Advances in
Analytical Chemistry and Instrumentation
Volume 4

Advances in
Analytical Chemistry
and Instrumentation

Edited by
CHARLES N. REILLEY
*Department of Chemistry, University of
North Carolina, Chapel Hill, North Carolina*

VOLUME 4

INTERSCIENCE PUBLISHERS
a division of
JOHN WILEY & SONS, INC.
New York • London • Sydney

INTRODUCTION TO THE SERIES

The scope and even the purpose of analytical chemistry has grown so amazingly in the last decade that even the dedicated analyst with time on his hands cannot follow the significant developments which appear now in ever increasing numbers. If analytical chemistry is to grow into its new and wider role and gain its rightful prestige, these new developments must become everyday working knowledge and be translated into practice. At present a series time lag still exists between evolution and practice. This new venture aims to bridge the hiatus by presenting a continuing series of volumes whose chapters deal not only with significant new developments in ideas and techniques, but also with critical evaluations and the present status of important, but more classical, methods and approaches. The chapters will be contributed by outstanding workers having intimate knowledge and experience with their subject.

It is the hope and belief that *Advances in Analytical Chemistry and Instrumentation* will offer a new medium for the exchange of ideas and will help assist effective, fruitful communication between the various disciplines of analytical chemistry.

These volumes contain articles covering a variety of topics presented from the standpoint of the nonspecialist but retaining a scholarly level of treatment. Although a reasonably complete review of recent developments is given, a dry and terse cataloguing of the literature without description or evaluation is avoided. The scope of the *Advances* is flexible and broad, hoping to be of service to the modern analytical chemist whose profession each day demands broader perspectives and solution of problems with increased complexity. The periodical literature is inherently specialized and the appearance of suitable monographs takes place only after many years. Reviews are often directed to the specialist and often lack adequate description or evaluation. *Advances* hope to fill in the resulting need for critical, comprehensive articles surveying various topics on a high level, satisfying the specialist and nonspecialist alike. Comments and suggestions from readers are heartily welcome.

THE EDITOR

CONTRIBUTORS TO VOLUME 4

K. A. CONNORS, *School of Pharmacy, University of Wisconsin, Madison, Wisconsin*

LYMAN C. CRAIG, *The Laboratories of the Rockefeller Institute, New York, New York*

DONALD C. DAMOTH, *The Bendix Corporation, Cincinatti, Ohio*

G. EISENMAN, *Department of Physiology, University of Utah College of Medicine, Salt Lake City, Utah*

L. N. FERGUSON, *Department of Chemistry, Howard University, Washington, D.C.*

F. H. FIRSCHING, *Science and Technology Division, Southern Illinois University, Alton, Illinois*

T. HIGUCHI, *School of Pharmacy, University of Wisconsin, Madison, Wisconsin*

A. M. G. MACDONALD, *Department of Chemistry, The University of Birmingham, Birmingham, England*

CONTENTS

CONTENTS

Recent Advances in Precipitation From Homogeneous Solution

F. H. FIRSCHING, *Southern Illinois University, Alton, Illinois*

I. INTRODUCTION

Precipitation is one of the oldest techniques used in chemistry, yet one of the least understood. It still has broad applications in commercial processes. However, its use has declined in the laboratory. This lack of understanding and decline in use is being corrected by the study of precipitation from homogeneous solution (PFHS), the gradual formation of a solid from an initially uniform solution.

PFHS produces large crystalline precipitates that possess superior physical properties, when compared to those precipitates formed from direct mixing methods. Filtering and washing are much easier. Vexing problems such as clogging of the filter, creeping of the precipitate, and colloidal dispersion, which are associated with finely divided and amorphous precipitates, are seldom found in a PFHS method.

Generally, the chemical purity of these large crystalline precipitates is considerably better than of those formed by direct mixing methods. Separations are usually improved. Coprecipitation is often drastically reduced. The precipitates are stoichiometric. Stated succinctly PFHS is superior chemistry.

Another important aspect of PFHS should be emphasized—the reproducible behavior of the precipitation process. This is theoretically important, for it makes possible the application of mathematical principles.

Using PFHS methods, definite reproducible data are being obtained in precipitation processes. Heretofore, studies conducted by direct mixing methods have yielded conflicting and confusing results, probably because of the arbitrary manner in which conditions were fixed by various workers. PFHS has made precipitation results meaningful, for now the process is reproducible. Extraneous variables such as the rate of mixing solutions, the concentration of the added precipitant, the order in which components are added, etc. have been eliminated.

The reproducibility of data obtained has led chemists using PFHS methods into a variety of other areas of chemistry. Kinetics, coprecipitation, and nucleation studies have often been incorporated into PFHS publications. This pronounced excursion of PFHS work into the theoretical area of chemistry is by far the most significant and far-reaching of the advances made. Such work has illuminated some obscure features of the precipitation process, and may lead to an eventual understanding of the precipitation process itself.

A host of diverse and clever processes for obtaining PFHS have recently been developed. PFHS is rapidly developing into a complete area of chemistry, and supplanting the older and less satisfactory precipitation methods. The need for using an unsatisfactory conventional direct mixing process is almost nil. Anyone using a precipitation process should take a long and careful look at the method. If the fundamental principles of PFHS are not incorporated in the method, then there is a high probability that the method is not as efficient as it should be.

PFHS has been in use for about thirty years. At first the number of workers were few and the number of publications were quite limited. With time the field has been expanding. Now it is surging forward at a remarkable pace.

The field of PFHS was well covered by the book, *Precipitation from Homogeneous Solution*, by Gordon et al. (1). They summarized the entire area up to 1958 and presented a thorough discussion of all phases of this work. Anyone who wishes to understand the fundamentals of PFHS should definitely consult this book.

Two other comprehensive summaries are available. A chapter entitled "The Analytical Chemistry of Thioacetamide," by Swift and Anson appears in Volume I of *Advances in Analytical Chemistry and Instrumentation* (2). This covers a much more limited field, but does explore this area in detail. Another comprehensive review of the entire field is given by Gordon (3) in a chapter entitled "Precipitation from Homogeneous Solution" in Volume IA of *Comprehensive Analytical Chemistry*. This covers some additional material beyond the book with the same title and is a more succinct source of information.

This chapter will try to include all the pertinent work in PFHS that is not mentioned in the above sources. This will roughly cover a five-year period, in which the rate of investigation was drastically increasing. A complete and thorough discussion of each paper cannot be accomplished. However, the important highlights of each paper will be mentioned, and if possible some important generalizations will be made from a series of papers. If some drastically different method or result is presented in any paper, it will be thoroughly discussed with the important features emphasized.

A look at the bibliography will give a vivid picture of just how much has been accomplished in a five-year period. Numerous review papers have discussed PFHS and reference to the more recent reviews (4–6) is incorporated in the bibliography.

In order to handle the accumulation of papers in a somewhat systematic manner, they have been arbitrarily classified into four general areas: inorganic, insoluble chelates, theoretical, and miscellaneous. Naturally, there is a considerable overlap in many articles. Even though this classification leaves much to be desired, it does facilitate the discussion of groups of papers in a more comprehensive way.

II. INORGANIC PRECIPITATES

The papers discussed in this section usually deal with precipitates that are clearly inorganic, such as the sulfides, phosphates, etc. Many of these papers are expansions or extensions of previous techniques. Even though the results often may not be startling or unusual, they do represent a great many useful methods that have substantially broadened the base of PFHS.

1. The Hydrolysis of Urea

The hydrolysis of urea, originally used in PFHS by Willard and Tang (7), still has numerous applications that have not been investigated. Even though methods using this fundamental scheme continue to appear, the possibilities that have not been explored are still quite broad.

The hydrolysis of urea in hot water provides a source of ammonia:

$$CO(NH_2)_2 + H_2O = CO_2 + 2NH_3$$

The ammonia formed internally reacts with any acid present:

$$NH_3 + H^+ = NH_4^+$$

thus lowering the acidity gradually and uniformly throughout the solution. An additional feature of urea hydrolysis is the stirring furnished by the carbon dioxide that forms and leaves the solution as a stream of small bubbles.

The gradual lowering of the hydrogen ion concentration makes possible the precipitation of various hydrous oxides or hydroxides in a dense crystalline form. Often an anion present in solution is incorporated in the precipitate.

Cartwright (8) used this fundamental idea to produce a precipitate of basic bismuth formate. Bromocresol green served to show when the hydrolysis should be terminated. Once the indicator turned to bluish-green (about pH 5.0), precipitation was quantitative. The easily handled precipitate made it possible to use up to 500 mg. of bismuth. Errors caused by adsorption and occlusion were negligible. Bismuth could be determined in the presence of 500 mg. of lead by igniting the precipitate to the oxide. This represents a marked decrease in the coprecipitation errors usually found in a direct mixing procedure.

Prasad and Sastri (9) published a preliminary report about the precipitation of beryllium as the oxide, using urea hydrolysis. Dense, easily handled, quantitative precipitates were obtained.

Norwitz (10) applied the precipitation of barium chromate, by means of urea hydrolysis, to a wide assortment of materials, in order to determine barium.

A somewhat different use was made of urea by Dembinski and co-workers (11), who precipitated urea uranate from homogeneous solution. The properties of the precipitated material were evaluated by means of x-rays and chemical methods. An analysis of the crystal structure was presented. A formula of $H_2UO_4(NH_2CONH_2)_2$ was assigned.

Holland and co-workers (12) used urea hydrolysis for two distinct reasons. The ammonia formed was used to lower the hydrogen ion concentration, while the carbon dioxide formed was used as the precipitant. This dual role produced a precipitate of calcium carbonate.

2. Formation of a Precipitant by Hydrolysis

One of the most useful general systems in PFHS is that of the hydrolysis of an ester to form a precipitant. A typical reaction is

$$(C_2H_5O)_2C_2O_2 + 2H_2O = 2C_2H_5OH + H_2C_2O_4$$

The ester, diethyloxalate, is hydrolyzed to form oxalic acid, which serves as the source of oxalate ions used to precipitate heavy metal cations.

The hydrolysis of a rather wide variety of substances has been studied in order to produce PFHS. The list of substances keeps increasing and there are still a multitude of untried materials that would provide a workable system. New applications are continually being developed. The following papers use this fundamental idea.

Ross and Hahn (13) have used metaphosphoric acid in order to determine bismuth. The method is rapid and is based on the hydrolysis of metaphosphoric acid. The bismuth phosphate that is formed is dense, crystalline, and easy to handle. The volume of this precipitate is roughly 1/40 of the volume of the direct mixing method precipitate. Metals usually alloyed with bismuth do not interfere.

The study of the hydrolysis of thioacetamide

$$CH_3CSNH_2 + H_2O = CH_3CONH_2 + H_2S$$

has attracted a great deal of attention. These papers are of two general types: those that deal with the quantitative nature or purity of the precipitate and those that deal with reaction rates, coprecipitation effects, etc. In many cases one paper deals with both topics.

McCurdy and co-workers (14) studied the quantitative separation of copper, cadmium, and zinc by precipitation of the sulfides, using thioacetamide hydrolysis. The coprecipitation of cadmium and zinc on copper sulfide and of zinc with cadmium sulfide was studied. In the case of cadmium and zinc mixtures, the contamination of the precipitate was serious and required a reprecipitation of the cadmium sulfide in order to achieve a reasonable separation.

Burriel-Marti and co-workers have published a series of papers (15–17) on the precipitation of molybdenum sulfide, using thioacetamide. The effect of three different acids—hydrochloric, perchloric, and sulfuric—on the precipitation has been investigated.

Krijn and den Boef (18) have used thioacetamide and EDTA in combination in order to determine zinc in the presence of other group II and group III cations. The use of EDTA in a precipitation of sulfides, when thioacetamide has been hydrolyzed, is the chief difference from other reported methods. The presence of the EDTA improves the separation by holding various cations in solution under specified conditions. The results show that zinc can be precipitated in this fashion with improved efficiency. As little as 0.6 mg. of zinc can be determined in the presence of a large excess of elements of groups II and III.

Several other papers dealing with thioacetamide hydrolysis are discussed in Section IV.

3. Oxidation–Reduction Reactions

The application of redox reactions to PFHS methods has been quite limited. However, some significant new approaches have been made recently. These include three fundamental schemes: a change in oxidation state of the cation, the oxidation of a complexing agent, and the decomposition of a peroxy compound.

A. CHANGE IN OXIDATION STATE OF THE CATION

This particular scheme has found limited use in the past. Recently two papers (19,20) have appeared that use the change in oxidation state of copper(II) to copper(I).

Davis (19) has used ascorbic acid as the reducing agent in order to precipitate cuprous tetraphenyl borate. A solution containing copper(II) and tetraphenylborate was prepared. The resulting solution was then stirred as 10 ml. of a $0.1M$ ascorbic acid solution was added slowly. The copper was reduced gradually, forming the cuprous tetraphenylborate precipitate. The final determination was made by oxidizing the organic compound, dissolving the resulting substance, and titrating with EDTA. Results indicate that most of the metals commonly found with copper do not seriously interfere.

Cuprous thiocyanate has been used for over a hundred years in a direct mixing precipitation procedure, although serious difficulties are presented because of the small particle size. Newman (20) has overcome most of these problems by using PFHS: A solution of copper(II) and thiocyanate is made and then hydroxylamine is added. On heating, the copper(II) is slowly reduced by the hydroxylamine to copper(I), thus forming the insoluble cuprous thiocyanate. Precipitation is complete in one-half hour. The precipitate is granular and has excellent filtration properties.

When tested with a variety of alloys, excellent results were achieved. This reaction is essentially specific for copper, even though most of the metals commonly found with copper were present in the solution. This method should be a practical alternative to electrolyzing copper from solution.

B. OXIDATION OF A COMPLEXING AGENT

PFHS can be realized by complexing the cations in solution, introducing a precipitant, and then oxidizing the complexing agent. Cartwright (21) studied this general procedure as applied to the destructive oxidation of EDTA by the action of hydrogen peroxide.

He found that the rate of EDTA oxidation, in the absence of cations, was essentially constant at pH 1–4 and increased rapidly at higher pH values.

However, when hydrated oxide precipitates were introduced, an increase in the decomposition of hydrogen peroxide resulted. In the case of hydrated bismuth oxide, the precipitate particles first formed decomposed all the hydrogen peroxide, and further oxidation of the bismuth–EDTA complex ceased. Phosphate ion stabilized the hydrogen peroxide and prevented this decomposition. The bismuth phosphate precipitate was found to be inert to hydrogen peroxide and even had a slight stabilizing effect.

A second publication by Cartwright (22) concerned the effect of a number of metal phosphates on the oxidation of EDTA. The general method was satisfactory for iron, lead, calcium, and barium. Bismuth phosphate was not quantitatively precipitated above pH 1.5.

Hydrogen peroxide was found to be random in its oxidation of metal–EDTA complexes. All metals present are released into solution, indicating that EDTA would be of no help in achieving a separation of metals. The chief purpose would be to control the release of cations and thus improve the physical properties of the precipitates.

Cartwright (23) also studied the effect of the solubility of the precipitate on the oxidation of EDTA with hydrogen peroxide. He found that selectivity is poor and showed that the use of EDTA without an oxidizing agent gave fairly good results. Barium sulfate was precipitated using the hydrolysis of sulfamic acid in the presence of a calcium-EDTA complex. The pH was adjusted to 2.5–3.0 and the barium sulfate was quantitatively precipitated, while the calcium was held in solution.

These papers are a demonstration of the more sophisticated approach that is being made when PFHS is used. There is a decided attempt to understand the processes involved and go considerably beyond the simple development of an analytical method.

Chan also used oxidation of an organic compound in order to produce an insoluble chelate. This is discussed more fully in Section III.

C. DECOMPOSITION OF PEROXY COMPOUNDS

Dams and Hoste (24,25) have worked on the determination of tungsten, tantalum, niobium, and titanium by precipitating the insoluble acid or hydrous oxides of these four metals from homogeneous solution by a somewhat original technique. The fundamental idea is to dissolve the insoluble acids with hydrogen peroxide, thus forming the peroxy acids. By heating the solution, the peroxy acids are decomposed and the insoluble oxy acids are precipitated.

The determination of tungsten has been thoroughly studied using this method. A comparison was made with the classical procedures for tungsten using cinchonine or β-naphthoquinoline. PFHS was found to be superior to the standard methods in all cases except for very small concentrations of tungsten.

A preliminary report (25) on tantalum, niobium, and titanium indicates that this same general technique would be suitable for these metals. The chief difference would be the pH at which these peroxy acids are decomposed.

4. Complexation and Replacement

Several entirely new concepts for inducing PFHS have been developed. One of these uses a complexing agent to remove most of the free cations from solution by keeping them in the form of the complex ion during the addition of the precipitant. A second cation, with a formation constant about the same as the cation to be precipitated, is then introduced slowly into the stirred solution. A competition for the complexing agent occurs. The cation to be precipitated is released from its complex ion, uniformly and slowly throughout the solution.

Several methods using this fundamental scheme have been developed. One of these is the precipitation and determination of barium chromate (26) using the complexation and replacement method. A barium solution is mixed with an excess of EDTA, and then chromate ion is added. A uniform solution results. To the stirred solution is added a dilute solution of magnesium ion. In this particular case the magnesium ion does not form a precipitate when added, because magnesium chromate is soluble. Instead, the magnesium ion is complexed by the excess EDTA. Once the excess is exhausted, competition for the complexing agent occurs. Magnesium, forming a more stable complex, displaces barium from its complex, releasing the barium ion homogeneously in solution.

Barium chromate precipitates and continues to precipitate as more magnesium is added. A very crystalline precipitate of barium chromate is produced, which has a uniform size and shape. With this method, a good separation from large quantities of strontium and lead is realized.

This scheme has also been applied to the PFHS of barium sulfate (27). However, in this particular operation a good separation from strontium was not obtainable.

Apparently this general idea has been used to separate strontium and calcium (28). To the solution of strontium and calcium complexed by EDTA and sulfate, magnesium ion is added. A good separation of strontium from calcium is obtained.

Ramette has mentioned the use of complexation and replacement to bring about a precipitation of nickel dimethylglyoximate (29). In this instance the nickel–EDTA complex was disturbed by the addition of zinc ions. A very crystalline precipitate of nickel dimethylglyoximate was produced.

An extension of complexation and replacement has been reported. Firsching (30) achieved an excellent separation of rare earths by using two complexing agents. This rather complicated system is best illustrated with the reported separation of lanthanum and praseodymium. Each cation forms a complex of definite stability with each complexing agent. Each complex that is formed has a discreet formation constant, with different cations forming complexes of different stabilities. In the case of the rare earths, the differences in formation constants are often very slight. Nevertheless, these slight differences can be used to advantage, especially if two are used in a supplementary way.

The two complexing agents used were hydroxyethylethylenediaminetriacetic acid (HEDTA) and diethylenetriaminepentaacetic acid (DTPA). The logarithm of the formation constants with HEDTA and the two rare earths are: lanthanum, 13.22; praseodymium, 14.39; and for the replacement ion, cadmium, 13.0. The logarithm of the formation constants with DTPA for these cations are: lanthanum, 19.96; praseodymium, 21.85; and cadmium, 18.93.

When equal molar quantities of lanthanum, praseodymium, HEDTA, and DTPA are added to a beaker, a precipitate does not form upon the addition of iodate. Under these conditions the concentration of free cations is quite low and most of the cations are in the form of the complexes. This situation is upset by adding a dilute solution of cadmium ion to the stirred solution. Cadmium forms a complex with HEDTA that is very close to that of lanthanum. However, cadmium does not form a complex with DTPA that even approaches the stability of the praseodymium complex. They differ by a factor of about 10^3.

This set of circumstances means that the introduced cadmium will compete about equally with lanthanum for the HEDTA, but will have a much lower competition for DTPA than praseodymium. This means that the essential disturbance would be with the HEDTA complex of lanthanum, if these were the only two complexes in solution. However, two other complexes are also present, lanthanum–DTPA and praseodymium–HEDTA. From a study of the respective formation constants, it is apparent that most of the lanthanum is in the HEDTA complex. This means that the chief disturbance from the addition of cadmium ion is to the lanthanum–HEDTA complex. Furthermore, lanthanum is a more insoluble iodate than praseodymium and should precipitate first.

This combination of conditions makes it possible to achieve the separation. The difference between formation constants for three cations with two complexing agents, and the difference in solubility are combined to increase efficiency in one step. Results show that when about 99% of the lanthanum is precipitated, the filtrate contains about 70% of the praseodymium and 1% of the lanthanum. This means that approximately 70% of the praseodymium can be recovered about 99% pure with respect to lanthanum, in one precipitation.

The Doerner-Hoskins logarithmic distribution coefficient was found to be in the order of about 13. The value is considerably greater than any previously attained in a precipitation process involving the trivalent rare earths.

This use of two complexing agents in solution has only been applied to the rare earths. Numerous applications are surely possible, that should lead to vastly improved separations using PFHS.

5. Volatilization of Ammonia

A somewhat different method of precipitating insoluble materials from homogeneous solution has been applied by Firsching (31) to insoluble silver compounds. This involves the complexing of metal ions with ammonia. When a precipitant is added, the solution remains clear. Ammonia is then allowed to escape from the solution, thus gradually and uniformly increasing the free cation concentration. An insoluble metal salt slowly forms and settles out of solution.

With this scheme, a good separation of iodide from bromide and chloride has been obtained. A fair separation of bromide from chloride is also possible. This means that from an equimolar mixture of these three halides, it is possible to determine all three using only one reagent, the silver ammonia complex.

One other unusual feature of this work is that anions are determined. Very few PFHS methods involve the determination of anions.

This same general idea has been applied to the determination of phosphate (32). As ammonia leaves the ammoniacal solution of silver and phosphate, a dense, crystalline, quantitative precipitate of silver phosphate slowly forms. Only 7.4% of the precipitate is phosphorous, making the gravimetric factor almost as favorable as the phosphomolybdate method.

III. INSOLUBLE METAL CHELATES

The use of chelates in precipitation from homogeneous solution is a recent development that has expanded swiftly. Before 1960, only a few papers were published on this topic. Since then a great many communications have appeared. Some of these uses are extensions of previous general techniques, while others are original approaches.

The surge of interest is partly due to the challenges involved. A precipitation system using chelates poses some difficult problems. Solubility, reaction rates, and other similar difficulties are present in all these methods. In order to accomplish a satisfactory PFHS, either the cation or the chelate anion must be released in solution or formed in solution. This release or formation must be at a reasonable rate, neither too rapid nor too slow, to be of any practical use.

The most elegant of these methods use synthesis, the actual formation of the chelating agent in aqueous solution.

1. Dimethylglyoxime Synthesis

A classic example of this synthesis would be the production of dimethylglyoxime, formed by reacting biacetyl and hydroxylamine in the presence of nickel(II) ions.

Salesin and Gordon (29,33) have done an extensive study on the precipitation of nickel dimethylglyoximate from homogeneous solution using a direct synthesis. The reaction proceeds at a satisfactory rate when biacetyl and hydroxylamine are added to a water solution of nickel(II) ions at a pH of about 7.5. The dimethylglyoxime slowly forms and gradually brings about precipitation of the red nickel compound. The filtering characteristics and handling properties of this precipitate are far superior to those produced by direct mixing methods. An additional advantage is the much larger amount of precipitate that can be handled. About four times as much nickel dimethylglyoximate can be manipulated as easily as the maximum amount possible using a conventional method.

This particular scheme, from a historical point of view, had been used by Barnicoat (34) in 1935 to determine biacetyl in butter. This was not classified as PFHS. Unfortunately, the significance of this reaction was not recognized for approximately 20 years, until it was independently developed into a method by Gordon and co-workers.

This reaction makes a very interesting lecture demonstration (35). The gradual changes in color, from bluish to yellow to red, as first the chelate and then the insoluble precipitate are formed, involve challenging chemistry. Students have the opportunity to observe the rather complicated set of reactions that are occurring in the solution. This may be the first opportunity for many students to see a slow process occurring, and thus stimulate their thinking in terms of reaction rates and kinetics.

The reaction of biacetyl and hydroxylamine was studied and will be discussed in the section on theoretical papers (Section IV).

Palladium was also precipitated from homogeneous solution, using the synthesis of dimethylglyoxime (36). Long yellow needles of palladium dimethylglyoximate were produced.

The separation of palladium from platinum and nickel was investigated. Despite the obvious superior physical properties of the precipitate formed from homogeneous solution, the chemical purity is essentially the same as that of the direct mixing method. No improvement in the separation was found. The only advantage was the handling and washing of the precipitate.

2. Synthesis of Other Oximes

Píno Pérez and co-workers (37) used a very similar scheme to precipitate palladium furfuraldoximate from homogeneous solution. In this case, furfural and hydroxylamine were reacted in water solution to synthesize the furfuraldoxime. A variety of metals were studied and only gold(III) proved to be a serious interference. Metals that form insoluble chlorides also interfered.

Pietrzak and Gordon (38) have used a very similar reaction, that of salicylaldehyde and hydroxylamine in the presence of copper(II) ions, to precipitate the insoluble copper chelate from homogeneous solution.

A study of the separation of copper from both nickel and iron showed that PFHS was just a bit less satisfactory than the direct mixing method. This is unusual and one of the very few instances of a more impure precipitate being produced by PFHS as compared to conventional methods.

Palladium (39) has been precipitated from homogeneous solution, using indane-1,2-dioxime synthesized in solution. Once again hydroxylamine reacts with a ketone or aldehyde in water solution to produce the corresponding oxime. Quantitative results were obtained, as the insoluble chelate was precipitated by the reaction of indane-1-one-2-oxime and hydroxylamine to form the chelate. The palladium indane-1,2-dioximate can be weighed directly after drying at 110°C. Numerous possible interfering ions, including iron and cobalt, were studied, and only platinum(IV) was a serious interference.

The synthesis of oximes by reacting hydroxylamine with various aldehydes and ketones appears to have rather wide applications. At present, only the four methods just described are available. However, the compounds involved are diverse enough to indicate that many similar structures should behave in a similar fashion and find useful application in PFHS.

3. Synthesis of Other Compounds

A somewhat different type of synthesis has been used by Heyn and co-workers. Two chelates were synthesized using nitrous acid and nitrite.

Cupferron (40) was produced by reacting phenylhydroxylamine and nitrite in water solution in the presence of copper, iron, and titanium. A preliminary communication indicates that these three chelates can all be satisfactorily precipitated using this synthesis of cupferron.

The reaction of 2-naphthol with nitrous acid in the presence of cobalt(II) produces the insoluble cobalt(III) 1-nitroso-2-naphtholate (41). The synthesized chelate serves to oxidize the cobalt(II) and then precipitate the cobalt(III). This precipitate is stoichiometric and can be weighed directly after being dried at 115°C. However, the conventional precipitate is not stoichiometric, being contaminated with reagent. This must be ignited to the oxide, giving a much less favorable gravimetric factor for the determination of cobalt.

One chelate oxidation method has been presented. Chan (42) used oxygen in the air to oxidize the 3,3′,4′,5,7-pentahydroxyflavanone (dihydroquercetin), in hot acid solution, to form the insoluble tantalum and niobium compounds of 3,3′,4′,5,7-pentahydroxyflavonates from homogeneous solution. Zirconium and molybdenum do not interfere, but titanium does. Reagent may accompany the precipitate, but ignition to the oxide overcomes this problem.

This is the only published example of the use of air oxidation to produce or synthesize the desired chelate in solution. The simplicity of this procedure should provide a stimulus to further development.

4. Hydrolysis of Urea

The useful method of the hydrolysis of urea has found several applications. There can be no question about the wide and useful possibilities of this idea. Only a small fraction of the potential applications have been reported.

Heyn and Finston (43) used urea hydrolysis for the separation of magnesium from sodium and potassium, with 8-hydroxyquinoline serving as the precipitant. In acid solution the magnesium chelate does not precipitate. In hot solution, the urea is hydrolyzed, lowering the hydrogen ion concentration and allowing the formation of the insoluble chelate.

Various magnesium precipitates were studied. The collected data showed that the precipitation of magnesium 8-hydroxyquinolate from homogeneous solution was a separation from sodium and potassium superior to any of the other methods studied.

A similar scheme was used by Kosta and Dular (44) to prepare the niobium 8-hydroxyquinolate. Urea was hydrolyzed to raise the pH and induce the precipitation of the niobium chelate. A study of various methods indicated that PFHS using urea hydrolysis yielded the best results. The product was crystalline and stoichiometric. Almost quantitative results (99%) were achieved. Previous methods had failed to give a definite compound; it had been necessary to ignite the indefinite composition to the oxide. However, PFHS using urea hydrolysis gives a reproducible and stoichiometric compound, $NbO(C_9H_6ON)_3$.

5. Hydrolysis of Esters

Numerous publications describe the use of simple hydrolysis to release a chelate in aqueous solution and produce PFHS.

A. HYDROLYSIS OF 8-ACETOXYQUINOLINE

This general scheme of hydrolysis of organic esters originally appeared when Gordon and co-workers used the hydrolysis of 8-acetoxyquinoline to precipitate the insoluble thorium 8-hydroxyquinolate. A series of papers on this topic have followed.

The first of the series (45) was concerned with the preparation of the compound. The 8-acetoxyquinoline must be very pure in order to be used in PFHS; otherwise, on its addition to the solution containing the cation, there will be an immediate precipitation due to any free 8-hydroxyquinoline present.

The thorium paper (46) was followed by reports dealing with aluminum (47), uranium (48), magnesium (49), zinc (50), indium (51), and gallium (51). Aluminum, uranium, magnesium, and zinc can all be weighed as stoichiometric compounds. The uranium can be precipitated in two different stoichiometric forms and weighed directly after drying. However, the thorium must be ignited to the oxide.

The procedure was not recommended for determination of indium and gallium. Under rigorously controlled conditions the indium 8-hydroxyquinolate could be obtained stoichiometrically and quantitatively, in a form that could be weighed directly after drying.

Coprecipitation of various ions was studied in the precipitation of zinc 8-hydroxyquinolate. Some remarkable improvements in precipitate purity were obtained in PFHS, compared to direct mixing methods.   In the case of lead(II), less than 0.3% was coprecipitated, compared to over 50% in a conventional method.

Howick and Trigg (52) independently made use of the hydrolysis of 8-acetoxyquinoline to precipitate aluminum 8-hydroxyquinolate. Their findings were essentially the same as those of Gordon and co-workers.

B. HYDROLYSIS OF 8-ACETOXYQUINALDINE

The hydrolysis of a very similar ester, 8-acetoxyquinaldine, has been investigated.   Graham and co-workers (53) have used this hydrolysis to bring about the precipitation of thorium 8-hydroxyquinaldate from homogeneous solution.   In order to produce a stoichiometric precipitate, conditions must be controlled carefully.

Gordon and co-workers have also studied the hydrolysis of 8-acetoxyquinaldine.   Both zinc (54) and indium (55) have been precipitated from homogeneous solutions by the 8-hydroxyquinaldate released in solution by the hydrolysis.   A comparison of the zinc 8-hydroxyquinaldate produced by PFHS with that obtained by a conventional direct mixing method showed higher purity of the PFHS precipitate.   Indium could be separated from lead, calcium, and magnesium using this technique.   Both the zinc and indium insoluble chelates are stoichiometric compounds that can be weighed directly after drying.

C. OTHER HYDROLYSIS REACTIONS

Gordon and co-workers (56) have also studied the hydrolysis of N-benzoylphenylhydroxylamine acetate as a source of the chelating agent N-benzoylphenylhydroxylamine.   This hydrolysis has been used to bring about a precipitation of the insoluble copper(II) chelate from homogeneous solution.   Unfortunately, the time required for hydrolysis (24 hr.) is a bit excessive for normal use.   Much lower coprecipitation was realized by PFHS than by direct mixing methods, when the possible interference of cobalt and cadmium was investigated.

Even though only three esters have been used in the reported work, the possible applications, with resulting improvements, seems to be very broad.   In every one of the reported methods, the precipitates were easy to filter and wash and generally gave improved separations.

Further study of hydrolysis reactions should prove very rewarding. Undoubtedly, many of the existing organic precipitants can be converted to esters, then used in PFHS methods. The vastly improved physical characteristics of the resulting precipitates as well as the usual decrease in coprecipitation should make the effort worthwhile.

The use of direct mixing methods with organic precipitants is rapidly being supplanted by PFHS procedures. Further development of PFHS methods should provide additional favorable alternatives.

6. Volatilization of Organic Solvent

Howick and co-workers (57) have developed an original approach to PFHS that uses insoluble chelates. The fundamental idea of this scheme is to bring about slowly a change in the precipitation media. Metal chelates are often insoluble in water but readily soluble in organic solvents. By making a solution that is a mixture of water and organic solvent, these organic chelates can be held in solution. If the organic solvent is allowed to volatilize slowly, then the solution becomes more water-like, and the metal chelates precipitate.

A series of papers describing the precipitation of aluminum (58), nickel (59), magnesium (60), and copper (61) 8-hydroxyquinolates have been presented. Some of the general advantages of this scheme are: rigorously pure reagents are not necessary, easily handled precipitates are formed, separations are generally good, and the pH can be predetermined by adding a suitable buffer system to the original solution.

Among the organic solvents used were acetone, acetone–chloroform, and acetone–ethanol. The fine results obtained with the reported metals indicate that this system should have many additional useful applications (62). Chelates other than 8-hydroxyquinoline should also prove to be useful in this general scheme.

IV. THEORETICAL

Many of the PFHS publications have gone beyond the simple development of an analytical method. Often the research moves into kinetic studies. Another interesting aspect is the work on nucleation and coprecipitation.

1. Thioacetamide

Among the most widely studied systems is that of thioacetamide, when it is used to precipitate various metal sulfides. Some of this work has emphasized the kinetics of this reaction.

Washizuka (63) investigated the rate of precipitation and quantitative separation of nickel sulfide using the hydrolysis of thioacetamide in an ammonia–ammonium nitrate solution. He concluded that the precipitation reaction of nickel sulfide in ammoniacal solution is a general base catalysis by hydroxyl ion and ammonia. An apparent rate equation with the value of various constants was given. This work supports the view that the reaction between thioacetamide and the bases is a rate-determining step in the precipitation of sulfides.

The crystal structure of the nickel sulfide was determined by an x-ray powder method and found to belong to the hexagonal NiAs type.

Pryszczewska (64,65) has investigated the amperometric determination of metals with the aid of thioacetamide. Included in this work is a study of the rate of precipitation of cadmium sulfide using the hydrolysis of thioacetamide in ammoniacal solution. Two rate equations were presented, for dilute ammoniacal solutions and for concentrated ammonia solutions.

Tanigawa and co-workers (66) studied the coprecipitation of zinc with cadmium sulfide, using the hydrolysis of thioacetamide as a source of sulfide. They found that the coprecipitation of zinc with cadmium sulfide belongs to a derichment system, which obeys the Doerner-Hoskins logarithmic distribution law. The distribution coefficient, λ, was found to be about 4×10^{-3} at 33°C. The distribution coefficient decreased with increasing temperature and with increasing quantities of zinc.

2. Thiourea

Soloniewicz (67,68) made use of the hydrolysis of thiourea as a source of sulfide in order to precipitate both bismuth and mercury. The hydrolysis reaction proceeds quite rapidly in hot solution. The quantitative nature of the bismuth sulfide and mercury sulfide precipitations was studied. The mercury sulfide was quantitative, but the bismuth results were only reliable within 1%.

Nakano (69) used thiourea to precipitate zinc sulfide from a zinc hydroxide suspension. The kinetics of this reaction were found to be second order with respect to $Zn(OH)_2$ and thiourea. The rate constant at pH 9–11 was 2.685×10^{-3} and the activation energy 25.4 kcal. The average diameter of the precipitate particles was in the 0.1–$0.2\ \mu$ range. X-ray analysis showed that the precipitates were of the zinc blende type.

Nakano (70) also studied the coprecipitation of silver with zinc sulfide. He compared the sulfide formed using hydrogen sulfide gas with those formed by the hydrolysis of thiourea.

3. Coprecipitation Studies

A. SULFATE SYSTEM

Cohen and Gordon (71) have studied coprecipitation in some binary sulfate systems. The fundamental scheme involved the hydrolysis of sulfamic acid to bring about the precipitation of alkaline earth sulfates. The distribution behavior of radiotracers was used to study the coprecipitation of strontium, lead, lanthanum, and yttrium on barium sulfate, and also the coprecipitation of lead, lanthanum, and yttrium on strontium sulfate.

The distribution coefficients were determined and an attempt was made to correlate them with the theoretical solubility ratios. There was a slight correlation. However, the divergence between theory and observation was so great that a quantitative correlation was not possible.

B. OXALATE SYSTEM

Block and Gordon (72) used the hydrolysis of dimethyloxalate to precipitate uranous oxalate from homogeneous solution in the study of the coprecipitation of cerium(III) and scandium(III). These systems obeyed the logarithmic distribution law. The distribution coefficient was found to be related to a first-order precipitation rate. When trace amounts of cerium were coprecipitated with carrier quantities of uranium, a modified distribution law, which included an ionic charge, was found to be satisfactory. The cerium(III) and uranium-(IV) oxalate system followed the modified form of the Doerner-Hoskins logarithmic distribution law more closely than the original.

More and more studies of this nature are appearing and eventually should result in a much more satisfactory picture of the rather complicated and poorly understood process of coprecipitation.

C. RARE EARTH SYSTEMS

Separation Efficiency. Callow (73) has studied the fractional crystallization and fractional precipitation of the rare earths. In some cases this involved PFHS. He determined the Doerner-Hoskins distribution coefficient, lambda, for several rare-earth systems. A mathematical formula using maximum entropy change was developed. The fundamental idea is that maximum entropy change corresponds to maximum separation efficiency. From the distribution coefficient, a calculation could then be made using the maximum entropy change. In this fashion it was possible to predict the fraction of one rare earth that should be precipitated to achieve maximum separation efficiency.

Examples of such calculations are presented. One calculation is shown to lead to an improved separation when tested experimentally (73).

Induced Nucleation. Pruitt and co-workers (74) have applied PFHS to the radiochemical determination of yttrium and promethium. They were able to improve the separation of yttrium from neodymium by providing nucleation sites for the immediate discharge of supersaturation, thus maintaining the iodate level at a low value and preventing the precipitation of yttrium iodate. Apparently the nucleation phenomena was side-stepped, and only crystal growth occurred. The introduction of about 0.1 mg. of talc ($MgSiO_3$) apparently provided an immediate site for the precipitation of neodymium iodate, thus eliminating any initial supersaturation that would otherwise have occurred.

The introduction of foreign particles into a solution may provide a means of separating two phenomena; nucleation and crystal growth. Apparently, foreign particles can drastically alter the initial supersaturation required for nucleation. A short communication by Adamski (75) deals with crystal nucleation in precipitation methods. By introducing foreign particles into the solution, different shaped crystals can be produced. By performing fractional precipitation, the number of crystalline forms decreases. The conclusion is that the final crystalline form is influenced by the foreign nuclei serving as the growing site for the crystal.

Further investigations of this nature may provide valuable information about the nucleation process.

4. Dimethylglyoxime Reaction

Gordon and co-workers (76) have made a rather thorough study of the reaction of biacetyl and hydroxylamine to form dimethylglyoxime. Simple kinetics were followed when nickel was absent. However, in the presence of nickel, there is definite evidence for complex formation between biacetyl monooxime and nickel. This complex and others formed with nickel determined the overall rate of formation of the nickel dimethylglyoximate precipitate.

Supersaturation concentrations in the order of several hundred times the equilibrium solubility were reached in nucleation experiments. These results provide a reasonable explanation of the persistent supersaturation that is often observed in this system.

A note (77) has appeared concerning additional intermediates that form when biacetyl and hydroxylamine react. Two intermediates or addition products of biacetyl form very quickly in solution. Apparently these intermediates are the substances that then proceed to bring about the PFHS of nickel(II) and palladium(II) using the dimethylglyoxime that is formed.

5. Formation Constant

Firsching and Brewer (78) used the volatilization of ammonia to bring about the precipitation of zinc and cadmium 8-hydroxyquinolates from homogeneous solution. Dense crystalline precipitates were obtained. However, the determination of either of these metals in the presence of metals commonly associated with them is not possible.

The determination of zinc is complicated by the formation of a previously unreported complex, the tris(8-quinolinato)-zincate(II) ion. An approximate formation constant of 3×10^4 was determined. Positive data for a cadmium tris complex was not found, although there were indications that such a complex may exist.

6. Nucleation

Three papers dealing primarily with nucleation using PFHS have appeared (79–81). The first was an introduction to the nucleation problem and summarized the developments up to that point.

Fundamentally the precipitation process involves two steps: nucleation and crystal growth. The nucleation process is of the greatest importance, for it fixes the number and therefore the size of the final crystalline particles. Previous experimental work in nucleation was evaluated and discussed.

Gordon and co-workers examined the supersaturation of silver chloride. Critical supersaturations were determined. These appeared to be different from the critical supersaturation of classical nucleation theory and appeared to depend on both the rate of nucleation and the rate of crystal growth. Furthermore, it was found that the rate of precipitation is not constant but varies quite markedly during the early part of the precipitation process. A slight control of this variation can be realized by altering the concentrations of the reagents.

The precipitation nucleus of silver chloride was also examined from the kinetic point of view, which indicated that the silver chloride nucleus consists of about five ions. These results support the findings of the Christianson-Neilson nucleation theory. One of the chief values of these papers has been the fact that theoretical problems of this type can be studied using PFHS. Perhaps this may eventually lead to an understanding of the precipitation process.

Fischer (82) reported on the nucleation of precipitates formed from homogeneous solution. He determined that the nucleation process actually fixes the size and numbers of crystals that are formed in any precipitation process. Nucleation occurs very early and only crystal growth thereafter. He concluded that precipitation from homogeneous solution was not occurring. He postulated that the precipitate was forming heterogeneously, during the direct mixing of the reacting solutions. Despite the fact that he had rigorously studied only three precipitations from homogeneous solution, he generalized to all PFHS.

Fischer's conclusions were challenged by Haberman and Gordon (83). They believe that this cannot possibly be true for many PFHS and gave supporting data for their claim. Part of their criticism was concerned with the critical supersaturation ratio. They felt that Fischer's calculations had not taken this into account. They also criticized Fischer's suggestion that speeding up the precipitation would be advantageous, for this would lead to increased coprecipitation. The chief discussion was centered on the assumption that all PFHS occurred by direct mixing and not from a true homogeneous solution.

Several examples were given that indicate that PFHS was occurring and precipitation by direct mixing was not possible.

Fischer countered that some supersaturation was necessary but he felt that critical supersaturation ratios as high as 30 were unrealistic. He also felt that many hydrolysis reactions, such as those that make use of thioacetamide or sulfamic acid, must have precipitation occurring on direct mixing. He did agree that all PFHS may not be really direct mixing causing the nucleation, but he felt that it frequently must be.

It appears that Fischer generalized excessively on the basis of the three systems he studied. Undoubtedly his conclusions are valid for these systems, but there is a gross uncertainty about applying this conclusion to all PFHS. In fact there are numerous PFHS systems where this generalization is not valid.

V. MISCELLANEOUS

This section contains a variety of papers that do not satisfactorily fit into other groupings. Three general types of papers are included: original approaches to PFHS, peripheral papers that involve PFHS, and subjects that are beyond the usual scope of analytical procedures.

1. Original Approaches to PFHS

Among the new methods for inducing a PFHS is that of electrolytic generation of sulfate. Klein and Fontal (84) used the electrolysis of thiocyanate to yield sulfate.

$$SCN^- + 4H_2O = SO_4^{2-} + HCN + 7H^* + 6e^-$$

A study was made of current efficiency, rate of formation, and other variables. On unfiltered solutions a critical supersaturation ratio of about 24 was found for barium sulfate precipitated with the electrolytically generated sulfate. For filtered solutions these ratios were in the 40–50 range, definitely indicating that a true PFHS was realized. Current efficiency was found to be 100% over a wide range of acid pH values.

Fabrikanos and Lieser (85) have used a two-phase system. an aqueous solution containing sulfate, and an organic solution of barium perchlorate in ethyl acetate. A narrow interface was maintained between the two solutions. The aqueous solution was agitated continuously. As barium perchlorate diffused slowly through the interface it was mixed to produce an essentially uniform solution.

With this original method of PFHS, critical supersaturation ratios very similar to values obtained by previous workers were obtained.

2. Peripheral Papers

Because of the widespread use of the hydrolysis of esters in PFHS, the following two papers should prove to be of interest. Howick and co-workers (86) studied the effect of pH on the hydrolysis of two similar esters, 7-acetoxyquinoline and 8-acetoxyquinoline. Wasmuth and Freiser (87) have studied the effect of copper(II) ions, apparently acting as a catalyst, on the hydrolysis of 8-acetoxyquinoline. Both these studies are concerned with the actual mechanism of the hydrolysis reaction.

Bordner and Gordon (88) have taken two different uranium 8-hydroxyquinolates, formed by PFHS, and studied the thermogravimetric behavior of both compounds.

Nickel dimethylglyoximate produced using PFHS was studied with the electron microscope (89). The larger crystals were convenient for study and showed that the direction of the long axis is the c axis. The material sublimed at 120°C. and changed to nickel oxide at 400°C.

3. Organic Reagent Precipitation

Weiss and co-workers have investigated the coprecipitation of trace metal ions on an assortment of organic precipitants. In a sense this is a variation of the usual use of PFHS. Normally, the insoluble chelate is formed between the metal ion and the organic molecule. This means that the solubility is exceeded and most of the results are predictable in a mathematical way. However, the quantities of metal studied by Weiss are extremely small, in the order of 10^{-8} g./liter. These ultramicro amounts coprecipitate on the organic reagent which is precipitated. Their solubility is not exceeded under these conditions. Nevertheless, essentially all of the ultramicro quantities can be precipitated using these techniques.

A variety of methods for inducing the precipitation of the organic molecule were used. Some of these are definitely PFHS while others may not be. It is difficult to be certain from the procedures that were described.

The following methods were used: (a) In hot solution all components were soluble; on cooling a precipitate formed. (b) Organic reagent was added with acetone; heating volatilized the acetone and caused precipitation of the organic reagent. (c) Salting out was done by adding ammonium chloride to a uniform solution, thus causing the organic compound to precipitate. (d) Ethyl alcohol was added to a uniform solution, causing the organic reagent to precipitate. (e) 8-Acetoxyquinoline was hydrolyzed to produce the 8-hydroxyquinoline. The hydrolysis was continued until the organic reagent precipitated.

An attempt was made to determine the mode of coprecipitation. In some cases the Doerner-Hoskins equation was followed, in others it was not.

The concentration of radiobarium (90), molybdenum (91), uranium (93), silver (95), and gold (96) in sea water were determined using these techniques. The cocrystallization of ultramicro amounts of alkali metals (92) iron, plutonium, cerium, and praseodymium (94) on various organic reagents was studied.

This work is in a somewhat distinct area of chemistry and involves a method that has not been used before in exactly this way. The variety of methods for inducing precipitation as well as the attempt to determine distribution coefficients makes these papers of general interest.

4. Inorganic Preparations

A series of publications dealing with inorganic preparations by Hayek and co-workers (97–99) has some interesting possibilities in terms of future applications. These preparations were made by PFHS. Several general techniques were used to produce a rather wide assortment of inorganic compounds.

The volatilization of ammonia was used with cations that form ammonia complexes: silver(I), copper(II), nickel(II), cobalt(II), cobalt(III), zinc, and cadmium. Some unusual salts, normally not encountered in PFHS, involving arsenate, molybdate, vanadate, etc. were prepared.

Complexing agents such as citrate, tartrate, and EDTA, were used. The complexes were made less stable by two methods: volatilization of a base such as ammonia, or hydrolysis of an acid ester. In both cases the hydrogen ion concentration would increase and render the complex less stable, thus bringing about a PFHS. A variety of inorganic compounds were prepared this way.

A suggestion that cyanide complexes could be decomposed by oxidation was also presented, but compounds were not prepared by this novel technique.

This series of papers has explored a number of very broad possibilities for analytical methods using PFHS.   These general cation release methods should prove to be most useful in the future.

5. General Diffusion Method

Despite the wide assortment of general methods that have been described in the literature for producing a PFHS, many possibilities have not been exploited. Some unpublished results (100,101) will give an idea of the almost unlimited possibilities that exist.

This general system is based on diffusion and uses the following technique. One beaker, containing the uniform solution in which the precipitation is to occur, and a second beaker containing the substance to be volatilized, are placed in a closed atmosphere, such as a polyethylene bag or an empty desiccator. Agitation is desirable in order to maintain uniformity during the diffusion.

An example of this system would be the precipitation of barium chromate using the diffusion of ammonia, instead of the hydrolysis of urea. A beaker containing an acid solution of barium and chromate ions is placed inside a polyethylene bag. A second beaker, containing an aqueous solution of ammonia, is also placed inside the bag and then the bag is closed and set on a shaker.

Ammonia diffuses to the surface of the acid solution one molecule at a time. Acid molecules are neutralized one molecule at a time. With agitation, this effect is made essentially uniform throughout the solution. Eventually, insoluble barium chromate precipitates.

This is approximately what occurs when urea is hydrolyzed. However, the solution does not have to be heated. The precipitation rate can be controlled by changing the concentration of the original ammonia solution or by placing a watch glass over the beaker.

Almost any volatile substance can be used in this fashion. Any volatile amine can bring about an increase in pH, while any volatile acid, such as hydrochloric or acetic, can bring about a decrease in pH.

Redox reactions can be produced by diffusion. Reducing agents such as formic acid or sulfur dioxide, and oxidizing agents such as

TABLE I

Analytical Determinations Using PFHS

Element	Nature of precipitate	Reagents or method used	Element determined, mg.	Other substance present, mg.	Coprecipitated error, mg.	Ref.
Al	8-Hydroxyquinolate	8-Acetoxyquinoline	10	Cd 10	1.8	47,52
Ba		Solvent volatilization	10	Cd 10	0.1	58
	Chromate	EDTA, MgCl$_2$	71.1	Sr 44	0.2	26
		Urea hydrolysis	300	—	—	10
	Sulfate	EDTA, MgCl$_2$	70.0	Sr 44	1.6	27
		EDTA, sulfamic acid	113.8	Ca 500	Trace	23
Be	Oxide	Urea hydrolysis	159.8	—	—	9
Br	Silver bromide	Ammonia volatilization	16.0	Cl 7.1	0.4	31
Bi	Basic formate	Urea hydrolysis	500	Pb 500	Trace	8
	Phosphate	EDTA, H$_2$O$_2$	254.2	Pb 500	30	21, 22
		Metaphosphoric acid	126.9	Cd 100	0.6	13
	Sulfide	Thiourea	350	—	—	67
Cd	8-Hydroxyquinolate	Ammonia volatilization	204	—	—	78
	Sulfide	Thioacetamide	168.6	Zn 9.8	5.9	14
Cl	Silver chloride	Ammonia volatilization	7.1	Br 16.0	0.7	31
Co	1-Nitroso-2-naphtholate	2-Naphthol, HNO$_2$	10.3	Ni 10	0.05	41
Cu	N-Benzoylphenylhydroxylaminate	N-Benzoylphenylhydroxylamineacetate	25.0	Cd 75	0.0	56
	8-Hydroxyquinolate	Solvent volatilization	30	Pb 480	0.1	61
	Salicylaldoximate	Salicylaldehyde, NH$_2$OH	43.01	Ni 100	0.15	38
	Sulfide	Thioacetamide	95.3	Zn 9.8	0.18	14
	Tetraphenylborate	Cu(II), ascorbic acid	24.99	Cd 100	Trace	19
	Thiocyanate	Cu(II), NH$_2$OH	622	Zn 359	Trace	20

In	8-Hydroxyquinaldate	8-Acetoxyquinaldine	25.48	Al 25	0.25	55
I	Silver iodide	Ammonia volatilization	25.4	Br 160	0.1	31
Mg	8-Hydroxyquinolate	8-Acetoxyquinoline	12.84	Ba 50	0.3	49
		Solvent volatilization	13.35	Ba 50	0.06	60
		Urea hydrolysis	69	Na 4000	0.001	43
Hg	Sulfide	Thiourea	500	—	—	68
Mo	Sulfide	Thioacetamide	66.5	—	—	15–17
Ni	Dimethylglyoximate	Biacetyl, NH$_2$OH	196.6	Co 40	0.0	33
	8-Hydroxyquinolate	Solvent volatilization	30	Ca 1400	0.7	59
Nb	8-Hydroxyquinolate	Urea hydrolysis	700	—	—	44
	Pentahydroxyflavonate	Pentahydroxyflavanone, air	20.0	Zr 60	0.3	42
Pd	Dimethylglyoximate	Biacetyl, NH$_2$OH	24.3	Pt 75	0.2	36
	Furfuraldoximate	Furfural, NH$_2$OH	28.5	Pt 20	0.3	37
	Indane-1,2-dioximate	Indane-1-one-2-oxime, NH$_2$OH	4.88	Co 28	0.03	39
P	Silver phosphate	Ammonia volatilization	186.3	SO$_4$ 2400	0.5	32
Sr	Sulfate	EDTA, MgCl$_2$	88	Ca 40	0.1	28
Ta	Pentahydroxyflavonate	Pentahydroxyflavanone, air	20.0	Zr 60	Trace	42
Th	8-Hydroxyquinaldate	8-Acetoxyquinaldine	35	—	—	53
	8-Hydroxyquinolate	8-Acetoxyquinoline	50.3	Ce 500	0.28	46
W	Tungstic acid	Peroxytungstate decomposition	251	Mo 22.2	11	24
U	8-Hydroxyquinolate	8-Acetoxyquinoline	28.0	—	—	48
Zn	8-Hydroxyquinaldate	8-Acetoxyquinaldine	50.03	Al 100	0.01	54
	8-Hydroxyquinolate	8-Acetoxyquinoline	50.02	Pb 100	0.24	50
		Ammonia volatilization	177	—	—	78
	Sulfide	EDTA, thioacetamide	6.0	Cd 3	0.0	18

bromine or iodine, can diffuse into a solution and bring about a slow redox reaction and thus induce a PFHS.

Precipitants can be introduced by diffusion. Hydrogen sulfide, hydrofluoric acid, and other volatile precipitants can be diffused into solution and bring about a PFHS.

The polarity of a solution can be altered by diffusion. As the composition of a solvent system is altered, the solubility of various substances is affected. Water can diffuse into an organic solvent and make it more "water-like," thus causing a PFHS. Organic solvents, such as acetone or alcohol, can diffuse into water solution and cause a PFHS.

Some examples of materials that have been precipitated from homogeneous solutions in preliminary experiments are: crystalline thorium fluoride precipitated by the diffusion of hydrogen fluoride, mercurous chloride precipitated by the diffusion of formic acid into a mercuric chloride solution, potassium iodate precipitated by diffusion of methyl alcohol into an aqueous solution, zinc 8-hydroxyquinolate precipitated by diffusion of water into an acetone solution, and polystyrene precipitated into a two-phase system by diffusion of water into a tetrahydrofuran solution.

The area of diffusion has not been exploited by workers in PFHS. The possibilities are very general and extensive.

6. The Future of PFHS

Even though the scope of PFHS has been broadened considerably in recent years, many possibilities are probably being overlooked. Additional developments should be possible by "crossing over" into other areas of scientific work and taking advantage of existing information. Undoubtedly there are numerous techniques in other areas of scientific endeavor that have not been used in PFHS.

The application of PFHS techniques in other areas of chemistry should be considered. Some preliminary work indicates that the purification of organic materials, including the fractionation of polymers, might be improved by using PFHS techniques.

All indications point to a further expansion of PFHS. The fundamental concepts of PFHS should find more and more applications throughout the entire field of chemistry.

VI. SUMMARY

In order to survey the applications of recent developments in PFHS, Table I has been prepared. Included in this table are the analytical determinations of various substances using PFHS. Other work of a more general nature could not be satisfactorily incorporated. The present situation in PFHS is very promising. The field is expanding rapidly. The less satisfactory direct mixing methods are being steadily replaced by PFHS methods. It is quite likely that in the near future PFHS will become the standard operating procedure for almost all precipitation work.

Because of the obvious advantages of PFHS, a careful examination should be made of all existing precipitation methods. Such an evaluation may disclose that a more efficient PFHS method is available or can be developed from the general schemes already in use.

At this time PFHS is firmly established. Further applications of PFHS into theoretical problems, as well as in the analytical area, are certain to continue. The fundamental principles of PFHS are being utilized in a more general manner than ever before. This trend shows every indication of continuing at an accelerated pace in the near future.

References

1. Gordon, L., M. L. Salutsky, and H. H. Willard, *Precipitation from Homogeneous Solution*, Wiley, New York, 1958.
2. Swift, E. H., and F. C. Anson, in C. N. Reilley, ed., *Advances in Analytical Chemistry and Instrumentation*, Vol. I, Interscience, New York, 1959, pp. 293–345.
3. Gordon, L., *Comprehensive Analytical Chemistry*, Vol. IA, Van Nostrand, New York, 1959, pp. 530–547.
4. Gordon, L., J. Block, N. Haberman, and E. D. Salesin, *Acta Chim. Acad. Sci. Hung.*, **33**, 299 (1962).
5. Williams, M., *Ind. Chemist*, **38**, 134, 186 (1962).
6. Firsching, F. H., *Talanta*, **10**, 1169 (1963).
7. Willard, H. H., and N. K. Tang, *J. Am. Chem. Soc.*, **59**, 1190 (1937).
8. Cartwright, P. F. S., *Analyst*, **85**, 216 (1960).
9. Prasad, T. P., and M. N. Sastri, *Current Sci.*, **32**, 67 (1963).
10. Norwitz, G., *Anal. Chem.*, **33**, 312 (1961).
11. Dembinski, W., A. Deptula, and B. Volavsk, *J. Inorg. Nucl. Chem.*, **25**, 320 (1963).
12. Holland, H. D., U. M. Oxburgh, T. V. Kirsipu, M. Boresk, and A. Mookerjee, TID-12366.

13. Ross, H. H., and R. B. Hahn, *Anal. Chem.*, **32**, 1690 (1960).
14. McCurdy, W. H., W. J. A. VandenHeuvel, and A. R. Casazza, *Anal. Chem.*, **31**, 1413 (1959).
15. Burriel-Martí, F., and A. M. Vidan, *Anal. Chim. Acta*, **26**, 163 (1962).
16. Burriel-Martí, F., and A. M. Vidan, *Anales Real Soc. Espan. Fis. Quim. (Madrid), Ser. B*, **58**, 777 (1962).
17. Burriel-Martí, F., and A. M. Vidan, *Anales Real Soc. Espan. Fis. Quim. (Madrid), Ser. B*, **59**, 43 (1963).
18. Krijn, C. C., and G. den Boef, *Anal. Chim. Acta*, **23**, 35 (1960).
19. Davis, D. G., *Anal. Chem.*, **32**, 1321 (1960).
20. Newman, E. J., *Analyst*, **88**, 500 (1963).
21. Cartwright, P. F. S., *Analyst*, **86**, 688 (1961).
22. Cartwright, P. F. S., *Analyst*, **86**, 692 (1961).
23. Cartwright, P. F. S., *Analyst*, **87**, 163 (1962).
24. Dams, R., and J. Hoste, *Talanta*, **8**, 664 (1961).
25. Dams, R., and J. Hoste, *Talanta*, **9**, 86 (1962).
26. Firsching, F. H., *Talanta*, **2**, 326 (1959).
27. Firsching, F. H., *Anal. Chem.*, **33**, 1946 (1961).
28. Berak, L., and J. Munich, *Nucl. Aci. Abstr.*, **16**, 31590 (1962) (CEA-tr-A-1135).
29. Salesin, E. D., and L. Gordon, *Talanta*, **2**, 392 (1959).
30. Firsching, F. H., *Anal. Chem.*, **34**, 1696 (1962).
31. Firsching, F. H., *Anal. Chem.*, **32**, 1876 (1960).
32. Firsching, F. H., *Anal. Chem.*, **33**, 873 (1961).
33. Salesin, E. D., and L. Gordon, *Talanta*, **5**, 81 (1960).
34. Barnicoat, C. R., *Analyst*, **60**, 653 (1935).
35. Gordon, L., and E. D. Salesin, *J. Chem. Ed.*, **38**, 16 (1961).
36. Kanner, L. J., E. D. Salesin, and L. Gordon, *Talanta*, **7**, 288 (1961).
37. Píno Pérez, F., F. Burriel-Marti, and L. Martínez Conejero, *Anales Real Soc. Espan. Fis. Quim. (Madrid), Ser. B*, **55**, 331 (1959).
38. Pietrzak, R. F., and L. Gordon, *Talanta*, **9**, 327 (1962).
39. Bark, L. S., and D. Brandon, *Talanta*, **10**, 1189 (1963).
40. Heyn, A. H. A., and N. G. Dave, *Talanta*, **5**, 119 (1960).
41. Heyn, A. H. A., and P. A. Brauner, *Talanta*, **7**, 281 (1961).
42. Chan, F. L., *Talanta*, **7**, 253 (1961).
43. Heyn, A. H. A., and H. L. Finston, *Anal. Chem.*, **32**, 328 (1960).
44. Kosta, L., and M. Dular, *Talanta*, **8**, 265 (1961).
45. Salesin, E. D., and L. Gordon, *Talanta*, **4**, 75 (1960).
46. Takiyama, K., E. D. Salesin, and L. Gordon, *Talanta*, **5**, 231 (1960).
47. Marec, D. J., E. D. Salesin, and L. Gordon, *Talanta*, **8**, 293 (1961).
48. Bordner, J., E. D. Salesin, and L. Gordon, *Talanta*, **8**, 579 (1961).
49. Corkins, J. T., R. F. Pietrzak, and L. Gordon, *Talanta*, **9**, 49 (1962).
50. Jones, J. P., O. E. Hileman, Jr., and L. Gordon, *Talanta*, **10**, 111 (1963).
51. Jones, J. P., O. E. Hileman, A. Townsend, and L. Gordon, *Talanta*, in press.
52. Howick, L. C., and W. W. Trigg, *Anal. Chem.*, **33**, 302 (1961).
53. Billo, E. J., B. E. Robertson, and R. P. Graham, *Talanta*, **10**, 757 (1963).

54. Hikime, S., and L. Gordon, *Talanta*, in press.
55. Jones, J. P., O. E. Hileman, and L. Gordon, *Talanta*, in press.
56. Ellefsen, P. R., L. Gordon, R. Belcher, and W. G. Jackson, *Talanta*, 10, 701 (1963).
57. Howick, L. C., and J. L. Jones, *Talanta*, 8, 445 (1961).
58. Howick, L. C., and J. L. Jones, *Talanta*, 9, 1037 (1962).
59. Howick, L. C., and J. L. Jones, *Talanta*, 10, 189 (1963).
60. Howick, L. C., N. L. Ford, and J. L. Jones, *Talanta*, 10, 193 (1963).
61. Howick, L. C., and J. L. Jones, *Talanta*, 10, 197 (1963).
62. Howick, L. C., and T. Rihs, *Talanta*, 11, 667 (1964).
63. Washizuka, S., *Bunseki Kagaku*, 12, 20 (1963).
64. Pryszczewska, M., *Acta Chim. Acad. Sci. Hung.*, 34, 135 (1962).
65. Pryszczewska, M., *Talanta*, 10, 135 (1963).
66. Tanigawa, Y., S. Hasegawa, and K. Takiyama, *Bunseki Kagaku*, 11, 1300 (1962).
67. Soloniewicz, R., *Chem. Anal. Warsaw*, 7, 625 (1962).
68. Soloniewicz, R., *Chem. Anal. Warsaw*, 7, 965 (1962).
69. Nakano, E., *Kogyo Kagaku Zasshi*, 65, 1772 (1962).
70. Nakano, E., *Nippon Kagaku Zasshi*, 84, 363 (1963).
71. Cohen, A. I., and L. Gordon, *Talanta*, 7, 195 (1961).
72. Block, J., and L. Gordon, *Talanta*, 10, 351 (1963).
73. Callow, R. J., *J. Chem. Soc.*, 1962, 4353.
74. Pruitt, M. E., R. R. Rickard, and E. I. Wyatt, *Anal. Chem.*, 34, 283 (1962).
75. Adamski, T., *Nature*, 197, 894 (1963).
76. Salesin, E. D., E. W. Abrahamson, and L. Gordon, *Talanta*, 9, 699 (1962).
77. Hileman, O. E., P. R. Ellefsen, R. J. Magee, and L. Gordon, *Talanta*, 10, 419 (1963).
78. Firsching, F. H., and J. G. Brewer, *Anal. Chem.*, 35, 1630 (1963).
79. Klein, D. H., and L. Gordon, *Talanta*, 1, 334 (1958).
80. Klein, D. H., L. Gordon, and T. H. Walnut, *Talanta*, 3, 177 (1959).
81. Klein, D. H., L. Gordon, and T. H. Walnut, *Talanta*, 3, 187 (1959).
82. Fischer, R. B., *Anal. Chem.*, 32, 1127 (1960).
83. Haberman, N., and L. Gordon, *Anal. Chem.*, 33, 1801 (1961).
84. Klein, D. H., and B. Fontal, *Talanta*, 10, 808 (1963).
85. Fabrikanos, A., and K. H. Lieser, *Z. Physik. Chem. (Frankfurt)*, 36, 232 (1963).
86. Elliott, D., L. C. Howick, B. G. Hudson, and W. K. Noyce, *Talanta*, 9, 723 (1962).
87. Wasmuth, C. R., and H. Freiser, *Talanta*, 9, 1059 (1962).
88. Bordner, J., and L. Gordon, *Talanta*, 9, 1003 (1962).
89. Takiyama, K., and L. Gordon, *Talanta*, 10, 1165 (1963).
90. Weiss, H. V., and M. G. Lai, *Anal. Chem.*, 32, 475 (1960).
91. Weiss, H. V., and M. G. Lai, *Talanta*, 8, 72 (1961).
92. Weiss, H. V., and M. G. Lai, *J. Inorg. Nucl. Chem.*, 17, 366 (1961).
93. Weiss, H. V., M. G. Lia, and A. Gillespie, *Anal. Chim. Acta*, 25, 550 (1961).
94. Weiss, H. V., and W. H. Shipman, *Anal. Chem.*, 34, 1010 (1962).
95. Lai, M. G., and H. V. Weiss, *Anal. Chem.*, 34, 1012 (1962).

34   F. H. FIRSCHING

96. Weiss, H. V., and M. G. Lai, *Anal. Chim. Acta*, **28**, 242 (1963).
97. Hayek, E., M. Hohenlohe-Profanter, and B. Marcic, *Congr. Intern. Chim. Pure Appl.*, **16**, 881 (1957).
98. Hayek, E., and M. Hohenlohe-Profanter, *Angew. Chem.*, **70**, 307 (1958).
99. Hayek, E., P. Inama, and B. Schetz, *Monatsh. Chem.*, **94**, 366 (1963).
100. Gordon, L. (Case Institute of Technology), private communication.
101. Firsching, F. H. (Southern Illinois University), unpublished results.

Manuscript Recieved by Publisher March 9, 1964.

Differential Dialysis

LYMAN C. CRAIG, *The Laboratories of the Rockefeller Institute, New York, New York*

I. INTRODUCTION

When a semipermeable membrane is used to stabilize the concentration gradient between a solution on one side and pure solvent on the other, the minimum requirements for simple dialysis have been met. The kinetic movement of the solute molecules will tend to drive them through the membrane in the direction of lower concentration. On the other hand, as a result of the osmotic pressure difference, the net movement of the solvent molecules will be in the opposite direction. However, depending on their size, shape, and other properties, the solute molecules may not be able to enter the membrane and will be completely excluded. We can call the more concentrated solution the "retentate" (1) and the more dilute solution the "diffusate."

This concept of dialysis was first proposed by Thomas Graham (2) in 1861 as a way of separating relatively small molecules from large ones. The test solutes he used were sucrose and gum arabic in aqueous solution. Obviously, this separation did not demonstrate a very high degree of selectivity, or separating power, since the molecular sizes differ so widely. Nonetheless it represented a very important advance in separation. Many of the solutes which diffused through the membrane could be crystallized. Graham, therefore, called the diffusable solutes "crystalloids" and those that would not pass the membrane "colloids."

As time passed, dialysis came to be used widely as a simple laboratory method of separating very large molecules from small, but little refinement in the method was accomplished. Graham, however, realized that it had considerable potential for separating mixtures of more closely related solutes. He thought of the process as being based on differential rates of diffusion and, therefore, capable of development as a separation process which would be analogous to distillation. It is the purpose of this chapter to deal particularly with those aspects of simple dialysis which contribute to the possibility of separating mixtures of closely related solutes. This is the reason for the title "Differential Dialysis" rather than "Dialysis." The success of dialysis in this connection will clearly depend on whether or not conditions can be found which will provide sufficient differences in the rates of diffusion of the solutes through the membrane. Any factor which is capable of modifying the rates differentially becomes of prime interest.

The rate of diffusion of any single solute through a membrane depends on many factors among which are:

1. The membrane
2. The solute
3. The solvent
4. The temperature
5. The physical setup

All these factors are interrelated, a state of affairs which contributes to the complication of any proposed study of the phenomenon.

Ideally, for a given solute, membrane, solvent, temperature, and physical setup, the overall rate of diffusion through the membrane can be described by an equation analogous to Ficks law for diffusion in free solution. This equation can be written as follows:

$$\text{Rate of diffusion} = -DA\,\frac{dc}{dx} \tag{1}$$

D is the diffusion constant, A is the cross-sectional area of the diffusion column, and dc/dx is the concentration gradient. In fact, one well-known way of measuring diffusion coefficients makes use of a sintered glass plate (3) as shown in Figure 1. In this method a correction for the effect of the sintered glass plate must be applied. The correction factor or cell constant is determined experimentally by studying solutes with known diffusion coefficients. In this cell the pores of the sintered glass are very much larger than the dimensions of the solute

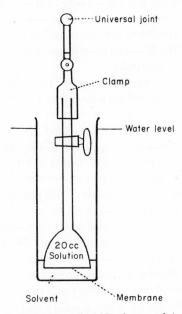

Fig. 1. Diffusion cell of Northrop and Anson.

molecules and, therefore, the cell constant corrects largely for the depth of the membrane and for the reduced solution volume within the sintered glass plate available for diffusion. The same approach can be used with membranes with presumably much smaller pores, but in this case the whole picture becomes much more complicated. Here the term "permeation constant" has been used for the comparison of membranes.

Unfortunately, the large majority of solutes, solvents, and membranes do not behave ideally, and any constant applied to the cell will usually hold only for a particular solute at a particular concentration range. The reason for this will become apparent later on.

The study of diffusion through membranes can be taken up from several different approaches each of which has been followed to some extent in the large and growing literature on the subject. Broadly speaking there is the theoretical approach, more appealing to the physical chemist, in which an attempt has been made to sort out and define the various factors controlling the phenomenon. The objective in this type of study is the discovery of relationships which can be expressed mathematically in terms of general equations. A recent excellent paper by Ginzburg and Katchalsky (4) can be taken as an example. Most of the informative studies in the literature have been carried out from this standpoint.

A basically different approach can be taken which may be of more significance from a practical standpoint to the subject of differential dialysis. This approach is more characteristic of the organic or natural products chemist who is interested in separating mixtures of solutes into pure individual compounds and in the use of the data so obtained for characterizing each fraction. Long experience has shown that for such a purpose there is no substitute for the extensive use of model solutes. The emphasis of this approach, therefore, is on the properties of the model solute and its behavior in the membrane rather than on the less certain and often confusing properties of the membrane. It is more empirical in nature. No assumption regarding the nature of the membrane need be made. Such an approach will be extensively developed in the present chapter. It can have a rather simple basis both experimentally and theoretically.

If the rate of diffusion for a given solute and membrane is proportional only to the concentration gradient across the membrane (eq. 1), it follows that the process is analogous to first-order reaction kinetics. When the logarithm of the decrease in concentration of the retentate is plotted against time, a straight line should result as shown in Figure 2 (5). Several years ago the author set about finding the most favorable conditions for experimentally producing such a result. It has been possible to achieve this adherence with a high degree of precision for a wide variety of solutes. Such a plot gives the following information almost at a glance:

1. It indicates that the solute is behaving ideally over the range of concentration covered.

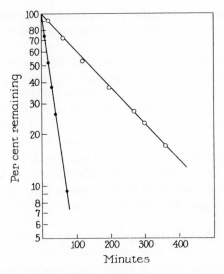

Fig. 2. Dialysis plots of two polypeptides; ● = bacitracin, mol. wt. 1422; ○ = subtilin, mol. wt. 3200.

2. It shows that the solute is homogeneous with respect to size within the limits of discrimination of the membrane.

3. The 50% escape time is a constant characteristic of the cell and the size of the solute, and useful for comparison with the 50% escape times of other solutes. It is a figure which does not represent a single measurement, but is the composite result from a number of determinations under fractionating conditions.

4. It is possible to interpret the deviation from a straight line, should this be found to occur, in terms of impurity, association, or dissociation, as will be shown later in this development.

Because of the interrelationship of all the factors, which influence the rate of diffusion through a membrane, it is difficult to decide which should be considered first in any general treatment of the subject. For example, the concept of ideality and how closely the solutes can be expected to adhere to it is of little concern when the problem is that of separating a small solute from a very large one. On the other hand, it may be all important if the problem is that of distinguishing between or separating two solutes, one of which is only twice as large as the other. Here, the required selectivity must be achieved in some way and the physical setup accordingly assumes much greater importance. The problem cannot be solved by speaking in terms of generalities. Therefore, before attempting any further treatment it would seem best to refer the reader to the analytical dialysis cell in Section V. This cell in the author's experience seems capable of yielding the most pertinent information for the study of differential dialysis.

It is not the purpose of this chapter to deal with the diffusion of charged solutes through membranes carrying fixed charges. This is a subject of great importance on the one hand to physiologists and on the other to industry. For a better understanding of the theory of this type of membrane action, the reader is referred to the classical work of Sollner (6) and the book by Tuwiner (7). Electrodialysis, a closely related subject likewise, does not come within the scope of the treatment.

The chapter will deal almost entirely with cellophane membranes, since these seem to be by far the most widely used and generally satisfactory membranes now available for laboratory work.

II. THE MEMBRANE

A dialysis membrane is a layer of some substance or mixture, usually a very thin layer, which forms a boundary between two solutions of different composition. It may or may not permit diffusion of one or all the solutes from one phase to the other. If it does permit diffusion of one solute, but not the others, it is said to be semipermeable. When to consider a membrane permeable and when semipermeable, however, is often an arbitrary decision depending on the differences in size of the solutes or other properties such as their charge.

In the literature describing the earliest use of dialysis one finds the use of parchment paper and various animal membranes. These included the bladders of fish, pigs, cattle, and other animals. The gut and peritoneal membrane were also tried. Later, membranes cast in the laboratory from pyroxylin or collodion solutions became popular. These could be made in almost any size, thickness, or shape desired. Ways of controlling the porosity within certain limits were later developed. In spite of intensive investigation directed toward improvement, the strength of the nitro-cellulose membranes was never developed to a completely satisfactory level. Their selectivity and reproducibility also left much to be desired.

In comparatively recent years, regenerated cellulose casings of remarkable properties and specifications have been developed for the meat packing industry. For such a purpose it was desirable to fill sausage casings by forcing ground suspended meat into long casings under considerable pressure. But it was also desirable, from the standpoint of the consumer, to have the skins on the sausages as thin as possible once they were formed. These requirements called for unusual uniformity in thickness and freedom from so-called pin holes, since the latter would invariably be a point of weakness in the membrane which would show up at the worst possible time during the filling of the casing. These are characteristics which are precisely those needed for dialysis membranes in the laboratory. By virtue of this fortunate coincidence, a superior membrane for laboratory dialysis has become available. Except for specialized purposes, it has now come to be the membrane of choice for laboratory dialysis.

The Visking Company, 6733 West 65th Street, Chicago 38, Illinois, markets two types of cellophane casing which are of particular interest in differential dialysis. One type, their "dialysis" tubing, is made specifically for this purpose. The other is the regular regenerated cellulose tubing which is not claimed to have the same reliability or uniformity of pore size.

Both types are marketed in rolls which are sealed in plastic bags to prevent their drying out. They contain glycerine and small amounts of other solutes which can be washed out easily. Once the plastic bag is opened in order to use a piece of the casing the roll should be put in the container again and the bag closed tightly. When stored in the refrigerator the porosity will remain nearly constant for long periods of time.

The sizes listed by the Visking Company are given in Table I.

TABLE I
Sizes of Visking "Dialysis" Casing Available

Identity	App. inflated Diam. (wet) in cm.	Wall thick., mm.	Lengths available, ft.
8 D.C.	0.62	0.05	100 or 1500
20 D.C.	1.55	0.02	100 or 1000
27 D.C.	2.1	0.025	100 or 1000
36 D.C.	2.8	0.02	100 or 1000
$1^7/_8$ S.S.	4.7	0.04	50 or 500
$3^1/_4$ S.S.	8.13	0.09	50 or 500

The identifying numbers relate to the size in fractions of an inch of the wet inflated casing at one point during manufacture. Thus, 8 is the same as $^8/_{32}$ in the older identification numbers.

A wider variety of sizes is available in the regenerated seamless tubing. The company gives the average pore size, determined by rate of flow of water under standard conditions, as 24 A. for the dialysis tubing. Data are not given for the other type. Thus far in the author's laboratory, the seamless tubing has proven to be nearly as reliable as the "dialysis" tubing.

When the porosity is compared by the rate of dialysis of known solutes as given in Section V, it will be found that the "dialysis" tubing is generally more permeable than the regular tubing. In the author's experience, the 20 D.C. is the most permeable and will allow ribonuclease (mol. wt. 13,600) in $0.01N$ acetic acid to pass slowly at 25°C. Even chymotrypsinogen (mol. wt. 24,500) may not be completely held back. On the other hand, sizes 18 and 23 of the regular tubing are completely impermeable to ribonuclease. The size 18 is of about the same thickness as 20 of the dialysis tubing, while 23 is a little thicker.

In recent times there has been considerable industrial interest in membranes, but often for purposes outside the stability range of cellulose. Strong acids or bases change its properties and weaken or degrade it. For use with these materials, synthetic resin membranes have been developed which are polymers of polyvinyl alcohol. While these membranes have great industrial potential they have not as yet come into general laboratory use as far as the author is aware.

Many membranes are ion selective by virtue of the fact that they carry fixed charges, either positive or negative. Animal membranes are generally of this type, since they appear to have a considerable degree of structure and contain protein or polypeptide material. While there are many specialized purposes for which ion exchange membranes could be very valuable, the fixed charges do introduce complications. One of the objections to the collodion membrane, other than lack of strength, is that it carries fixed negative charges of somewhat indefinite nature. It would seem best from the standpoint of simple dialysis to use either a membrane free of fixed charges or one with a known high number of positive or negative charges.

Cellophane membranes are extraordinarily free from fixed charges, even carboxyl groups. This point has been well substantiated (8) in the author's laboratory. Apparently, in the manufacturing process, great care is taken to prevent oxidation of the cellulose, since the point of attachment of a carboxyl group in the cellophane would constitute a point of mechanical weakness in the membrane.

The synthetic resin membranes made from polyvinyl alcohol also can be non-ion selective. Moreover, membranes made from this polymer can be made to contain either fixed anions, or cations, by incorporating a second polymer with the appropriate groups.

For a long time two theories of the way uncharged membranes permit certain solutes to pass, but reject others, have been under consideration. In one, the solute is thought simply to dissolve in the membrane. It is considered to have the properties of a viscous liquid with no "pores" through which the solute may diffuse. Transport takes place by normal diffusion through the liquid. Solutes not soluble in the viscous liquid are totally rejected.

In the other theory, the membrane is considered to be a matrix of anastomosing pores like a sponge or something more analogous to an irregular pile of sticks. The matrix does not "dissolve" the solute but the "pores" are filled with the same solvent in which the solutes on either side of the membrane are dissolved. Such a membrane may be scarcely porous in the dry state, but it usually has a definite affinity for the solvent and "imbibes" a certain definite proportion of solvent, thereby becoming swelled and considerably less rigid. The porosity of this type of membrane can be a function of the solvent, as well as of the membrane, since the degree of swelling will differ with different solvents. Of course, membranes which do not interact with the solvent are known, porous Kel-F for instance.

The synthetic resin membranes in some cases can be considered hybrids of the two limiting types. Here there appears to be microscopic islands of dense impermeable but crystalline material throughout the membrane (9). These islands do not imbibe the solvent but the amorphous polymeric material around them does and in this way an overall physical medium something like a sponge is formed. The amorphous part has the properties of a gel and permits permeable solutes to diffuse through it.

An example of a membrane operating according to the solution mechanism is to be found with a membrane made from pure rubber. Hydrocarbons will diffuse through it but not hydrophyllic solutes like the amino acids. Cellophane on the other hand is one which clearly operates by the "pore" mechanism, as later experiments will show.

If a membrane operates by the pore mechanism it has more of the characteristics of a simple sieve and will allow solutes of various sizes to diffuse through differentially according to their size. On the other hand solution membranes may show a size parameter as would be expected of any diffusion process but they may also allow diffusion preferentially on the basis of solubility properties.

With a semipermeable membrane which operates by the "pore" mechanism it would be expected that the relative rates of diffusion of two different sized solutes would be in proportion to their effective diameters. With perfect spheres this diameter would be in proportion to the inverse cube of the volume, since $V = \frac{4}{3}\pi r^3$, where V is the volume and r is the radius of the sphere. This behavior can be approximately substantiated in experiments with cellophane. The inverse square relationship, however, is often quoted as the proportionality which seems to apply.

1. Types

A. ALTERATION OF POROSITY BY STRETCHING

Wet cellophane is really a gel which can be stretched and deformed rather easily. But if it is stretched more than a certain critical distance it will not return to the original size and shape, but will remain permanently deformed. A length of dialysis tubing will thereby become longer but more narrow in diameter. When the porosity of such a stretched membrane is determined in the cell of Figure 3 by measuring the escape rate of a standard solute and compared with that determined in an unstretched membrane, a marked retardation will be noted (10). Figure 4 gives an example of this with ribonuclease as the solute. Membranes can be stretched conveniently a measured amount by the simple apparatus shown in Figure 5. The decreased rate of diffusion in the stretched membrane can be explained on the basis of deformation of a hypothetical average shape of the pores as shown in Figure 6a,b.

This deformation in shape can be partly prevented by applying hydrostatic pressure to the inside of the tubing at the time it is being stretched. The per cent of linear stretch can be measured, and sufficient hydrostatic pressure applied, so that the per cent of increase in the circumference of the tubing is similar to that of the linear. When this is done the membrane becomes much more porous as measured by

solute permability (10).   In Figure 4 this effect is shown with ribonuclease.

The stretching equipment (10) shown in Figure 5 includes a shallow
pan of sufficient length, two C clamps, and two glass collars each
connected to the C clamps with loop of nylon cord (fishing line) tied

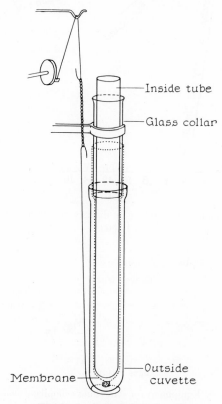

Fig. 3. Analytical dialysis cell.

around each glass collar.   One glass collar carries a solid rubber
stopper, the other a stopper through which passes a glass tube.   The
glass tube is connected to a rubber tube leading to a water reservoir.
Controlled pressure on the water is applied by air pressure.   The
cellophane tubing is held on the glass collar which later becomes the
glass collar of Figure 3, by a sufficient number of loops of tightly

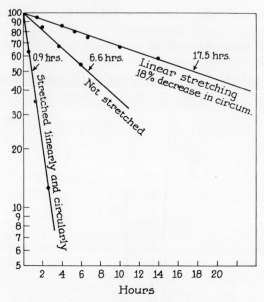

Fig. 4. Effect of membrane stretching on dialysis rate with ribonuclease, mol. wt. 13,600.

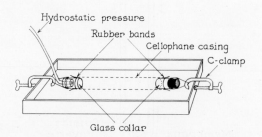

Fig. 5. Equipment for stretching cellophane casing.

stretched rubber bands. After the stretching process the rubber bands are removed and the sac is tied off as in Figure 3.

In Figure 7 one curve shows an escape rate obtained with an unstretched membrane with ribonuclease molecular weight 13,600. The other curve was obtained with chymotrypsinogen, molecular weight 25,000, with the same membrane when it was stretched approximately 20% both linearly and circularly. One sphere with twice the volume

(a)   (b)

Fig. 6. Concept of pore deformation by stretching. a = uniform linear and circular; b = linear.

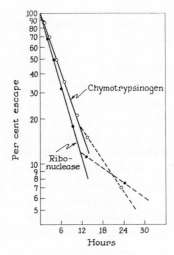

Fig. 7. Comparison of ribonuclease and chymotrypsinogen in appropriate membranes.

of another would have a 25% larger diameter. Here the length of the sac was adjusted to provide the same total membrane area in both cases. The geometry of the above comparison is not entirely correct since the membrane becomes stretched in two dimensions only, not three, and, therefore, becomes somewhat thinner during the stretching process. The experiment nonetheless does offer strong support for the pore theory. Even stronger support, however, is offered by the body of evidence built up by the many published (5,11–13) experiments with solutes of known size.

In Section VIII, dealing with the theoretical aspects of dialysis, it will be shown that the limiting pore size is very important in determining selectivity.   Maximum selectivity is obtained when a particular solute is barely able to diffuse through the membrane.   It, therefore, becomes very important to adjust the pore size to either smaller or larger dimensions to suit the size of the molecules under study. While the mechanical stretching experiments described above have permitted adjustment within a limited range, it has become necessary to use other techniques for a wider adjustment.   These include an acetylation procedure for reducing the pore size (10) and a swelling procedure with zinc chloride solution to increase the pore size.   These procedures have permitted adjustment to be made so that solutes anywhere in the range of 100 to 100,000 will either pass the membrane or be almost totally rejected.

B.   THE ACETYLATION PROCEDURE

Since this procedure is used only to reduce the pore size, it has proven advisable to select a particular casing which already has been shown to have as small a pore size as possible.   Thus far in the author's experience the choice has proven to be either the $^{23}/_{32}$ or $^{18}/_{32}$ size.   Neither of these sizes are sold by the Visking Company as dialysis tubing, but are obtainable from them as regenerated cellulose tubing.   The wet casing is stretched linearly as far as possible. Acetylation not only reduces the pore size but it also makes the membrane somewhat less flexible if carried too far.   A flexible membrane provides a more uniform retentate film, and from this standpoint is more desirable.

The wet stretched membrane tied off and attached to the glass collar as given in the above section is washed inside and out with pyridine and then filled with 25% acetic anhydride in pyridine.   It is suspended in the acetic anhydride mixture at 60–65°C. for an arbitrary time depending on the tightness of the membrane desired.   Heating at 65°C. for 7 hr. has been found sufficient nearly to exclude the passage of amino acids.   The reaction mixture is removed from the membrane by repeated washing with $0.01N$ acetic acid.   Complete removal of the pyridine may require several hours.   An acetylated membrane is less hydrophyllic than the unacetylated one.   It will maintain the porosity determined by calibration for a long time, if treated properly.   Aqueous $0.1N$ ammonium hydroxide at 40°C. was found to increase the porosity of highly acetylated membranes but not those lightly acetylated.   Dilute acetic acid did not.   Strong urea solutions caused the porosity to increase slowly with certain highly acetylated membranes.

C. THE ZINC CHLORIDE SWELLING PROCEDURE

The effect of zinc chloride on cellophane dialysis membranes was first described by McBain and Stuewer (14) who recommended a 64% solution. This is a rather viscous solution which will completely disintegrate the membrane if given sufficient time.

An arbitrary length of the tubing is attached to the glass collar as above and tied off at the bottom with sufficient of the cellophane tubing to allow a second knot to be tied into a loop. A glass rod longer than the tubing is bent to form a hook which is inserted into the loop at the bottom of the sac. Sufficient of the 64% zinc hydrochloride at 25°C is then poured into the sac and into a graduate cylinder in which the sac is suspended so that the level inside is no more than 1 cm. higher than on the outside. The membrane soon becomes quite plastic and with an appreciably higher pressure inside the tubing will become enlarged in an uneven way. After an arbitrary period of time, 1 to 15 min. depending on the porosity desired, the zinc chloride solution is carefully poured off from both inside and outside, all the while maintaining nearly equal levels inside and out. This can be done by the use of the glass rod attached to the bottom of the sac. The zinc chloride is washed out with $0.01N$ hydrochloric acid using care on the first washing to avoid any pressure on the inside by filling it more rapidly than the outside.

Membranes treated in this way are not as stable as the untreated or acetylated ones but still there is sufficient stability for many repeated runs to be made on a single membrane after standardization. For this treatment it is best to select the most porous casing available, thus far in our experience the $^{20}/_{32}$ size.

For certain purposes it could be desirable to reduce the concentration of the zinc chloride somewhat, and compensate for this by use of a longer treatment time. Pierce and Free (15) have increased the porosity in this way.

D. CALIBRATION OF MEMBRANES

Most of the literature dealing with membranes treats the problem of calibration from the standpoint of "average pore size." The rate of flow of a solvent, usually water, through a unit area of the membrane is determined for a given pressure drop across the membrane. From this filtration rate a figure is calculated by a formula which gives a measure of the average pore size. While this method may have certain advantages for the theoretical interpretation of membrane structure, it does not provide a basis for comparison which is the most useful from the standpoint of selectivity and the understanding of differential dialysis.

A serious objection is immediately obvious when it is realized that membranes are more or less deformable gels and that their porosity can be altered by mechanical stress as shown in a previous section. It would seem that membranes should be calibrated by a method which avoids stress as nearly as possible.

In any case the selectivity of a membrane is not determined by the "average pore size" but by the distribution in size of those pores which barely permit the solute of interest to pass. The molecular size of this solute is ordinarily much larger than that of a simple solvent such as water. A considerably more realistic way of calibrating a membrane, therefore, would seem to be, by determination of the actual rate of dialysis under standard conditions, of a solute of known size and shape which is barely able to diffuse through the membrane. The experimental procedure for doing this is given in Section V along with the description of the analytical cell.

Calibration of membranes by this procedure is made much easier by the availability of relatively pure preparations of model solutes of widely different sizes varying from molecular weights of the order of

TABLE II
Solute Models

Solute	Mol. wt.
1. Glycine	75
2. Tryptophan	204
3. Oxidized glutathione	612
4. Bacitracin	1,422
5. Subtilin	3,200
6. Ribonuclease	13,600
7. Chymotrypsinogen	25,000
8. Pepsinogen	45,000
9. Serum albumin	68,000

100 to those of 68,000. In Table II a list of models thoroughly studied in the author's laboratory is given. These models are convenient to use since with the exception of glycine and oxidized glutathione the necessary concentrations can be determined by optical density at a suitable wave length in an ultraviolet spectrophotometer. Glycine and oxidized glutathione can be determined either by direct residue weight or by the ninhydrin procedure (16).

Since the rate of dialysis for most of the larger solutes is a function of the solvent and the temperature, as discussed in Sections IV and V, these always must be specified.

III. THE SOLUTE-SOLVENT INTERACTION

The solvent is a very important factor in dialysis for a number of reasons. It can influence the rate of dialysis by viscosity effects, by solvation, by conformational effects on the solute, and by influencing the state of association in the case of those solutes which associate strongly.

A solute dissolved in a given solvent may have relatively little attraction for the solvent, or it may bind one or more molecules of the solvent with considerable strength. In the latter case it can be the molecular size of the solvate which determines the diffusional capability of the solute. Solvation may or may not appreciably change the effective size depending on the nature of the solute. Pertinent information on this point is difficult to find in the literature because of the lack of a reliable way to measure the effect. It seems significant, however, that diffusion coefficients of polyhydroxy solutes like the sugars are considerably lower than those for amino acids or polypeptides of the same molecular weight. This difference is amplified when comparative rates of dialysis are considered. Thus, for example, glucose with a molecular weight of 180 was found to dialyze at a rate comparable to leucyl tryptophan whose molecular weight is 317. Other examples support this experience. If each hydroxyl of glucose should bind firmly one molecule of water the effective diffusional size of glucose would be that expected from a molecular weight of 270 rather than 180. Both conformation and hydration could well play a role in the dialysis of sugars.

The role of the solvent becomes more complex and important when the shape or conformation is not entirely fixed by covalent bonds.

Molecules of larger size such as polypeptides are capable of assuming more than one conformation. In one extreme the molecule may be fully extended and in the form of maximum length, while in the other extreme it can be coiled or twisted in some way so that its shape approaches a spherical form. The latter would be expected to have a much higher diffusability for more than one reason. With solutes of this type the shape is determined by a balance of interactions. The chain is capable of folding back on itself and will tend to do so if the attractive interactions between the different portions of the chain are greater than the solute-solvent interaction. The diffusability of the spherical conformation should be greater not only because of the shape but also because this shape would be solvated to a lesser degree and thus would be smaller.

Protein and peptide chemists have been greatly interested in the intrachain interactions of polymeric molecules. They have tried to describe more precisely the forces which determine the shape of the molecule. At present these are considered to be: (1) charge interactions, (2) hydrogen bonding, (3) charge transfer, (4) hydrophyllic bonding, and (5) hydrophobic bonding.

For example, a synthetic polymer of ethylene glycol would not be expected to show much intrachain interaction and should behave as a chain partly extended and partly coiled or folded in a completely random manner. While monodisperse preparations are not available, ones with rather narrow ranges of molecular weights can be purchased, the "Carbowaxes." These are water soluble materials which can be studied well by thin film dialysis. The smaller ones give curved escape patterns indicative of mixtures as expected, but require a more porous membrane for their study than do the so-called linear peptides of the same molecular weight. Obviously, their diffusional size is much larger. A long peptide chain can be tightly coiled or folded in solution even though the arrangement may be more or less random.

It would be expected that the solvent not only would be very important in determining the shape of such molecules but would similarly affect the porosity of the membrane. A solvent with a strong affinity for the membrane will cause greater imbibition or swelling, and thus cause the membrane to become more porous. This has long been known in membrane technology (7). Obviously, when the dialysis rates of two solutes are to be compared, the solvent composition must be exactly the same in both cases.

The effect on the membrane of small changes in composition of the solvent can be studied by the use of model solutes held in a specific conformation by covalent bonds. Certain cyclic peptides and polysaccharides are excellent for this purpose. These include bacitracin (17) and the Schardinger dextrins (13). Cellophane membranes have been found to be relatively little influenced by pH changes between the range of 2 and 10, or by aqueous salt solutions or by urea solutions.

On the other hand, the rates of dialysis of certain peptides and proteins (12) may be influenced by changes of pH but the majority are more or less strongly influenced by relatively small concentrations of salt in the solvent. Each peptide seems to be influenced to a different degree. Thus, the polypeptide hormone, ACTH, dialyzes rapidly at pH 3.3 in a salt-free solution, but at less than one tenth this rate when the solution contains $0.1M$ ammonium acetate. It dialyzes only slowly in urea solution. The hormone bradykinin, on the other hand, seems relatively little influenced by salt. A polymeric molecule of another type, yeast sRNA, which contains approximately 100 nucleotide units, will readily diffuse through a membrane of suitable porosity when the solvent is a salt solution but will not dialyze at all in salt-free water (18). This behavior can be explained best on the basis of conformational changes in the molecule which result from charge interaction and the shielding effect of salt.

When the solute shows a tendency to associate to form dissociable dimers, trimers, and higher forms, the solvent can play a strong role (19). If the equilibrium is not too strongly in favor of the polymers, little effect on the dialysis rate will be found, but where the higher forms predominate and only slowly transform to the monomers, the rate of dialysis is strongly retarded. In this case a component added to the system which is capable of binding to the monomer can strongly influence the rate of dialysis. Obviously, dialysis phenomena can become very complicated when strong association occurs and when equilibrium between the various forms is not instantaneously established. In spite of this it can be a very useful tool for studying systems that associate. Apparently, a considerable degree of rapidly reversible association has little effect on the dialysis rate.

IV. THE TEMPERATURE

For simple diffusion with an ideal solute, the effect of changing the temperature can be calculated (20). The rate of diffusion will increase in direct proportion to the absolute temperature, and inversely as the viscosity of the solvent changes. This follows from the Stokes-Einstein relationship in equation 2 where D is the diffusion coefficient, n is the viscosity, r is the radius of the molecule, and N is Avogadro's constant.

$$D = RT/6\pi\eta rN \tag{2}$$

It might be expected that the rates of dialysis of ideal solutes would follow a similar relationship. However, this was found not to be the case (20) for those experiments in which a highly selective membrane

TABLE III
Temperature Coefficients (Ratios of Half Escape Times)

Compound	M.W.	0.01N HAc 25–40°C.	0.01N HAc 40–60°C.	0.15N NH₄Ac pH 5.57 25–40°C.	0.15N NH₄Ac pH 5.57 40–60°C.	Deionized water 25–40°C.	Deionized water 40–60°C.
Tryptophan	204	2.5	—	2.3	1.55	2.1	1.4
Triglycine	189	2.5	1.35	—	—	1.53	1.62
Tetraglycine	246	2.7	1.44	1	3.6	1.54	1.57
Leu·Tyr	294	2.1	2.2	2.1	—	1.38	2.4
Leu·Try	317	3.2	2.2	1.6	1.7	1.36	1.57
Val·Tyr·Val·His	516	1.7	—	1.45	1.75	1.9	2.5
Ala·Ala·Try·Gly·Lys	531	2.9	3.1	1.85	2.1	—	—
Oxidized glutathione	612	—	—	12	1.8	0.9	1.6
Val·Phe·Val·His·Pro·Phe	744	1	1	1.9	2.8	1.8	1.8
Asp·Arg·Val·Phe·Val-·His·Pro·Phe	1015	2.3	2.5	3.0	2.7	2	1.1
B chain from insulin		2.5	—	—	—	—	—
Ribonuclease		1.44	2.3	1.0	—	2.1	2.5ᵃ
Lysozyme		1.48	—	2.1	—	—	—
Cytochrome c		1.42	—	1.36	—	—	—
Chymotrypsinogen		1.89	—	1.57	—	—	—
Ovalbumin		1.53	—	—	—	—	—

ᵃ Temperature interval = 40–65°C.

was used, one which would barely allow the solutes to pass. Only in the case of certain solutes and for certain temperature intervals did the relationship appear to hold. This is shown in Table III where the rates are compared on the basis of 50% escape times for the temperature intervals 25–40°C. and 40–60°C. Ideally, each of these temperature intervals on the basis of equation 2 should increase the rate of dialysis by a factor of 1.44.

Deviation from this factor could arise from a change either in the solute or in the membrane. However, the fact that the expected factor was found experimentally for a number of the test solutes would seem to indicate that the discrepancy was to be found in the solute. Two possibilities may be considered for the case where the factor is too large; a change in the degree of solvation or a change in the conformation of the molecule.

In the interpretation of these data it should be kept in mind that only relatively small changes are involved because of the high selectivity of the membranes. Data have been presented (13) which show this type of diffusion amplifies greatly, perhaps ten fold, any differences noted by comparing free diffusion coefficients.

In a few cases, the data in Table III show the temperature interval factor to be less than 1.44. This could mean a change in conformation at the higher temperature which would result from a slight expansion of the molecule. It would not be surprising to find this taking place with peptides. However, too much confidence should not be placed in any one value in Table III. It was not possible to check carefully all the values because the membranes used finally developed pin holes and were no longer usable.

V. THE ANALYTICAL CELL

The cell (10) which has proven thus far to have the most favorable characteristics for deriving the data for the type of plot shown in Figure 2, is shown schematically in Figure 3. It is designed to be used with commercially available cellophane casing.

A glass collar A is made by cutting off approximately the top 5 cm. of a test tube chosen of such diameter that it will be about 3 mm. larger in diameter than the wet inflated cellophane casing. The cut end is carefully fire polished so as not to increase the thickness of the glass. The end of the wet casing is enlarged by working it while it is kept well wetted, over the tapered end of a tapered glass tube shown in Figure 8b. After stretching it in this way it will easily slide over the glass collar. This part of the casing is allowed to dry and will be fixed on the glass collar in this way. The unstretched part of the casing below the glass collar must never be allowed to dry.

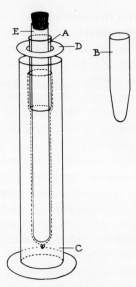

Fig. 8. A preparative dialysis cell and tapered glass tube for stretching the opening of the casing.

The casing is tied off a suitable distance from the glass collar depending on the length of the cell desired. It can be tied with silk thread or by making a knot in the cellophane tubing. The former makes a more efficient sac.

An inside tube sealed off at the bottom, is chosen so that its diameter is only slightly less than the inflated diameter of the casing. This is the only critical dimension of the cell. When it drops into place the solution which is to become the retentate, about 0.3–0.5 ml. in volume, is spread evenly over the entire surface of the membrane. With approximately 50 sq. cm. of dialyzing membrane, the retentate solution film will then be of the order of 0.1 mm. in thickness.

The outside cuvette is of such diameter that approximately 3 ml. of the solvent will fill it to the upper edge of the dialyzing membrane. It is enlarged a sufficient amount for a distance of approximately 1 cm. from the top so that it will slide easily over the lower edge of the glass collar. The solvent thus fills the cuvette to within a little more than 0.5 cm. of the top.

Stirring is accomplished by a small slow speed motor driving an eccentric. A small timing motor with a gear reduction affording 10–

30 r.p.m. is excellent. The eccentric raises and lowers a nylon cord which passes over a bent glass rod. The other end of the cord is attached to a wire loop that supports the cuvette C. The cuvette is thus raised and lowered a distance of approximately 0.5 cm. 10–30 times/min. This produces a piston-like action which provides excellent stirring of diffusate and the retentate film alike, since the membrane is flexible and responds to the small difference in pressure.

The arrangement shown in Figure 3 offers another convenience. It can be lowered into a constant temperature bath to nearly the top of the cuvette. Temperature coefficients can be determined very simply.

In the regular procedure used to determine an escape rate, the membrane is prepared and pure solvent run as a blank until the analytical procedure used, usually a spectroscopic method, shows a low level or response. For instance the cellophane membranes currently obtainable seem to show with $0.01N$ acetic acid a blank of 0.010–0.020 at 280 mμ even after prolonged washing. This may be due to a little colloidal cellophane being shed from the membrane. The solutions can be withdrawn or added most conveniently by the use of hypodermic syringes with appropriate sizes and lengths of Kel-F tubing thrust into the tip in place of the needle.

After achieving a low blank, the solvents are withdrawn and the required volume of solution of a known concentration is placed without delay inside the sac together with the pure solvent in the cuvette. The change must be made in such a way that the membrane does not dry. The time is recorded. After an arbitrary time period, the diffusate is withdrawn and replaced with fresh solvent. This is repeated until the major part of the solute has emerged in 6–10 diffusate portions. Since the diffusate approximates ten fold the volume of the retentate, the diffusion through the membrane takes place against essentially O concentration.

At the end of the run, the retentate is removed and the sac rinsed. All the diffusates and the retentate solutions are then analyzed and the recovery calculated. If this figure does not add up to total recovery, a reliable estimate of the rate cannot be made. In case the recovery is too low, adsorption in the pores of the membrane should be suspected and elution of the membrane for an hour or more with the solvent may reveal further material. In any case, this should be done in order to be certain that the blank is low for the next run. It may even be necessary to elute the membrane with a solvent of higher eluting power, for instance, a stronger solution of acetic acid. If the recovery should be too high this may indicate a mistake or incomplete elution from a previous run.

Each time a diffusate is set aside and fresh solvent replaced, the inner tube B should be pulled up and allowed to fall back in again. This is done by grasping the knot with one hand when the tube is pulled up. It may show a tendency to stick slightly due to evaporation on the outside of the membrane. Here a little manipulation of the membrane by the tips of the operator's fingers may be required. Therefore, this operation should be done only with well washed hands in order not to contribute absorbing impurities. If the tube B should tend to stick on replacing it, the retentate can be forced up sufficiently to wet the surfaces again. A film of the solution spread over the surface is an effective lubricant.

Dialysis is ordinarily thought to be a slow process requiring days for its accomplishment. It need not be. The diffusion processes taking place through membranes in living tissues are not such slow processes. On this point, a little reflection will bring out the realization that the transfer takes place through thin membranes of relatively enormous surface area in relation to the volume of retentate. The retentate is in fact spread over the membrane in a very thin film. The consequences of this are at once obvious from equation 1.

The arrangement in Figure 3 is an attempt to make a cell in which the retentate is spread as thinly and reproducibly over a dialysis membrane as possible. If an ordinary Visking cellophane dialysis membrane is used, 99% of the total sample of a small solute like an amino acid or peptide will at room temperature diffuse through the membrane in a few minutes.

This is not only important in the saving of time but it also permits the study of those membranes with relatively low porosity or, conversely, the study of the dialysis of solutes thought to be of too large a size to be dialyzable. In this case it was found that the discriminating power of the procedure was relatively much greater than with small solutes. A theoretical explanation of this selectivity has been proposed many years earlier by Elford (21) and by Ferry (22).

The cellophane membranes in the dialysis cell described above have surprising stability when preserved properly. They will retain the original calibrated porosity after repeated use over a period of months when they are preserved in $0.01N$ acetic acid and stored in the cold room.

1. Small-Scale Preparative Dialysis

Perhaps the simplest procedure for small scale preparative dialysis is the method customarily employed in most biochemical laboratories. A sac of appropriate size is made by tying a knot in one end of a piece of wet cellophane casing. The sac is then filled with water to test for leaks, emptied, and the solution to be dialyzed placed inside. The top is tied off and the closed bag suspended in water stirred in a large vessel, often with a stream of water flowing through the vessel. The temperature is usually near $0°C.$ and the time of dialysis is overnight or for several days.

Many an investigator has found to his surprise that part of the expected material though of relatively large molecular size, has mysteriously gotten through the membrane in some way. This can result from a faulty membrane with pin holes, a leaky knot, a stretched membrane resulting from the tying procedure, or pressure built up inside during the dialysis. A stretched membrane is considerably more porous as demonstrated in Section II. The knot should be tied in such a way that no strain is applied to the part that becomes the dialyzing membrane. Leakage through the knot is seldom a problem, but can be eliminated by a second knot tied slightly below the first. Leakage through the first knot can then be detected by the accumulation of solution between the knots.

If the osmotic pressure of the retentate is considerable, the volume can be expected to increase accordingly. Therefore, the knot which closes the sac should be tied above the retentate a distance sufficient to account for the expected increase in volume. The empty upper part is allowed to collapse before tying so that little air is in the closed sac. Larger volumes can be accommodated by the preparation of a number of such sacs.

For a more controlled and rapid dialysis the arrangement shown in Figure 8 can be highly recommended. Here the dialysis sac is the same as described under the analytical cell but usually longer to provide more capacity. The collar A is flared at the top so that it rests on a plastic collar D. The solution to receive the diffusate is held in a graduate cylinder. It may be stirred by a magnetic stirring bar on the bottom of C.

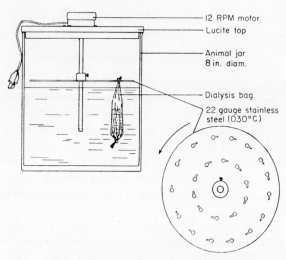

Fig 9. The dialyzer of Durrum et al.

If greater capacity is desired, a number of such sacs may be prepared and suspended through a corresponding number of holes in a stiff plastic sheet. Sacs prepared in this way may be tested and used repeatedly when they are properly preserved as described previously in this section. Greater capacity can be easily provided by reducing the size of E and allowing a longer time for dialysis. Pressure cannot develop in this type of dialyzer. Space for expansion of the retentate volume can be provided by reducing considerably the diameter of E just inside the collar A above the membrane.

Many different types of laboratory dialyzers have been described in the literature (7,23) and a number are available commercially. It scarcely appears necessary to describe them here. A convenient type somewhat more elaborate than the multiple type described above is shown in Figure 9. It was devised by Durrum et al. (24).

2. Filtration

A dialysis membrane may be used as a filter with the use of either vacuum or pressure to cause the solution to flow slowly through it. In this case, the larger size tubing must be supported to avoid undue stretching. If the flow is from the inside the cellophane sac can be placed in a sac made of some kind of netting (cotton, silk, or nylon),

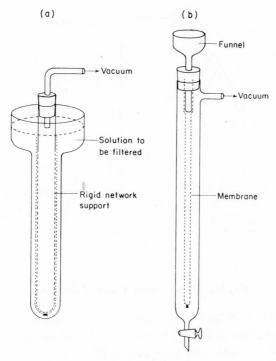

Fig. 10(a) and (b). Two ultrafiltration devices for small volumes.

which is scarcely larger than the cellophane tubing. If the flow is from the outside in, a rigid tube made from plastic sieve material and only slightly smaller in diameter than the inflated diameter of the cellophane tubing is inserted in the sac (Fig. 10a). The tubing can be of structural material with many slits in it. Frames of this kind are sold commercially.

The subject of ultrafiltration is an extensive one and many different types of filters are available on the market. The best known are the Millipore filters. Ultrafiltration is outside the scope of this chapter but will be treated only briefly because of its close relation to dialysis when the same membrane is used both for filtration and dialysis. Indeed the two processes can be profitably combined.

Several types of simple filters which permit this are shown in Figures 10 and 11. The arrangement in Figure 11 suggested by Berggard (25) is the easiest to assemble. The cellophane tubing used

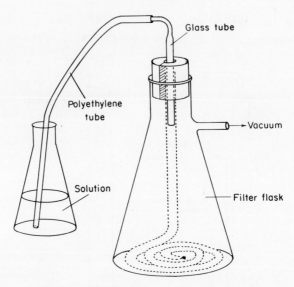

Fig. 11.   Ultrafiltration device of Berggard.

for this is Visking size $^8/_{32}$, the smallest tubing sold commercially by
Visking.   Because of the small diameter, the tubing does not require
support and will withstand a vacuum of 100 mm. or more of mercury.
It will, however, become considerably larger and more porous under
this vacuum.   A knot is tied on the end of the tubing inside the flask
and the other end is slipped over a glass tube which passes through a
flexible rubber stopper.   The rubber stopper is cut perpendicularly on
one side of the hole so that it can be opened to receive the glass tube
with the tubing pulled over it.   The cellophane tubing is, therefore,
held between the rubber stopper and the glass tubing.

When vacuum is applied the solution will be drawn slowly up
through the polyethylene tubing and into the filter.   The rate of filtration is increased by having as long a coil of the cellophane inside
the flask as possible.   This filter provides an excellent way to concen-
trate dilute solutions of proteins (25) with molecular weights larger
than 20,000, or to remove such solutes from considerably smaller ones.

The arrangement in Figure 11b is for smaller volumes and has certain conveniences.   The sac is prepared on the funnel as described for
the analytical dialysis cell.   The tube of the funnel should be of thin
glass.   Here again the rubber stopper is slit to insert the funnel so

that the membrane is held on the tube of the funnel. This arrangement permits a convenient combination of dialysis and filtration by drawing solvent into the outer tube through the lower stopcock so that it surrounds the membrane.

Filtration does not have as good selectivity as dialysis for a number of reasons. The pores tend to become clogged and the porosity does not remain constant during the filtration. In dialysis the pores are probably purged by the osmotic flow of the solvent toward the retentate. Moreover, the pressure exerts a deforming effect on the membrane, even when it is supported by a network. The total rejection point for dialysis will be for a molecule of the order of half of the size as for filtration when the same membrane is compared in both cases.

VI. COUNTERCURRENT DIALYSIS

Experiments (5,8,13) with the analytical cell described in Section V have revealed the possibility of a surprisingly high selectivity for a single step. It is, therefore, logical to try to develop a countercurrent process in which single-stage selectivity could be multiplied many times as has been done in countercurrent distribution, chromatography, or distillation. The two latter, however, are continuous processes in which there are no discrete stages. Actually, considerable work has been done to try to develop a countercurrent dialysis method. Signer and co-workers have developed an ingenious stage-continuous train (26) and Kolff (27) has published the description of an arrangement in studies designed to develop an artificial kidney. Neither of these devices has achieved wide application for laboratory separation.

A basic difficulty stems from the fact that high resistance to diffusion in a membrane seems to be required for high selectivity. This means that a high concentration gradient must be established across the membrane and the process is slow unless a relatively large membrane area is provided. While the latter does not make a countercurrent process difficult, the former does because a high concentration gradient can only be established at the expense of an extremely dilute solution to receive the diffusate. Concentration of the dilute diffusate on each stage becomes a problem. Nonetheless, a few stages are entirely practical as will be shown in the following treatment, where a membrane of relatively high selectivity has been used.

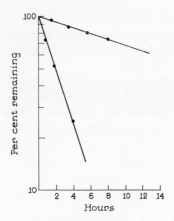

Fig. 12. Comparative escape patterns of sucrose, mol. wt. 342 and stachyose, mol. wt. 666.

The test mixture (5) will be a 50–50 mixture of 1 g. each of stachyose and sucrose. The former is a tetrasaccharide roughly twice the size of sucrose, a disaccharide. The basic data needed to evaluate the separation is given in Figure 12 which compares their relative escape rates at 25°C. From these patterns it can be derived that with a dialysis time of 5 hr., 82% of the sucrose would be in the diffusate but only 18% of the stachyose. This will give the optimum symmetrical pattern shown in Figure 13. The scheme requires two identical cells or four separate runs with the same cell. Each circle represents a separate dialysis experiment. It can be seen that in the direction of the arrows leading to the right the diffusate must be evaporated after each stage in order to place it inside the sac on the next stage. This is made feasible by use of an appropriate rotatory evaporator (28). The scheme in Figure 13 represents only two stages. Successful experiments have been made in the author's laboratory, in which this scheme was extended to five stages with five identical cells and five parallel rotatory evaporators.

The pattern in Figure 13 is identical in principle to the well-known "dry exchema" used for years in fractional crystallization and in countercurrent distribution, where the mathematics of the binomial expansion can be applied. It assumes that concentrations are sufficiently low so that each solute will behave as if the other were not present. While this ideal is not strictly true in actual practice, it is

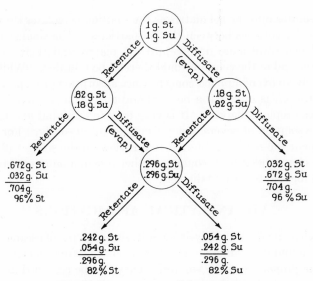

Fig. 13. Countercurrent dialysis scheme.

approached well enough to make the system useful for the investigation of many mixtures. It would obviously be better to carry out the dialysis at a higher temperature to shorten the time. A temperature of 50°C. could easily reduce the time of dialysis 2.5 hr. and would tend to reduce solute interaction. On the other hand, even if the solutes do have sufficient stability as would be expected of these two solutes, the selectivity factor could be reduced by hydration or conformational effects. These would be revealed by determining the individual rates of Figure 12 again at the higher temperature.

A technique known as "Gel filtration" (29) or "Sephadex" chromatography should be discussed briefly in this connection. In this technique a solution is filtered through a column made from a synthetic crosslinked dextran preparation. The preparation is called "Sephadex." It is commercially available from the Pharmacia Fine Chemicals, Inc., 501 Fifth Avenue, New York, in several different degrees of crosslinking. With aqueous solutions it forms a gel which has properties almost ideal for the purpose of separating many mixtures of solutes on the basis of their size. When used like an adsorbent in chromatography it gives discrete effluent bands. These are thought to arise by the different rates or degree of penetration of different sized solutes into the gel matrix as the solution percolates through the interstitial volumes between the gel particles. The smaller particles would penetrate more deeply into the matrix and their emergence from the end of the column would thereby be retarded. While this is probably an oversimplified concept since adsorption often plays a role, gel filtration is one of the best separation techniques available and often can replace dialysis. It is very easy to carry out and may give good resolution of several components simultaneously. For further treatment the reader is referred to a review on the subject (29). Its success has tended to discourage further research on a more practical device for countercurrent dialysis.

VII. ANALYTICAL APPLICATIONS

When an analytical dialysis is made, several types of escape patterns can be found depending on whether or not a mixture is being studied and the properties of the solutes. They can be classified as follows:

(a) Straight-line behavior.

(b) An apparent break in the straight line to give two slopes.

(c) More than one apparent break.

(d) A continuously curving line.

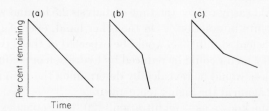

Fig. 14. Types of escape patterns.

Straight-line behavior as in Figure 14a indicates that the preparation behaves ideally under the conditions used and is homogeneous with respect to size, at least within the limits of selectivity of the membrane. A less porous membrane could still reveal impurity. Likewise, a different solvent or different temperature should be tried.

Where a break in the curve is found, as in Figure 14c, inhomogeneity should be suspected. This can be definitely confirmed in several ways. If the rate of escape is determined by more than one type of analysis, comparison of the escape curves from the different methods may be instructive. Residue weight is particularly useful in this connection. The second could be optical density, a color reaction or biological assay. A pure preparation will give matching curves regardless of the analytical technique used, whereas if this is found not to be the case, impurity is revealed. If residue weights have been determined a progressive quantitative shift in properties is apparent.

A mixture, however, can still give matching curves with the different analytical techniques. Where a break in the curve is noted, the first diffusates corresponding to the more rapidly dialyzing solutes should be recovered separately from the last more slowly emerging solutes. These two should then be compared again in separate runs. A difference in rate here definitely reveals impurity.

With certain solutes neither of the two criteria discussed above reveal impurity and yet the curve seems to show a break. The direction of the break may be as shown in Figure 14b. This almost certainly indicates that the solute is not behaving ideally but is more highly associated at the initial or highest concentration than at the final and lower concentration. Such curves have been observed with insulin (30), a solute known to associate strongly and with other solutes. A continuous curve with this type of negative curvature indicates dissociation with several sized molecular species involved. The curve can often be made to give a straight line by adding some component to the solvent which is capable of exerting a strong dissociating effect. Polymers can give straight line behavior if they are predominantly in one form. Thus, the tetrameric molecule hemoglobin (19) was found to give a straight line.

A positive break, Figure 14c, may not always indicate impurity. The solute may exist in solution in more than one conformational form and require time for readjustment (31). It may also be adsorbed slightly on the membrane and cause this type of deviation.

Adsorption can be detected rather easily in the following way. A standard run is set up and allowed to proceed part way to completion. It is then interrupted and both retentate and diffusate analyzed. The recovery now should be within about 5–10% of the theoretical described in Section II. A short elution time with fresh solvents will reveal the amount retained within the membrane. It is of considerable interest that as much as 30% of the sample can be adsorbed in the membrane (8), and yet a straight-line escape pattern still be found.

In this case the adsorption can accelerate the rate of diffusion through the membrane. Depending on the binding sites and the isotherm, however, adsorption can cause a positive break in the curve.

Where more than one apparent break is observed the above possibilities are multiplied accordingly. A continuous curve may indicate a mixture of many components or a combination of complications.

When it has been conclusively established that one or more breaks in an escape curve are due to the presence of a corresponding number of components it will be permissible to draw conclusions about the quantitative composition of the mixture by extrapolation of the rate curves. Siggia et al. (32,33) have exploited this procedure, but it must be used with considerable care since the approach may lead to error. One solute may influence more or less the rate of dialysis of the other. Where preliminary experiments have shown the possibility of this procedure it becomes important to use a membrane of maximum selectivity so that the rates are separated as far as possible and the breaks are maximal. The extrapolation then becomes more certain.

There seems little doubt but that dialyzability can be a measure of molecular size, but to what precision it can be used for this purpose is a question which requires discussion. Perhaps it is more accurate to say that dialysis can be a measure of effective diffusional volume. When membranes of high selectivity are used, the shape of the molecule, and probably its flexibility, also become important. It should be remembered that the membrane in reality is a rather stiff gel but may have a degree of flexibility or distortability on a molecular level.

While there is now good evidence to believe the membrane acts mainly as a sieve, there is no reliable way of measuring the real size or tortuosity of the pores. Therefore, the most reliable basis for size measurement is by the use of model solutes of known size and shape. Size approximations of unknown solutes can then be made on a comparative basis. A number of studies of this type are now in the literature in which sugars (13), amino acids (8), peptides (17), and proteins (11) have been compared. A correlation with free diffusion data has been demonstrated (13). By a careful study of homologous cyclic sugars of known size and shape it has been possible to estimate a selectivity limit in terms of relative molecular diameters. If all other parameters are equal, one solute should show a measurably different dialysis rate from another if its effective diameter is 2–3% larger.

VIII. POINTS OF THEORETICAL INTEREST

From the introduction and the various sections preceding this one it should be apparent that the major problem connected with differential dialysis would seem to be that of "selectivity." While "selectivity" may be defined (11) simply as the ability to distinguish or separate one solute from another, an operational definition may actually have more meaning when it is applied to differential dialysis.

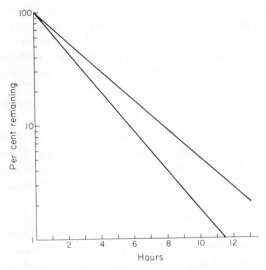

Fig. 15. Plots illustrating the meaning of selectivity.

This can be given in terms of escape plots. Thus, two solutes differing little in diffusional size might give the escape plots in Figure 15, when compared in the same membrane. Since they both give straight lines, they obviously behave as ideal solutes and do not show concentration dependence, at least within the selectivity limits of the particular membrane.

The plots of Figure 15 give a clear concept of the meaning of selectivity with the particular membrane and conditions, except for one possibility. The two test solutes may show sufficient interaction with each other when a mixture is studied, so that the individual escape rates become modified. Such behavior cannot be predicted, but can easily be detected by an experimental test with the mixture. In this case, an analytical method for detecting quantitatively one component in the presence of the other will be required for analysis of the diffusate fractions.

Interaction can be of considerable theoretical interest. It often can be overcome by changing the pH or solvent components of the system. In case the membrane has sufficient selectivity to prevent entirely the diffusion of one of the components, study of the phenomenon becomes very simple. Binding constants in this case can be determined by estimating the concentration of the diffusable solute on both sides of the membrane after allowing the concentration to build up on the diffusate side, until no more change occurs; equilibrium dialysis. The thin-film diffusion cell in Figure 3 and the calibrated membranes are ideal for this type of study, since equilibrium is established with greater speed when the retentate is a thin film.

Following the preceding brief discussion of the meaning of selectivity, the next most important topic to be discussed is that of how to achieve a high selectivity when it is based exclusively on the diffusional size of the molecule. The reason for using the term "diffusional size" will be discussed later. Since we have chosen not to discuss electrodialysis and dialysis through ion-exchange membranes, we need consider only size and shape effects.

A good theoretical approach for the development of selectivity was proposed many years ago by Ferry (22) in his studies on ultrafiltration. If we consider a round pore of a given cross-sectional area, a spherical solute molecule whose size is much smaller than the pore would have little difficulty entering the pore by diffusion. Essentially, the total cross-sectional area of the mouth of the pore would be available for the diffusion. But for a solute nearly as large as the pore this would not be true. Here the difference between the pore area A and $2\pi r$ is the important area, where r is the radius of the solute sphere. The actual area available for diffusion is given by the relationship of equation 3, where R is the radius of the cross section of the

$$A = A (1 - r/R)^2 \qquad (3)$$

pore. While even more refined equations than equation 3 are in the literature to express frictional effects (4), it would seem sufficiently refined to show that as the size of the solute molecule approaches the limiting pore size, the size parameter would be expected to become increasingly critical.

Thus, greater selectivity should be observed when the solutes in question are barely able to diffuse through the membrane pores. The data presented in the preceding sections give ample proof that this is true.

Therefore, it follows that the achievement of high selectivity basically implies a slow process. This is true in terms of the amount of solute diffusing through unit area of the membrane. However, to overcome this disadvantage, the area of the membrane per unit volume of retentate can be increased. Thus, the concept of "thin-film dialysis" was introduced (5). Experimentally, retentate films of the order of 0.01 mm. in depth have been shown to be very practical. It is interesting to speculate concerning the selectivity which should be obtainable if films 0.01 mm. in depth could be reproducibly made in membranes with tenfold the dialyzing area of those in Figure 3. Even if this were possible, an inherent practical difficulty would result.

In order to reach the selectivity required to make practical the separation of two solutes differing in diffusional size by a factor of two, the pore size must be adjusted rather precisely in terms of the escape rates of the solutes. Half-escape times of several hours are needed. This difficulty would necessarily be greatly increased in order for the use of 0.01 mm. films to become fully effective.

The temperature of the dialysis is important in this connection, since the rate of dialysis becomes more rapid with increase in temperature. Thus, exclusive of changes in the conformation of the solute, hydration, etc., the highest temperature practical contributes to selectivity, since it permits a less porous membrane to be used.

Following the previous development, a few statements regarding the porosity of a membrane may be in order. Since the precise nature of a "pore" is unknown, it would seem possible to draw conclusions only in a statistical way from the diffusional behavior of solutes of known size. It has always been accepted, and certainly with a good probability, that the membrane actually presents a distribution of pore sizes. If this is true, the selectivity does not depend on all the available pores in the membrane, but only on the larger ones. The smaller ones at the total exclusion point play no role because they do not allow the solutes to enter. Although there is good reason to believe that cellophane presents a relatively narrow range of pore sizes, precise information on this point is lacking. The manufacturers give a value of 25 A. for the average pore size of the more porous membranes, a figure probably calculated from the rate of filtration of water under pressure. This would seem a reasonable figure, but since ribonuclease with a diameter in the range of 30 A. slowly dialyzes through the most porous one, while chymotrypsinogen, with an effective diameter only 25% larger, does not. The range of pore size, therefore, cannot be too broad.

On general principles it would seem reasonable to assume that a very narrow range of pore size would contribute to selectivity. This would allow the consequences of equation 3 to be better realized and at the same time contribute to a more rapid dialysis, since then more nearly all the pores would be available for the diffusion instead of only the larger ones.

The factors which contribute to selectivity in differential dialysis are the same factors which are of interest in the study of osmotic pressure when the solute is not completely held back by the semipermeable membrane (34). Here the escape of the solute through the membrane is measured by the decrease of osmotic pressure with time, whereas in dialysis, with the arrangement of Figure 3, the solute escape rate is measured directly. There is a very large literature on the study of osmotic pressure (35) which cannot be made part of the present discussion. However, that part which deals with leaky membranes is certainly very pertinent to differential dialysis, particularly the theoretical concepts based on the frictional effects encountered by the solute as it finds its way through the membrane. These have been treated from a theoretical standpoint by Staverman (34,36), and mathematical relationships proposed from which frictional coefficients can be calculated. Numerous later papers (4,37) have treated permeation and the diffusion of solutes through thin membranes from this standpoint.

It would seem well to point out that while many of these studies are illuminating from a theoretical standpoint, they require assumptions which may not apply to a particular differential dialysis condition. For instance, the recent study of Ginzburg and Katchalsky (4) was made with solutes far below the limiting pore size of the membranes where only a low selectivity for differential dialysis would be observed. Since we do not know the real nature of the membrane on a molecular level, it seems best to rely on an approach which makes wide use of different model solutes for interpretation.

In dialysis the membrane must be relatively thin and flexible. This means it is always flexing to a degree, and certainly to an appreciable degree in the arrangement of Figure 3 where stirring is provided. The effect this has on the pores is not known, but even apart from the mechanical stirring, the pores may be quite flexible on a micro level. In any case the unstirred quiescent layer of the solution on each side of the membrane postulated by Ginzburg and Katchalsky (4) does not play a significant role in the more selective differential dialysis because of the slowness of the dialysis rate per sq. cm. of dialyzing surface. The effect of stirring in thin-film dialysis has been shown (10) to be worth considering, but not to be of the greatest importance.

Irrespective of the possibility of a certain flexibility in the porosity of the membrane, the data obtained thus far with thin film dialysis through cellophane strongly indicate that the separation factor depends on the size, shape, and perhaps the flexibility of the molecule. Where strong solvation of the solute occurs, it is the size and shape of the solvate that matters. However, since there are varying degrees of solvation, it seems best to use the term "diffusional size" when comparing solutes. This term implies the possible role of the various factors mentioned.

References

1. Turner, E. G., and J. A. Feinberg, *Nature*, **184**, 1139 (1959).
2. Graham, T., *Trans. Roy. Soc., London*, **151**, 183 (1861).
3. Northrop, J. H., and M. L. Anson, *J. Gen. Physiol.*, **12**, 543 (1928–29).
4. Ginzburg, B. Z., and A. Katchalsky, *J. Gen. Physiol.*, **47**, 403 (1963).
5. Craig, L. C., and T. P. King, in D. Glick, Ed., *Methods of Biochemical Analysis*, Vol. 10, Interscience, New York, 1962, p. 175.
6. Sollner, K., in H. T. Clarke, ed., *Ion Transport Across Membranes*, Academic, New York, 1954, p. 144.
7. Tuwiner, S. B., *Diffusion and Membrane Technology*, ACS Monograph No. 156, Reinhold, New York, 1962.
8. Craig, L. C., and A. Ansevin, *Biochem.*, **2**, 1268 (1963).
9. Michaels, A. S., and H. J. Bixler, *J. Polymer Sci.*, **50**, 393 (1961).
10. Craig, L. C., and Wm. Konigsberg, *J. Phys. Chem.*, **65**, 166 (1961).
11. Craig, L. C., T. P. King, and A. Stracher, *J. Am. Chem. Soc.*, **79**, 3729 (1957).
12. Craig, L. C., Wm. Konigsberg, A. Stracher, and T. P. King, in A. Neuberger, Ed., *Symposium on Protein Structure*, Methuen, London, Wiley, New York, 1958, p. 104.
13. Craig, L. C., and A. O. Pulley, *Biochem.*, **1**, 89 (1962).
14. McBain, J. W., and R. F. Stuewer, *J. Phys. Chem.*, **40**, 1157 (1936).
15. Pierce, J. G., and C. A. Free, *Biochim. Biophys. Acta*, **48**, 436 (1961).
16. Moore, S., and W. H. Stein, *J. Biol. Chem.*, **211**, 907 (1954).

17. Craig, L. C., E. J. Harfenist, and A. C. Paladini, *Biochem.*, **3**, 764 (1964).

18. Goldstein, J., and L. C. Craig, *J. Am. Chem. Soc.*, **82**, 1833 (1960).

19. Guidotti, G., and L. C. Craig, *Proc. Nat. Acad. Sci.*, **50**, 46 (1963).

20. Craig, L. C., *Biochim. Biophys. Suppl.*, **1**, 112 (1962).

21. Elford, W. J., *Proc. Roy. Soc.* (*London*), **B105**, 216 (1930); *Trans. Faraday Soc.*, **33**, 1094 (1937).

22. Ferry, J. D., *J. Gen. Physiol.*, **20**, 95 (1936).

23. Stauffer, R. E., in A. Weissberger, ed., *Separation and Purification*, (Technique of Organic Chemistry, Vol. III, Part I, 2nd ed.), Interscience, New York, 1956, p. 79.

24. Durrum, E. L., E. R. B. Smith, and M. R. Jetton, *Science*, **120**, 956 (1954).

25. Berggard, I., *Ark. Kemi.*, **18**, 291 (1961).

26. Signer, R., H. Hanni, W. Noestler, W. Rottenberg, and P. von Tavel, *Helv. Chim. Acta*, **29**, 1984 (1946); **30**, 334 (1947).

27. Kolff, W. J., *J. Mt. Sinai Hosp.*, **14**, 71 (1947).

28. Craig, L. C., J. D. Gregory, and W. Hausmann, *Anal. Chem.*, **22**, 1462 (1950).

29. Porath, J., *Adv. Protein Chem.*, **17**, 209 (1962).

30. Craig, L. C., T. P. King, and Wm. Konigsberg, *Ann. N. Y. Acad. Sci.*, **88**, 571 (1960).

31. Craig, L. C., T. P. King, and A. M. Crestfield, *Biopolymers*, **1**, 231 (1963).

32. Siggia, S., J. G. Hanna, and N. M. Serencha, *Anal. Chem.*, **35**, 365 (1963).

33. Siggia, S., J. G. Hanna, and N. M. Serencha, *Anal. Chem.*, **36**, 638 (1964).

34. Staverman, A. J., *Rec. Trav. Chim.*, **70**, 344 (1951).

35. Kupke, D. W., *Adv. Protein Chem.*, **15**, 57 (1960).

36. Staverman, A. J., *Trans. Faraday Soc.*, **48**, 176 (1948).

37. Durbin, R. P., *J. Gen. Physiol.*, **44**, 315 (1960).

Manuscript received by Publisher July 10, 1964.

The Oxygen-Flask Method

A. M. G. MACDONALD, *The University of Birmingham, England*

I. INTRODUCTION

In 1955, Schöniger (127,128) showed that the oxygen-flask method of decomposing organic materials, which now often bears his name, could be applied on the microscale with an accuracy equal to that of the lengthy classical procedures of microanalysis. The method has the advantages of utter simplicity and great rapidity, and it has, therefore, completely changed the aspect of virtually all laboratories for organic analysis. Essentially, the method consists of confining the sample in some suitable container (e.g., paper), suspending it in a closed vessel filled with oxygen and charged with a suitable absorption solution, and igniting it; total decomposition is complete within seconds and the required ion can be determined in the absorption solution by whichever method the analyst prefers. If the absorption solution is chosen sensibly, then in most cases, the only interferences that need be considered are those arising from the organic material itself. Methods are now available for the determination of halogens, sulfur, phosphorus, arsenic, carbon, and many metals and metalloids. Qualitative tests are possible as well as many applications to radioactive materials.

The basic technique is old but only during the past 8 years has it become widely known and applied. In the years following the appearance of Schöniger's papers, there was a spate of publications, but since 1962, the volume of material appearing has decreased to more reasonable proportions. In 1960, the hope was expressed (93) that workers would not be "blinded by the obvious and so overburden the literature with a useless collection of papers describing methods of finish (and absorption solutions) which have already been applied to other methods of decomposition." Unfortunately, a continual though now milder rash of trivial modifications of modifications continues to mar the literature and debase the name of microchemistry. It has been clear for years that any method of finish suitable for inorganic analysis or for other methods of decomposition in organic analysis can be used after a flask combustion.

Several reviews of oxygen-flask methods already have been published (92,94,129,130); it is hoped that a certain amount of repetition in the present review will be forgiven in the interests of completeness and convenience.

II. HISTORY OF THE METHOD

The oxygen-flask method of combustion of organic materials was first introduced in 1892 by Hempel (66) for the determination of sulfur in coals and other materials, as a simplification of the Berthelot bomb technique. The 0.5-g. sample was ignited electrically in a platinum-gauze basket suspended from the stopper of a 10-liter bottle which had

Fig. 1. Hempel's flask (66).

been filled with oxygen (Fig. 1). Oxidation with bromine water was then followed by a gravimetric determination as barium sulfate. About a year later, Meslans (107) proposed a method for fluorine in gaseous alkyl fluorides in which the gas was fed into a partially evacuated flask containing oxygen, over an incandescent platinum spiral, the determination being completed by a titration of excess of alkali in the absorbent, or gravimetrically as calcium fluoride. The work on fluorine seems to have passed virtually unnoticed but a few workers did investigate Hempel's method further. Graefe (56) recommended cotton thread or filter paper as a fuse instead of electrical ignition, and provided oxygen from sodium peroxide in the absorbing solution. The method was first extended to the determination of halogens by Marcusson and Döscher (99), with a gravimetric determination as silver halide after reduction of any halogen produced with Devarda's alloy. Thereafter, only isolated efforts were made to apply the general technique, for its advantages and inherent accuracy seem to have been overlooked in the upsurge of interest in Pregl's microanalytical methods during the second quarter of this century. In 1922, Votoček (152) used a large separating funnel as the combustion vessel so that the absorbent could be more readily transferred to a convenient flask for titration. Chlorine was determined in this way by titration with mercuric nitrate solution in presence of sodium nitroprusside as indicator. In 1950, Roth (124) determined traces of sulfur by ignition of samples, mixed with Eschka mixture, by means of a paper fuse impregnated with potassium nitrate; a 2-liter flask was used and the determination was completed by the spectrophotometric methylene-blue method after reduction of sulfate with hydriodic acid. Mikl and Pech (108), closely followed by Pražák et al. (120), showed that the combustion process was suitable for routine control analysis for sulfur and chlorine on a semimicro scale. The work done by Schöniger (127,128) then, proved how versatile and accurate the procedure could be for micro work; it is from Schöniger's papers that virtually all later investigations have been derived.

III. GENERAL APPARATUS AND TECHNIQUES

The oxygen-flask method is very versatile. It is quite possible to obtain quantitative decomposition with a milk bottle (British style), a rubber stopper, a length of platinum wire, a piece of filter paper, and a match. At the other extreme, combustion can be done in a specially designed clamped flask in a safety box with special black paper and focussed light for ignition. While the former system is a trifle primitive for reliable routine use, the latter system certainly seems like "science" run riot.

The commonest apparatus for micro work (Fig. 2) consists of a 250- or 300-ml. flask fitted with a ground-glass stopper or air leak, into which is sealed a length of platinum wire (0.5–1 mm. diam.). To the end of the wire, an oblong (15 mm. × 30 mm.) of platinum gauze is attached, into which the wrapped sample can be clamped. In the general procedure, the sample is weighed from a weighing tube on to a piece of filter paper (Fig. 3); the paper is then carefully folded and clamped with the fuse protruding in the gauze hinge, which has been heated previously to ensure freedom from deposits. A suitable absorption solution is placed in the flask, which is then flushed with a rapid flow of oxygen for a few seconds. The tip of the fuse is ignited in a flame and the stopper is immediately inserted, the flask being tilted as soon as the

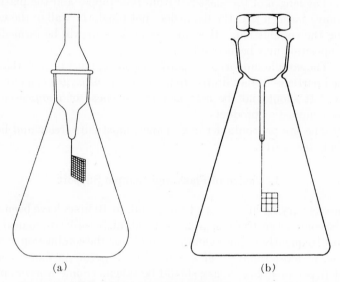

(a) (b)

Fig. 2. Conventional flasks for microdeterminations (a) airleak design (94); (b) stopper design (127).

Fig. 3. Filter paper for wrapping sample (127).

stopper is firmly seated, so that the absorption solution forms a seal round the stopper. The combustion is complete within 5–10 sec., and during this time, the flask and stopper must be held together firmly. The flask is then shaken for about 10 min., or for 3–4 min. after the cloud of combustion products seems to have disappeared; alternatively, the flask can be left on the bench for about 1 hr. The stopper is then removed and rinsed along with the sample holder and wire; the solution is then ready for whichever finish is preferred.

The essential points in the choice of apparatus are as follows:

(a) The vessel must be large enough to contain sufficient oxygen for complete combustion of the sample *and the sample container*.

(b) The length of the glass rod from the stopper and the platinum wire must be such that the flame does not touch the wall of the vessel during the combustion. If it does touch it, soot will be formed and decomposition may be incomplete.

(c) The sample support, e.g., platinum gauze, must be such that unburned particles cannot drop through it, whereas oxygen can circulate easily. It should not be attacked by the heat of combustion, or by the combustion products.

(d) The sample container, e.g., paper, must burn freely and be essentially blank free.

1. Choice of Flask and Sample Support

Vessels varying in capacity from 25 ml. to 10 liters have been used for the combustion process. A 250- or 300-ml. borosilicate conical flask is most frequently required and is suitable for the combustion of up to 25 mg. of most samples; if soot formation occurs, a more sensibly sized paper or a larger flask should be taken. Some workers prefer an iodine flask to the more usual Erlenmeyer design. A 500-ml. flask is suitable for samples up to 50–60 mg., while a 1000-ml. flask is satisfactory for samples up to 100 mg. Apparatus for much larger amounts have been described (see below).

For the sample support, 30–40 mm. of 0.5–1 mm. diam. platinum wire fused into a glass rod from the stopper, or into a suitably cut air leak suffices. The length of glass is chosen so that the sample support lies just above the center of the flask (if the flask is to be inverted). The platinum gauze should be about 30 mesh and is attached to the wire by welding.

A complete specification for 300- and 500-ml. flasks (Fig. 4) has been given (31). Suitable equipment is now available from most large suppliers, although it is much more economical and as effective to make one's own from standard ground-glass apparatus. Flasks are generally made of borosilicate glass. Since this glass can cause difficulties in some determinations, e.g., fluorine, boron, and alkali metals, flasks

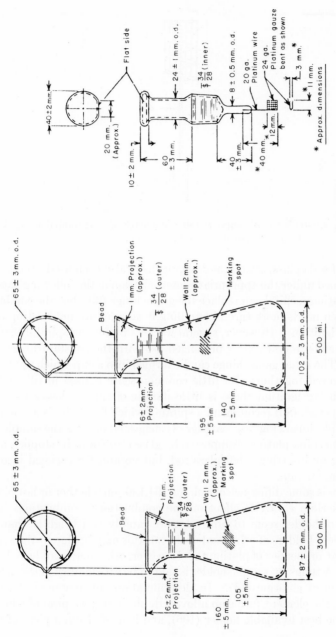

Fig. 4. American specification for borosilicate oxygen combustion flask (31).

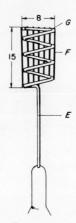

Fig. 5. Kirsten's sample support (80); diameter of longitudinal wires (F)
0.7 mm; diameter of spiral wire (G and E) 1 mm.

made of soda glass, quartz, and plastic, have also been used; these are
mentioned under the appropriate determination in the following pages.

A platinum spiral can replace the gauze hinge (90), but the combustion then needs more careful handling if samples are not to drop out during ignition. However, several workers prefer the spiral, because gauze tends to crack after prolonged use with the constant hinge action. The usual gauze hinge can be formed into a cup which need not be squeezed together; if a little common sense is used in tilting the flask during ignition there is little danger of sample losses (48,95). Kirsten et al. (80) recommend a spiral to which finer wire is welded to form a platform (Fig. 5). Archer (4) suggested placing the sample on a platinum-foil platform supported by glass rods from the stopper, and igniting by inserting a hot glass rod, but obtained occasional incomplete combustion.

There is some difference of opinion (94,130) on whether or not platinum exerts a catalytic effect on the combustion; combustions in a platinum holder seem to proceed more rapidly and brightly than in equivalent holders of other materials, but this may be due to the superior heat properties of platinum. However, other materials have been used. A tungsten sample holder is said to be satisfactory in the determination of chlorine (18). In determinations of arsenic and some metals, the element forms an alloy with platinum; a spiral of silica is then the best available holder (106), and is made from a piece of rod

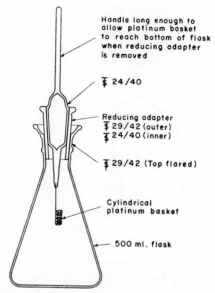

Handle long enough to
allow platinum basket
to reach bottom of flask
when reducing adapter
is removed

⊺ 24/40

Reducing adapter
⊺ 29/42 (outer)
⊺ 24/40 (inner)

⊺ 29/42 (Top flared)

Cylindrical
platinum basket

500 ml. flask

Fig. 6. Adaptor flask for sample support (48).

75–100 mm. long and 3–5 mm. thick, the spiral being tapered at the lower end to help to prevent losses of sample during ignition. Eder (38) recommends a Pyrex glass hook for all purposes; the sample is folded into an apron-shaped paper and the two fuses hang downwards when the paper is balanced on the hook. Haack (61) has described a stopper with glass rod fitted with a Teflon sleeve so that the actual sample supports of various shapes and materials, are interchangeable. If it is necessary to immerse the sample holder in the absorption solution after the combustion to remove adherent deposits, e.g., if an organometallic compound is being analyzed, a reducing adaptor can be placed in the neck of the flask (48) (Fig. 6).

Because of the consumption of oxygen and the formation and absorption of carbon dioxide, a slight vacuum is created within the flask after the combustion. The effect only rarely makes it difficult to open the flask but some workers have suggested placing a side arm with a tap either at the top (135) or the bottom (146) of the flask.

Various shapes of vessel have been recommended for different purposes and scales of working. Lehner (86) proposed a useful design (Fig. 7) for trace analysis; a large volume of oxygen is made available.

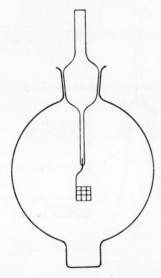

Fig. 7. Flask for trace analysis (86).

while the combustion products can be absorbed in a conveniently situated small volume of liquid.   This design is also suitable for potentiometric titrations (64,86).

If it is necessary to transfer the absorbent from the combustion flask to another vessel, the combustion can easily be carried out in a separating funnel (63,69,152).

For ignition of semimicro samples (up to 100 mg.), a few workers (2) prefer a round, flat-bottomed, 1-liter flask, since the flame is less likely to touch the wall.   Barney et al. (5) burned 100-mg. samples of motor oils and additives in 1-liter bottles; the sample support consists of a small platinum cup suspended only 1 in. above the bottom of the bottle and used with a thimble-shaped sample container.   Lisk (88a) used cellulose acetate cones as sample containers for the determination of residual pesticides in samples weighing about 70 mg.   A 1-liter flask contained sufficient oxygen for complete ignition, but cellulose burned more fiercely than paper, and so a rubber balloon was attached to a sidearm to take care of the excess pressure.   A similar idea was used in the combustion of up to 10 g. of plant materials in a 5-liter flask (58,60).   This method was applied for the determination of residual pesticides and fungicides via various elements.

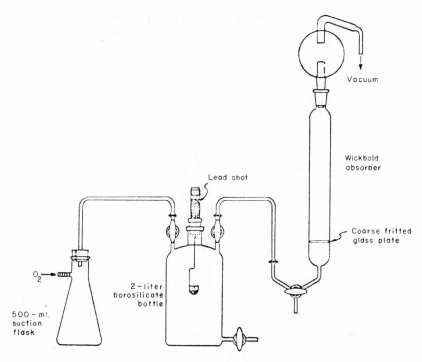

Fig. 8. Assembly for analysis of gram samples (42).

2-liter flasks have been used quite often but larger sizes, e.g., the 10-liter flask of Hempel, tend to make the equipment impossibly un-wieldy, yet samples of 1 g. or more are often desirable for analysis of traces in inhomogeneous materials. For this purpose, Farley and Winkler (42) have described an amalgamation of the flask combustion with a conventional absorber (Fig. 8); up to 8 g. of material contained in a sample cup made from an extraction thimble can be burned off without difficulty with an oxygen flow rate of 45 liter/min. High-melting solids are pelleted and moistened with *iso*-octane before ignition, whereas liquids are mixed with a flame retardant such as magnesium oxide.

At the other end of the analytical scale, samples of 50 μg. can be burned in a 25-ml. flask (Fig. 9) (9–11); the flask wall is moistened with a suitable absorbent and after a standing period, the wall and sample support are rinsed with about 2 ml. of liquid into the bottom chamber

(2.5–3 ml. capacity), where the required ion can be titrated.   Samples are wrapped in very thin polyethylene film with a linen or cotton thread fuse.   The platinum supporting wire is 0.3 mm. diam. and the platinum gauze (13 × 3.5 mm.), which can be shaped as a hinge or a cup, is 80 mesh; thicker platinum conducts too much heat away from the combustion, causing incomplete decomposition.

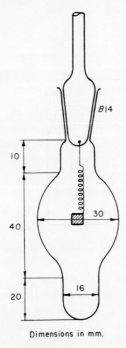

Dimensions in mm.

Fig. 9. Flask for 50-μg. samples (11).

To avoid the need for transferring samples to combustible carriers in analysis of 250–400 μg. samples, Kirsten (79) describes "hot-flask" methods for halogens.   The main oxygen-filled chamber is surrounded by a vertical furnace at 850°C and is 60 mm. long with an inner diameter of 14 mm.; the sample in a quartz cup on a quartz rod is inserted into the hot chamber, which is immediately sealed with a small cup containing about 0.5 ml. of a suitable absorbent.

2. Sample Containers

Filter paper is the commonest material for the sample container; suitable papers of low ash content are Schleicher and Schüll (No. 589 or 1575) or Whatman (No. 44 or 54). Any material must, of course, be checked for its blank value. For microanalysis, a 2.5–3 sq. cm. with a fuse 2–3 mm. wide and 2.5 cm. long is sufficient; slightly larger sizes are needed for larger samples. Cigaret paper can be used (34, 120), but its effect as a combustion accelerator is smaller and its ash value and blank variability are greater than those of filter paper. Cellulose sheet is said to be as good as filter paper (4). Very thin polyethylene film is excellent for microgram work; if it is washed with ethanol, the blank value for 1 sq. cm. does not exceed 0.5 μl. of 0.01N solution for any determination.

While paper is excellent for solids and can even be used for viscous liquids if they are weighed into an M-shaped piece of paper (36), it is obviously unsuitable for most liquids. Schöniger (127,128) weighed liquids of boiling point greater than 100°C in glass capillaries with a thin-walled bulb in the middle, which are wrapped in filter paper and crushed just before the ignition. Bennewitz (16) recommends weighing volatile liquids (b.p. > 63°C) in thin-walled bulbs (6–7 mm. diam.) drawn to a capillary; these are wrapped in filter paper and are burst by the heat of combustion.

However, most workers prefer a purely organic sample container because of the danger of unburned sample remaining in a glass capillary. Gelatin capsules are suitable for liquids with boiling points above 100°C; capsules from different sources give varying blank values and it is advisable to check these carefully for each elemental determination. To minimize losses through handling, Dobbs (37) suggests placing a drop of a hot mixture containing 1 g. of gelatin in 6 ml. of glycerol and 2 ml. of water, into the lid of a gelatin capsule which then becomes sealed to the bottom. The liquid sample is injected with a hypodermic needle through this gelatin plug and the plug seals itself hermetically as the needle is withdrawn. Capsules are also useful if it is necessary to carry out a combined fusion and combustion (48).

Methylcellulose capsules are also available commercially and these are reported to be much more satisfactory than gelatin as regards blank values. They may also have a beneficial effect on the completeness of decomposition of samples. Schöniger (130) measured the temperature in the combustion zone and found temperatures of 1000–1100°C with filter paper wrappers and of 1150°C if dekalin was added; with methylcellulose capsules the temperature rose to 1250°C.

Liquids of low boiling point, e.g., carbon tetrachloride or carbon disulphide, can be weighed and burned effectively in small envelopes of cellulose adhesive tape with a filter-paper lining (34,134); the tape is formed into a small pocket, the sample is injected on to the filter paper and the pocket is sealed. Capillaries made from polyethylene surgical tubing (15 mm. long and 1 mm. diam.) are also satisfactory (77); a little cotton wool is inserted to prevent too rapid volatilization of the sample. The sample is injected and the capillary is sealed with a soldering iron or with minute quartz stoppers. In all these procedures, a strip of filter paper is fitted to the side of the sample container as it is fixed in the platinum support, to act as the fuse.

If large solid samples are taken, it is usually advisable to pellet them before ignition. Samples such as oils can be weighed and burned in containers cut from micro-extraction thimbles, the thimble being supported in a suitable platinum gauze cup (5,42). Cones made from cellulose acetate film (88a) and from cellophane (75) have also been recommended. These cups are useful when a solution or extract must be evaporated before ignition.

3. Electrical and Other Ignition Systems and Safety Precautions

The questions of safety in the use of the oxygen flask and of electrical ignition are intertwined. Initially, a main advantage of electrical ignition was said to be that thermally unstable compounds could be ignited in a closed system (100). But, if a sensible length of fuse is used in the normal manner, no heat reaches the sample until the stopper has been inserted. Accordingly, the only real utility of electrical ignition appears to lie in its greater safety, since it can be done from behind a screen. Electrical ignition systems have been described in which the paper fuse is ignited by means of a heating coil (100,115,120, 154) or an electrical discharge (37,64); usually these are initiated from outside a safety box. In another safety system (83,115) the flask is placed in a box and combustion is started by focussing the light from a projection lamp on a black fuse attached to the sample. Both systems are available commercially, but as far as safety is concerned they are totally unnecessary and appear to benefit only the manufacturers.

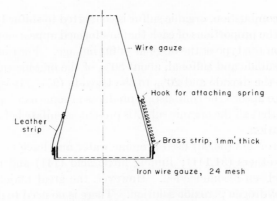

Fig. 10. Protection jacket (54).

Although most workers state that combustions were done behind a safety screen, one suspects that this is honored more in the breach than in the observance. The only explosions that are known to the writer to have occurred have involved large samples of petroleum products. Regularly one reads the words "although so far no explosions have occurred, a safety device . . ." In the writer's laboratory, the method has proved entirely safe on the micro and semimicro scales even in the hands of teenage trainees and undergraduates; the only safety precaution is a warning label on the alcohol wash bottle.

If protection of some sort is considered desirable, and this may be so with samples of over 50 mg., the most sensible arrangement is that described by Gouverneur and Eerbeek (54). This is a simple, readily detachable jacket made from wire gauze (Fig. 10) and is now commercially available. If an explosion does occur, the glass fragments, including the flask stopper, are retained entirely in the jacket.

IV. DETERMINATION OF SULFUR

The advantages of the oxygen-flask method perhaps appear more clearly in the determination of sulfur than in that of any other common hetero-element. Not only is it easy to decompose compounds which give trouble in many classical procedures, but the fact that the final solution can be virtually pure sulfuric acid simplifies the choice of a direct titration; for all known rapid titration methods for sulfate are sensitive to the presence of large amounts of even neutral salts.

In the combustion, organic sulfur is converted to sulfur trioxide and dioxide; the proportions of each that are formed appear not to depend strongly on the type of the original sulfur linkage. For example, with benzyl disulfide and sulfonal, about 80% of the organic sulfur is converted to the dioxide and 20% to the trioxide (95). It is, therefore, essential to absorb the combustion products in some oxidizing solution to ensure that all the organic sulfur is present as sulfate before the final determination.

Early workers (56,66) used bromine water and have been followed by a few others (51,141); fuming nitric acid (141) and nitrite (80) have also been recommended. However, the great majority prefers aqueous hydrogen peroxide solution. There is no need to use alkaline solutions (85) for complete absorption, even on a semimicro scale. It is essential, of course, to have sufficient peroxide present to ensure total conversion to sulfate, but it is also necessary to beware of adding so much that peroxysulfates are formed (153). For micro work, 3–5 drops of 30% (100 vol.) hydrogen peroxide in an absorbent volume of 5 ml. (128) is quite sufficient; 6–7% peroxide solutions have been recommended (90,112), but this high concentration is not only unnecessary for total oxidation, but often means that the excess of peroxide must be removed before the final titration.

1. Methods of Completion

If no acid-forming element other than sulfur is present, either in the sample or in the sample container, a direct titration with sodium hydroxide solution is satisfactory (108,128).

Many other procedures have been suggested but a direct titration with a barium solution is by far the most widely applied. Fortuitously, an excellent titrimetric determination of sulfate (47) was described at about the same time as the micro version of the oxygen-flask method (127), and conjunction of the two procedures has virtually solved the long-standing problems of determination of organic-bound sulfur.

Wagner (153) was the first to apply this titration after a flask combustion. Sulfate in 80% alcoholic medium is titrated with 0.005–0.01M barium perchlorate solution in the same medium; thorin (thoron, thoronol, APANS; 2-(2-hydroxy-3,6-disulfo-1-naphthylazo)-benzene-arsonic acid) is used as indicator, the color change being from yellow to pale pink. Since the color change is not very distinct, although it is very sharp, methylene blue is often added as a screen. The satisfactory performance of thorin as an indicator seems to vary considerably depending on the commerical source of the reagent.

The micro method which has been used in the writer's laboratory for the past 7 yr. is outlined below; it is essentially that of Wagner and similar procedures have been described on many occasions in the literature.

2. Recommended Method

A. PREPARATION OF $0.01M$ BARIUM PERCHLORATE SOLUTION

Dissolve ca. 3.2 g. of AnalaR barium hydroxide octahydrate in water, neutralize with ca. 50% perchloric acid (methyl red indicator), and dilute to 200 ml. with water. Alternatively dissolve ca. 3.4 g. of AnalaR anhydrous barium perchlorate in 200 ml. of water. Add isopropanol or ethanol nearly to the mark of a 1-liter volumetric flask, and add perchloric acid dropwise to give an apparent pH of 3–4 (narrow-range indicator paper). Dilute to the mark with the alcohol and mix well. Standardize the solution against standard $0.01M$ sulfuric acid, as in the titration described below.

If stored in a well-stoppered bottle, this solution should retain its titer for several months.

B. PROCEDURE

Weigh 3–6 mg. of sample on to the usual paper square and ignite in a 250-ml. flask, with 10 ml. of water and 4 drops of 100-vol. hydrogen peroxide (micro-analytical reagent grade) as absorbent. Shake the flask for 2–3 min. after all vapors seem to have been absorbed.

Rinse the stopper and gauze thoroughly with alcohol (whichever is used in the titrant preparation) and add 40 ml. of alcohol in all. Titrate with the barium perchlorate solution, using 3 drops of aqueous 0.2% thorin indicator screened with 1 drop of aqueous 0.01% methylene blue. Titrate slowly near the end point and use magnetic stirring under "color-matching" lighting.

The titration is applicable to semimicro samples by appropriate adjustment of solution strengths and volumes, and has proved valuable for undergraduate teaching purposes (97). It can also be scaled down to cope with the 50-μg. sample range, with results nearly as accurate as those achieved on the microscale (9). Traces of sulfur can also be determined (86).

Malissa and Machherndl (98) studied the barium perchlorate method in conjunction with ignition of different samples in a 350-ml. flask on the microscale and could find no statistical correlation between the standard deviation, the nature of the sulfur linkage, and the sulfur content; standard deviations of $\pm0.076\%$ at the 68% confidence limit and of $\pm 0.23\%$ at the 99.7% confidence limit were found.

C. INTERFERENCES

Hydrogen peroxide does not interfere with the titration and need not be boiled out after the combustion.

Chloride and bromide ions do not interfere in the amounts normally present in organic compounds. However, if the sample contains comparatively large amounts of chlorine and nitrogen (e.g., chlorthiazide), there may be an additive interference leading to results which are $0.34–1.2\%$ high (134). For the determination of $0.2–2\%$ sulfur in highly chlorinated polymers, it is advisable to evaporate to dryness to remove hydrogen chloride after addition of nitric acid; a preliminary step involves evaporation to dryness after addition of ammonia (157).

Iodine does not interfere provided that it is largely removed by boiling before alcohol is added. Iodate is never formed in sufficient amount to interfere (19). Fluorine does not interfere in small amounts, but within the $10–30\%$ fluorine range, some boric acid should be added to the absorbent solution; to prevent interference of larger amounts (up to 70%), it is better to add $10–20$ mg. of boric acid to the sample before ignition (95).

Phosphate interferes seriously with the titration (9,30,47,95) and must be removed. This is probably best done with a suspension of silver oxide, the silver ion being subsequently removed by ion exchange with Amberlite IR-120 (30) [cf., Dixon (36)]. Magnesium carbonate (47) or oxide (9) can also be used.

Most metals affect the titration (47). However, alkali metals in the amounts normally present in organic compounds do not interfere; of course, the sample holder must be rinsed with water to ensure dissolution of metal sulfate. According to White (157), sodium in amounts equivalent to sulfate does not interfere, whereas potassium does and should be removed on an ion-exchange column.

The titration is quite satisfactory for virtually all types of nitrogen-containing compound (1,95,101,153), although very high nitrogen contents may lead to slightly high results (149).

3. Alternative Procedures

The use of thorin as indicator is not entirely without snags but it appears to be the best available.   Alizarin sulfonic acid has been recommended with 0.02M barium nitrate as titrant (19,85), and Russian workers (112,113) prefer carboxyarsenazo (O-[7-(O-carboxyphenylazo)-1,8-dihydroxy-3,6-disulfo-2-naphthylazo] benzenearsonic acid; color change from violet to blue) with the same titrant.   Wagner (153) examined several analogues of thorin for titration with barium perchlorate but found nothing that was better.

Other procedures involving precipitation as barium sulfate which have been described after flask combustions are:

1. Precipitation with excess of barium chloride and back titration with EDTA solution (7,20,128,148).
2. Conductimetric titration with barium chloride (119) or acetate (36) solution.
3. Titration with barium chloride solution to tetrahydroxyquinone indicator (141).
4. Gravimetric semimicro method (90).
5. Spectrophotometric determination after treatment with barium chloranilate, for which it is claimed that phosphate does not interfere (91).

Titration with lead nitrate, in presence of dithizone indicator in acetone medium, as initially recommended by Archer (3), had its adherents (134,155), but later seems to have given way to the barium methods.   The disadvantages of the method are that a close control of pH (80) and removal of peroxide (53) are essential; further, it is about as sensitive to interferences as the barium–thorin method.   However, the end point is more easily seen though basically it is no sharper than that of the barium titration.   Kirsten (80) has described a modified procedure in which a pyridine–nitric acid buffer is used and interfering ions are removed on an aluminum oxide-exchange resin column.   Titration with lead nitrate may also be used with an amperometric end point (51), and with thorin indicator (41).

Reduction of sulfate to sulfide can be followed by a photometric finish as methylene blue (124) or by an iodimetric titration (39). These methods would be useful where large amounts of foreign ions were present, but otherwise are unlikely to supplant the direct barium procedures.

4. Applications

The flask combustion appears to be satisfactory for many different materials. The method has been used for the determination of sulfur in pharmaceuticals (149), petroleum products (88), rubbers (24), and solid fuels (21), the final titration being either with alkali or with barium solution in presence of a thorin indicator. Traces of sulfur have been determined in large samples by a modified burning technique (42).

V. DETERMINATION OF CHLORINE

Few difficulties are found in the combustion of organic materials containing chlorine. Highly halogenated materials may give low results and it may be advisable to add some auxiliary combustible material to assist complete decomposition. Paraffin wax (108), potassium nitrate (43), sodium nitrate (32), and sucrose (102) have been recommended; compounds such as trichloroethylene and 1,3-dibromopropane can then be dealt with (43). It should be emphasized, however, that many highly chlorinated materials decompose completely under the usual conditions of combustion and that the literature is confusing on the subject. On the basis of corresponding information in the literature on fluorine compounds, an organic additive would seem preferable.

In several early methods (108,120,152), water alone was used as the absorption solution. Schöniger (127) recommended 0.2N sodium or potassium hydroxide containing a few drops of hydrogen peroxide as absorbent. Other absorbents which have been recommended are alkaline bisulfite solution (4,63,64), ammonium hydroxide containing peroxide (89), a slightly acidic solution containing sodium nitrite (78), alkaline hydrazine sulfate (110), and dilute ammonia solution (102, 109). Mázor et al. (102) found that complete absorption of the combustion products of highly halogenated materials in alkaline peroxide solution could not be achieved in under 35 min., whereas with ammonia, recoveries were complete within 4–6 min. Most of these recommendations seem to be based on the misconception that chlorine or oxychlorides are formed in the combustion process and must be reduced to chloride. Such formation seems highly improbable considering the large amounts of hydrogen available in a sample wrapper, and excellent results can be obtained even on the microscale by simple absorption in water (53,94,117). Recently, it has been confirmed that the combustion products of chlorinated materials contain no chlorine (28). However, the addition of peroxide is useful to ensure that organic nitrogen and sulfur are present in the nitrate and sulfate states, respectively.

1. Methods of Finish

As in the case of sulfur, a multitude of finishes has been proposed; titrations with silver or mercury(II) solutions are the most popular, the former being more widely applicable and the latter more convenient for many purposes.

Schöniger (127) originally recommended the Vieböck mercury(II) oxycyanide method, which is very convenient after absorption in an alkaline peroxide solution. This method in its original (151) or modified (15) form gives good results on the micro (127,147) and semimicro (2) scales. Phosphate does not interfere (105). Spectrophotometric methods for 0.05–15 mg. of chloride based on reaction with mercury-(II) chloranilate have been described (89); sulfate and phosphate do not interfere. However, where possible, a direct titration with mercury(II) solution is to be preferred. Semimicro titrations to nitroprusside (152) or diphenylcarbazide (108,120a) indicator in aqueous media have been reported but the end points are poor. Cheng (25) utilized the remarkable improvement in the end point of diphenylcarbazone and in the precision of the titration obtained with an 80% alcoholic medium. This method has been followed by many later workers and is therefore given in detail.

2. Recommended Method

A. PREPARATION OF STANDARD $0.01M$ MERCURY (II) NITRATE

Dissolve ca. 3 g. of mercury(II) nitrate in 500 ml. of $0.05M$ nitric acid and dilute with water to 1 liter. Standardize the solution as follows: pipet a few (2 or 5) ml. of standard $0.01M$ sodium chloride and add water to give a total volume of 10 ml. followed by 40 ml. of ethanol or isopropanol. Add 1 ml. of $0.05M$ nitric acid and 15 drops of alcoholic 0.5% diphenylcarbazone solution and titrate. The reaction is not stoichiometric, hence factors should be obtained for the range of chloride required, or a calibration graph should be prepared. If 5 ml. of $0.01M$ sodium chloride is taken, the factor obtained is applicable over the range 1–2 mg. of chloride. Alternatively, the solution can be standardized against standard organic samples.

B. PROCEDURE

Burn a sample containing 1–2 mg. of chlorine in the usual way, absorbing in 10 ml. of water, or 10 ml. of $0.1N$ potassium hydroxide, containing 3–4 drops of 100-vol. hydrogen peroxide. Shake for 10 min. (Cheng absorbs in 1 ml. of $0.5N$ potassium hydroxide and 15 ml. of 6% hydrogen peroxide and later boils out the peroxide; this is unnecessary if only a little is added). Rinse the sample holder and flask wall with ethanol or isopropanol adding 40 ml. altogether, add 2–3 drops of alcoholic 0.05% bromophenol blue indicator and neutralize; then add 1 ml. of $0.05M$ nitric acid to give pH 3.5. Add 15 drops of the diphenylcarbazone indicator and titrate to the red end point.

If water is used as the absorbent and if the sample contains average amounts of acid-forming elements, the preliminary pH adjustment is unnecessary (94).

It is essential to avoid contamination of sample holders, etc., with chloride, e.g., from sweat; gloves should be worn for handling sample containers.

The titration in alcoholic medium is not very satisfactory on a semimicro scale, where the oxycyanide method is preferable, but gives excellent results on a submicro scale for 50-μg. samples (11). Mercury(II) perchlorate can be used instead of nitrate (135).

C. INTERFERENCES

Bromide is titrated quantitatively under the above conditions but iodide is not (see p. 99). Organic nitrogen does not interfere. Moderate amounts of fluoride do not interfere (95), but it may be advisable to take greater care over the pH adjustment (156). This is also true for phosphate (156). Organic sulfur is generally thought not to interfere but addition of 1 ml. of $0.1M$ barium nitrate after acidification has been recommended (156).

3. Alternative Methods

Potentiometric titration with silver solution was first used by Lehner (86) for analysis of traces of chlorine in pharmaceuticals. Since then, the method has been quite widely used (2,18,34,63,64,78,109,110) sometimes in conjunction with a specially designed flask to simplify insertion of the electrodes (86,111), or with combustion in a separating funnel to simplify transference of the solution (63,69). A potentiometric end point with coulometric titration has also been suggested (117). Essentially, any potentiometric setup for argentimetric titration can be applied; procedures of known reliability are those of Ingram (see p. 527 of ref. 93) and the Analytical Methods Committee (2). A disadvantage of the potentiometric method is that the absorption solution must be transferred unless a special flask is used; this removes one of the virtues of the flask combination — that normally there is no possibility of losses through transference of solutions.

A micro-Volhard titration (19,24) has been recommended. For direct titration with silver solutions, suggested indicators are variamine blue (40,102), dichlorofluorescein (50) in alcoholic medium, and dithizone in acetone medium (4). Silver halide can be filtered and reacted with potassium tetracyanonickelate, the released nickel being titrated with EDTA solution (67).

4. Applications

Combustion by the flask method has been applied for determination of chlorine in vinyl plastics (120), pulp and papers (18), polymers and plasticizers (63,64), pesticide formulations and other technical chemicals (2), petroleum products (88), rubbers (24), and chlorinated pesticide residues (60,88a). Traces of chlorine in oils have been determined by burning off 3 g. samples (42).

VI. SIMULTANEOUS DETERMINATION OF SULFUR AND CHLORINE

If aqueous hydrogen peroxide is used as absorbent, these two elements can be determined by titration of the total acidity followed by a titration of chloride alone by some mercurimetric method (108,128); of course, this is not satisfactory when other acid-forming elements are present. Böetius et al. (19) titrated sulfur with barium solution in

presence of alizarin sulfonic acid indicator and followed this immediately with a Volhard titration of chloride. Some workers, however,
prefer to take aliquots (24). More elegantly, the titration with barium perchlorate to thorin indicator in 80% alcoholic media can be followed by neutralization of the solution and immediate titration of
chloride with $0.01M$ silver perchlorate solution to dichlorofluorescein
indicator in the same medium (50). Titration with mercury(II)
nitrate solution can also follow the barium–thorin method, if the solution is appropriately diluted (157); the silver–variamine blue B procedure is also applicable (40).

VII. DETERMINATION OF BROMINE

Essentially all the methods of absorption and completion that have
been described for chlorine can also be applied for bromine. Organi-
callybound bromine is quantitatively converted to bromine in the
flask combustion (28) so that a reductant (e.g., peroxide) should be
present in the absorption solution if a final determination as bromide
is to be used. The mercurimetric and argentimetric titrations are
probably the most widely used, but both types suffer from the disadvantages of poor conversion factors. The method described for chlorine on p. 96 is applicable for bromine if the mercury solution is
standardized against bromide. The most accurate method for micro
samples involves oxidation of bromide with hypochlorite, followed by
destruction of excess hypochlorite with formate and iodimetric titration of the bromate formed (127,128). This is an excellent method,
though it is not fool proof; it gives a six-fold amplification factor and
is virtually free of interferences (except for iodine). Suitable procedures are given in most standard texts of organic analysis; for the
flask combustion, the buffered hypochlorite solution provides an excellent absorbent. The method is also suitable for submicro work (10).

VIII. DETERMINATION OF IODINE

By far the best method for the determination of iodine is based on
the Leipert oxidation procedure, first applied to the flask combustion
by Schöniger (127). The method possesses an excellent conversion
factor and is virtually specific for iodine. The method described below is an amalgam of previous work (15,127), which has proved en-

tirely satisfactory for years; the omission of the usual acetate buffer leads to greater clarity of end points and better precision.

1. Recommended Method

Burn a 3–6 mg. sample in the usual way, absorbing in 6 ml. of $1N$ sodium hydroxide. After complete absorption, rinse the sample holder and flask wall with water and neutralize with $1N$ sulfuric or phosphoric acid using an aqueous solution of methyl red as indicator; do not add so much acid that the indicator becomes clear pink. Add 1.5 or 2 ml. of saturated bromine water, stopper the flask, and leave for 5 min. Destroy the excess of bromine by dropwise addition of concentrated formic acid, and remove any bromine from the gaseous phase by suction. Test for complete removal of bromine with methyl red. Add 5 ml. of $2N$ sulfuric acid and ca. 0.3 g. of potassium iodide and titrate with 0.01 or $0.02N$ sodium thiosulfate, using Thyodene as indicator.

The method can readily be scaled down for 50-μg. samples (10). It can be applied after titration of sulfate with barium solution in aqueous solution (19). The virtues of the Leipert method after a flask combustion have been very widely realized but other methods have also been suggested. Titration with silver nitrate solution, either to variamine blue B indicator (40), or potentiometrically (110) can be applied. However, the conversion factor is very poor and a preliminary reduction to iodide is essential. Titration with mercury(II) nitrate solution by the Cheng method suffers from the same disadvantages. Cook (32) has recommended reduction with 3–4 drops of 10% hydrazine solution; the titration with mercury(II) nitrate is not satisfactory unless pyridine buffer is present. Hydrazine has been recommended as the reductant by other workers (67,110). The iodide formed can be precipitated as the palladium salt which is ultimately determined by EDTA titration (67).

If the products of combustion from compounds containing only C, H, O, and I are absorbed in water, organically bound iodine is said to be converted wholly to elemental iodine (28); but if the compound contained other elements, other oxidation states of iodine would be present. A limited method has been described (158) in which the sample is burned in a dry flask; the iodine is solidified and determined colorimetrically after addition of carbon tetrachloride, or by direct titration with thiosulfate after addition of carbon tetrachloride and water.

The flask combustion is entirely satisfactory for the analysis of iodine-containing pharmaceuticals (72).

IX. DETERMINATION OF FLUORINE

The very early and interesting application of a flask method to the analysis of alkyl fluorides by Meslans (107) has already been mentioned. Schöniger (128) found little difficulty in analyzing a selection of fluorinated materials; water is used as absorbent and the fluoride is titrated with cerium(III) solution in methanolic medium with murexide as indicator. Because of the rather poor end point, samples should be taken in the 7–15 mg. range, but the method has been confirmed as satisfactory (see ref. 130). The titration with cerium(III) solution is improved when the murexide is screened with naphthol green B (144). This method is useful for the determination of fluorine in the presence of phosphorus and arsenic if these are previously converted to the pentavalent state and separated on a zinc carbonate suspension; the zinc ions in solution must, however, be removed on a column of Amberlite IR-120(H) resin before the titration. This removal of zinc is unnecessary if a thorium titration is applied (13).

Despite these apparently straightforward applications, many difficulties have been reported in the determination of fluorine by the flask method. These can be traced to three basic sources: the stability of fluorinated compounds, the reactivity of hydrogen fluoride, and the lack of a really satisfactory method for completing the analysis. With regard to stability, many workers have recommended the addition of auxiliary combustible materials to the sample before ignition. Sucrose (123) sodium peroxide (132,142), potassium chlorate (12), and paraffin wax (84) have been suggested; Levy and Debal (87) tried these reagents, as well as glucose and potassium and ammonium nitrates, without obtaining much improvement in results. It seems possible that the successes originally claimed were due to some compensation of errors by the introduction of a foreign ion; notably, the workers who recommended sucrose (123) and glucose (87) also used a quartz flask for combustion (see below). The use of such aids to combustion does not, in fact, appear to have much effect on the completeness of decomposition. Compounds containing only C–F bonds or trifluoromethyl groups decompose quite readily in a straightforward combustion, whereas fully fluorinated compounds usually do not decompose completely whether or not an auxiliary addition is made (95). There seems to be no simple criterion by which to judge whether or not a perfluoro compound will be completely decomposed; the writer does not apply the flask method routinely to materials containing over 45% of fluorine because the results are so uncertain. Compounds such as Teflon appear to decompose quite readily, whereas highly fluorinated ring compounds are generally difficult. Such compounds can be decomposed much more effectively by fusion with potassium in a bomb. As might be expected, highly volatile stable perfluoro compounds cannot be dealt with by the flask method.

The reactivity of hydrogen fluoride causes trouble when combustions are done in flasks of borosilicate glass. Rogers and Yasuda (123) used quartz flasks to avoid interference from boron and aluminum in the glass. From published work, it appears that the errors incurred in the use of borosilicate glass are not significant with amounts of fluorine below 10%; possibly differences in the composition of certain glasses account for some early successes (128,130). However, it has now been repeatedly confirmed (44,71,87,118) that the results obtained with quartz flasks are much more accurate than those with borosilicate flasks. Fairly typical results at different fluorine levels are shown in Table I. Of course, quartz flasks are expensive. Preliminary tests indicate that cheap, stout polypropylene flasks are equally effective (44); the attack by heat is negligible if the flasks are manipulated appropriately during the combustion and a spectrophotometric finish can readily be used. Since dilute hydrofluoric acid can

TABLE I

Results for Standard Compounds After Combustion in Flasks of Various Materials[a]

		F content found after combustion in		
Compound	F content (%)	silica	boron-free glass[b]	borosilicate glass
p-Fluorobenzoic acid	13.56	13.55	13.47	13.03
m-Trifluoromethylbenzoic acid	29.98	30.00	29.95	28.81
Polytetrafluoroethylene	76.0	75.8	75.9	72.1

[a] From reference 71.
[b] Containing 3% alumina.

easily be titrated in borosilicate vessels, it must be assumed that hydrogen fluoride is lost on to the walls of borosilicate flasks before its absorption in water. Pretreatment of borosilicate flasks with hydrofluoric acid is said to improve results (118), but this is doubtful since the calibration curve for the finish used was prepared from combusted samples. With a titrimetric finish, prior rinsing with hydrofluoric acid has no significant effect (95).

1. Methods of Completion

Many methods of completion have been recommended. The combustion products are generally absorbed in water though 0.1–2N sodium hydroxide has been used (45,132). Konovalo (81) absorbs in a solution of calcium chloride and titrates the hydrochloric acid released. Apart from the cerium(III) titration (128), the only other titrimetric finish which has been applied after a flask combustion involves thorium nitrate with alizarin red S as indicator. Such titrations were apparently preferred by a majority of workers in a collaborative test (140). Visual comparison (8,95), visual direct (84) and photometric direct (142) titrations have been used. Spectrophotometric finishes utilizing the bleaching effect of fluoride on iron(III) salicylate (123), iron-(III) sulfosalicylate (87) and the zirconium–eriochrome cyanine R complex (45,132,133) have been proposed. A spectrophotometric method based on the reaction with thorium chloranilate has been recommended (118). The only known direct color-forming reaction for fluoride, that with the cerium(III)–alizarin complexan complex (alizarin fluorine blue), can be utilized with 100-μg. samples (12) or with 5 to 25-mg. samples if aliquots of the absorption solution are used (71).

Given so many divergent recommendations in the literature, it is impossible to single out any particular method as distinctly preferable to others. If a titrimetric method, the snags of which have been thoroughly examined and publicized, is desired, then a thorium nitrate procedure must be preferred; with this method, nitrogen and moderate amounts of other halogens do not interfere but sulfate, phosphate, arsenate, and most metals do, so that separation of fluorosilicic acid by a Willard-Winter distillation or removal of the offending ion by some other means becomes essential. The best of the spectrophotometric methods appears to be that involving alizarin fluorine blue; this method is less susceptible to anionic interference than most colorimetric procedures for fluorine, and so is particularly appropriate for organic analysis. However, since water is a suitable absorbent, the final solution for the determination contains only hydrofluoric acid, apart from other ions arising from the sample itself; accordingly, the analyst is entirely free to follow his own preference in regard to the final procedure. In analysis for fluorine, faith in one's method seems to be as important as scientific rectitude.

Soep (133) has used a flask combustion for the determination of fluorine in paper spots after chromatographic separations.

X. DETERMINATION OF PHOSPHORUS

The actual state in which phosphorus is present after an oxygen-flask combustion is uncertain. When organic materials are burned, most of the phosphorus almost certainly appears as orthophosphate but the residual amount has been considered variously as pyro- and metaphosphate (29,105) and as lower oxides of phosphorus (14,48).

The first workers to apply the flask method to the determination of phosphorus, Fleischer et al. (46), absorbed the products of the combustion in 5 ml. of 1:2 nitric acid and boiled the solution for a few minutes to ensure complete conversion to orthophosphate. This treatment would hydrolyze other phosphates to the *ortho* form and would also presumably oxidize any lower oxides of phosphorus. Several later workers have used similar absorption solutions (5,17,49,126). Many others (22,29,35,48,88,105) prefer sulfuric acid as the absorbent, for the application of a sensitive spectrophotometric finish is then simpler. Acid strengths varying from 0.2 to 6N have been recommended and the solution is generally boiled for 10–40 min. Cohen and Czech (29) and Merz (105) report no difficulties but Gedansky et al. (48) in analyzing petroleum products, confirmed an earlier report (14) that low results are obtained unless an oxidizing absorbent is used. On the other hand, Dirscherl and Erne (35) showed that oxidation with permanganate after absorption in sulfuric acid did not improve the low results. Gedansky et al. (48) overcame the difficulty by mixing the sample in a gelatin capsule with anhydrous sodium carbonate so that a simultaneous combustion–fusion was performed; their work has been confirmed for petroleum products (88) and a similar technique has been found necessary in the analysis of cokes (22). After various tests, Dirscherl and Erne (35) ascribed their low results to the formation of an unspecified carbon–phosphorus compound with carbon deposits on the platinum sample holder, and recommended mixing the sample with 10–20 mg. of ammonium persulfate before combustion of micro samples in a 500-ml. flask. However, the occurrence of low results is not, in the writer's experience, directly connected with carbon deposits, which are quite rare. Belcher and Macdonald (14) used an alkaline hypobromite solution with excellent results; this is suitable for micro (14,76) and semimicro (97) work. Other absorbents which have been recommended are pure water (122) and aqueous hydrogen peroxide (103); boiling times of 10 and 30 min., respectively, are used.

The question of whether it is hydrolysis or oxidation that is required to ensure the quantitative presence of orthophosphate for the end determination, has not been definitely answered. Some recent evidence (44), obtained in studying a different problem, indicates that a certain amount of phosphite is present when combustion products are absorbed in water. Gedansky et al. (48) obtained low results as the amount of phosphorus increased above 0.4 mg., which was ascribed to a deficiency of oxygen in the immediate vicinity of the combustion leading to incomplete oxidation of the phosphorus. Oxidizing absorbents are certainly satisfactory and should be preferred unless contraindicated by the chosen method of finish; if other absorbents, e.g., sulfuric acid, are applied it would seem essential to watch for low results and if necessary add some reagent to give a simultaneous fusion in the combustion.

Most workers shake the flask for the normal time to obtain complete absorption but it has been proved that shaking the flask for only 30 sec. is quite effective (48).

1. Methods of Finish

Fleischer et al. (46) recommended precipitation of magnesium ammonium phosphate and titration of the precipitate with EDTA for semimicro work, and a spectrophotometric molybdenum blue method involving a mixed ammonium molybdate–bismuth subcarbonate–ascorbic acid reagent for micro determinations. The semimicro method requires a correction and is little used. Colorimetric finishes predominate. Molybdenum blue finishes involving reduction with ascorbic acid, tin(II) chloride (29,76) hydrazine (48), methyl-p-aminophenol sulfate (Photorex) (105) and other reagents (22,49) have been described. Obviously, any satisfactory reductant of the many described in the literature can be used; hydrazine or ascorbic acid appears to be least troublesome. Other workers (5,35) have preferred the less sensitive phosphovanadomolybdate procedure. None of the methods appears to be so clearly superior to the others that a recommended procedure can be given. The choice of a colorimetric method depends on the range of phosphorus content in the samples, on the ready availability of apparatus and on the regularity with which analyses for phosphorus are required. Spectrophotometric methods are uneconomic for occasional use, hence many workers prefer titrimetric methods.

In one of the earliest applications of the flask method to the phosphorus determination (14), the phosphate produced is precipitated as quinoline molybdophosphate, which can be immediately filtered, washed, and dissolved in standard sodium hydroxide, excess of which is back-titrated. This method has the advantage of an excellent and unequivocal conversion factor and a high tolerance for most foreign ions. It is also applicable for semimicro work (97).

Bennewitz and Tänzer (17) describe a titrimetric method for 1–6 mg. of phosphorus in which the nitric acid absorbent is adjusted to pH 10 and a slight excess of magnesium chloride is added; this is back-titrated with EDTA solution in presence of eriochrome black T indicator. An empirical standardization is necessary and cyanide is added to prevent interference of platinum. A somewhat similar method with lead nitrate solution (103) appears to give very low results. Püschel and Wittmann (122) recommend absorption in water followed by direct titration with cerium(III) solution to eriochrome black T indicator in a hot hexamine-buffered medium. Cyanide addition is again necessary to prevent interference of platinum. Nitrogen, chlorine, bromine, iodine, and sulfur in the compound do not interfere, but fluorine, arsenic, and silicon do.

If a titrimetric finish is required, the choice appears to lie between the quinoline molybdophosphate and the cerium(III) methods. Both are applicable over the 0.2–0.5 mg. range of phosphorus and neither depends on an empirical standardization; the cerium(III) titration is of course quicker but more sensitive to interference. In the writer's laboratory. the quinoline method gives the more reliable results.

2. Applications

Applications of the flask combustion with a spectrophotometric molybdenum blue finish have been described for petroleum products (48,88); diluted sulfuric acid is used as absorbent, and sodium carbonate must be mixed with the sample. A vanadomolybdate finish is also suitable for analysis of motor oils and additives (5). Cokes should be sieved to 240 mesh and mixed with Eschka mixture before combustion (22). Flame-proof fabrics can be burned without difficulty (6). Pharmaceuticals can be analyzed readily (82). A modified combustion process can be applied for samples of up to 5 g. (42).

XI. DETERMINATION OF ARSENIC

It has been shown (15a) that arsenic is converted mainly to arsenic(III) on combustion of organic samples in an oxygen flask, and that some arsenic forms an alloy with the usual platinum sample holder. Because combustion in quartz or other metal sample holders is less satisfactory than that obtained with platinum, some workers (15a,145) prefer wet-combustion procedures to the flask method. The latter has, however, been applied on several occasions with successful results.

Corner (34) used a platinum spiral to hold the sample and distilled arsenic trichloride before an iodimetric finish. Merz (106) recommended a quartz spiral but found that a special "phosphorus-resistant" platinum could be used for compounds containing no hetero-elements other than arsenic. A major difficulty with quartz spirals is that particles of sample and paper drop through the spiral before complete ignition; even the more rapid combustion obtained with filter paper impregnated with potassium nitrate does not prevent this (121). A small layer of quartz wool wrapped around the spiral after insertion of the sample container is said to allow complete combustion without losses (121). If the compound contains much arsenic the spiral should be left on the flask during the subsequent boiling period.

An oxidizing absorbent is needed. Merz (106) absorbed in a dilute iodine solution and finally determined arsenate by a spectrophotometric molybdenum blue method, hydrazine being used as the final reductant. Püschel (121) used $0.01N$ sodium hydroxide containing 2 drops of 100-vol. hydrogen peroxide, the solution being boiled to ensure complete oxidation. The arsenate is titrated with $0.01M$ lead nitrate in hot hexamine-buffered solution in presence of pyridylazo-resorcinol or SNAZOXS as indicator; the former indicator gives more precise results but the latter is less easily blocked. Corrections are required for moderate amounts of sulfur, chlorine, and bromine. Precipitation as silver arsenate with an ultimate EDTA titration is possible (137).

Traces of arsenic can be determined in large samples of plant materials (60).

XII. DETERMINATION OF BORON

Organic boron is converted to borate by the combustion. Some compounds, e.g., substituted borazoles and silylbenzene–boronic acid derivatives may be difficult to decompose; in such cases, complete decomposition can be achieved by the addition of powdered sucrose (159) or potassium hydroxide (34). Difficulties from the use of borosilicate glass can be avoided by coating it with a silicone repellent, e.g., Beckman Desicote (159); soda-glass flasks can also be used (15a).

The boric acid formed on absorption of the combustion products in water can be determined by any straightforward mannitol method, after boiling out carbon dioxide (15a,34,114); a coulometric mannitol method has also been described (159).

XIII. DETERMINATION OF MERCURY

Excellent results can readily be obtained for mercury by flask combustion methods. Metallic mercury, mercury(I) and mercury(II) are formed in the combustion and concentrated nitric acid is generally used as the absorbent to ensure that all the mercury is finally present as mercury(II) (136). If chlorine is also present, the absorbent must be heated under efficient reflux to oxidize mercury(I) chloride. The mercury(II) can be titrated amperometrically with 0.1 or $0.01M$ EDTA solution. Visual titrations are unsatisfactory because nitrogen oxides destroy the usual indicators; mercury is lost if these oxides are boiled out (136). Trouble with chlorine-containing compounds can be avoided by absorbing in alkaline hypobromite solution, and visual titration with EDTA solution can then be applied (150). This procedure is simpler and faster than absorption in nitric acid but is less accurate (96) than that described by Gouverneur and Hoedeman (55). In this method, mercury is absorbed in nitric acid and titrated with sodium diethyldithiocarbamate solution (125). Chlorine and bromine do not interfere and, in fact, chlorine can be determined after the mercury titration.

1. Recommended Method (55)

Burn a sample containing not more than 10 mg. of mercury or 3.5 mg. of chlorine in a 250-ml. flask in the usual way, absorbing in 3 ml. of nitric acid (s.g., 1.42) introduced into the previously *dried* flask. Shake the flask for 1 min. and allow to stand for 15 min. (or for 5 min. if only mercury is to be determined). Wash the stopper and gauze with 2 ml. of nitric acid. Boil under a water-cooled condenser for 15 min., cool, and rinse the condenser, the gauze, etc., with water. Add 10 ml. of 10% (w/v) tartaric acid solution and 1 ml. of copper solution (100 mg. of copper(II) acetate mixed with 2.5 ml. of 20% (v/v) sulfuric acid and diluted to 100 ml. with water). Adjust the pH to 9–10 with 25% (v/v) ammonia (universal indicator paper) and add 5 ml. of chloroform. Titrate with standard 0.01N "carbamate" solution until the organic layer changes sharply from colorless to yellow. Prepare the titrant by dissolving 2.5 g. of sodium diethyldithiocarbamate trihydrate in 1 liter of water and standardize daily against standard 0.01N mercury(II) sulfate in 0.4% v/v sulfuric acid.

For a subsequent determination of chlorine, filter the above titrated solution through paper, wash with water and neutralize to methyl red indicator with 30% (v/v) nitric acid, adding 12 drops in excess. Then titrate the chloride potentiometrically with 0.01N silver nitrate solution.

Traces of mercury in 10-g. samples of dried apples can be determined after combustion in a 5-liter flask by a spectrophotometric dithizone procedure (58).

XIV. DETERMINATION OF OTHER METALS

Several metals can be determined very easily by combustion of the organometallic compound in the oxygen flask. Zinc, cadmium, and magnesium complexes cause no trouble (15a); 1N hydrochloric acid is a good absorbent and the metal can be determined after suitable pH adjustment, by titration with EDTA solution. Later work (96) has shown that calcium, cobalt, and barium complexes can be analyzed similarly without difficulty. Copper has also been determined (143).

Manganese and nickel traces in plant materials treated with pesticides have been determined (60).

Alkali metals can be determined after combustion in cooled polythene flasks (see ref. 130).

Gubser (57) suggested the use of flask combustions in trace analysis for selenium. Since selenium attacks platinum, it is necessary to use a quartz spiral (104), but this is said (68) to give inaccurate results and a special, electrically fired sample holder has been described (68). An oxidizing absorbent, e.g., bromine water or a mixture of sulfuric and nitric acids, appears to be essential if a final iodimetric titration is to be applied (68). The determination of selenium in dried plant materials involving a spectrophotometric finish with 3,3'-diaminobenzidine hydrochloride has been described (59).

Although the flask combustion gives satisfactory results for a number of metals, it is not a general method. Some elements, e.g., lead, bismuth, and iron, form alloys with a platinum sample support, or adhere very strongly to other supports, whereas other elements, e.g., nickel and aluminium, form oxides which are exceedingly difficult to dissolve. No doubt such difficulties could be overcome by appropriate treatments but the simplicity and speed of the flask method would be lost; in complicated cases, it seems better to use a simple and well-tried digestion process.

XV. DETERMINATION OF CARBON

Complete combustion of a small sample is not easily achieved by ignition with an electrical coil since the sample tends to melt or volatilize away from the coil before it ignites; the filter paper wrapper is therefore normally retained even by enthusiastic advocates of the electrical technique. The problem of a combustible inorganic sample wrapper has not been solved. Juvet and Chiu (73) placed the sample on a loose glass-wool mat which was then folded round a Nichrome heating coil for ignition; the carbon dioxide formed was absorbed in $0.5N$ sodium hydroxide and titrated with $0.1N$ acid between the phenolphthalein and methyl orange end points. The method is not very satisfactory. Cheng and Smullin (26,27) improved the ignition by placing the 2–4 mg. sample in a porcelain boat inserted into a platinum wire coil and covering it with a small piece of platinum gauze before heating the coil for ignition. The carbon dioxide is absorbed in alkaline barium chloride solution and barium carbonate is filtered off and titrated acidimetrically.   Nitrogen, halogens, and sulfur do not interfere.   The method requires considerable care, according to its originators, and, of course, hydrogen cannot be determined simultaneously.

Combustion in a 5-liter flask has been used for determination of carbon in soils (59); the pelleted sample is ignited with a filter paper fuse, for which a blank correction is made.   The method of finish is similar to that of Juvet and Chiu.

Ingram (70) has developed a method for determination of carbon and hydrogen in which a closed oxygen-filled chamber is combined with a high-temperature (900°C) furnace.   The sample is pushed into the hot zone for combustion and an oxygen stream is then used to sweep the combustion products through a conventional absorption system.   This method of combustion would appear to be ideally suited for instrumentation and automation purposes, since no control of the actual combustion process is necessary.

XVI.   ANALYSIS OF RADIOACTIVE MATERIALS

Decomposition by the flask method has been applied for the assay of organic materials labeled with tritium, carbon-14 and sulfur-35. Götte et al. (52) determined carbon-14 after absorption of carbon dioxide in $1N$ sodium hydroxide and precipitation of barium carbonate. Sulfur-35 can be determined similarly after precipitation of barium sulfate (62).   Later workers have preferred liquid scintillation counting.   Kelly et al. (75) determined carbon-14 and tritium in 200-mg. samples of biological tissues and fluids by burning in a 2-liter filter flask fitted with a stopcock; carbon dioxide is absorbed in Hyamine X-10 or ethanolamine, and water is frozen out before dissolution in a suitable phosphor for counting.   Modifications of this method have been described (37,74,116); 2-phenylethylamine is said to be the best absorbent for the carbon-14 and sulfur-35 combustion products (37, 116).   Most of the combustions are done with electrical or infrared ignition after the flask has been sealed.   Dobbs (37) described procedures for ^{14}C, ^{35}S, and ^3H which a single absorbent-phosphor mixture is injected into the flask after the combustion.   He noted a peculiar effect in the analysis of azobenzenes, which gave unexpectedly low count rates; the compounds obviously burned to completion and Dobbs suggested that some product with very strong quenching properties was formed.   For low carbon-14 activity, an ionization chamber method has been recommended (131).

XVII. QUALITATIVE APPLICATIONS

The application of flask combustion to qualitative elemental analysis is an obvious extension. Stephen (138,139) drew attention to its advantages in qualitative work, with particular reference to fluorinated materials. Haslam et al. (65) applied the flask decomposition for detection of "additional" elements ($< 2\%$ S,F,Cl,Br,I,P,N) in plastic materials with 20-mg. samples; the combustion products are absorbed in 5 ml. of N sodium hydroxide and when suitable aliquots are taken, semiquantitative results can be obtained.

The detection of the ions formed can clearly be done by any normal test of appropriate sensitivity. The detection of nitrogen is the most interesting application in this area. Haslam et al. (65) found the Griess-Ilosvay test too sensitive, for excessive blanks were obtained from filter paper containers. They preferred a test involving nitrosation of resorcinol and reaction with iron(II); positive tests were found with amides, amines, nitroso, azo, and nitro compounds, but a stabilized diazonium salt gave only a faint test.

Campbell and Munro (23) studied the detection of nitrogen further and showed that 0.5-mg. samples burned in a 100-ml. flask with 2 ml. of 0.1M sodium hydroxide as absorbent gave sufficient nitrite to be detected by the Griess reaction when only a drop of the absorption solution was taken. With a 15-mm. square of Whatman No. 44 paper, the blank test was never sufficiently positive to be confused with a sample test. Fluorine, chlorine, and iodine in the sample did not interfere, but bromine, which is produced quantitatively on combustion in a platinum sample holder, oxidized the nitrogen oxides formed to nitrate. To avoid this interference, copper or silver gauze was found necessary instead of platinum; the bromine then reacted preferentially with the gauze and the nitrogen oxides could be detected in the usual way as nitrite.

Combustion in air instead of oxygen is satisfactory for qualitative purposes and a steel prong can be used instead of the normal platinum arrangement (33); this makes the method particularly suitable for field use.

References

1. Alicino, J. F., *Microchem. J.*, 2, 83 (1958).
2. Analytical Methods Committee, Society for Analytical Chemistry, *Analyst*, 88, 415 (1963).
3. Archer, E. E., *Analyst*, 82, 208 (1957).
4. Archer, E. E., *Analyst*, 83, 571 (1958).
5. Barney, J. E., II, J. G. Bergmann, and W. G. Tuskan, *Anal. Chem.*, 31, 1394 (1959).
6. Bartels, U., and H. Hoyme, *Chem. Tech.* (*Berlin*), 11, 156 (1959).
7. Bartels, U., and H. Hoyme, *Chem. Tech.* (*Berlin*), 11, 600 (1959).
8. Belcher, R., E. F. Caldas, S. J. Clark, and A. M. G. Macdonald, *Mikrochim. Acta*, 1953, 283.
9. Belcher, R., A. D. Campbell, P. Gouverneur, and A. M. G. Macdonald, *J. Chem. Soc.*, 1962, 3033.
10. Belcher, R., Y. Gawargious, P. Gouverneur, and A. M. G. Macdonald, *J. Chem. Soc.*, 1964, 3560.
11. Belcher, R., P. Gouverneur, and A. M. G. Macdonald, *J. Chem. Soc.*, 1962, 1938.
12. Belcher, R., M. Leonard, and T. S. West, *J. Chem. Soc.*, 1959, 3577.
13. Belcher, R., and A. M. G. Macdonald, *Mikrochim. Acta*, 1956, 900.
14. Belcher, R., and A. M. G. Macdonald, *Talanta*, 1, 185 (1958).
15. Belcher, R., A. M. G. Macdonald, and A. J. Nutten, *Mikrochim. Acta*, 1954, 104.
15a. Belcher, R., A. M. G. Macdonald, and T. S. West, *Talanta*, 1, 408 (1958).
16. Bennewitz, R., *Mikrochim. Acta*, 1960, 54.
17. Bennewitz, R., and I. Tänzer, *Mikrochim. Acta*, 1959, 835.
18. Bethge, P. O., and T. Tröeng, *Svensk. Papperstid.*, 62, 598 (1959).
19. Böetius, M., G. Gutbier, and H. Reith, *Mikrochim. Acta*, 1958, 321.
20. Boos, R. N., *Analyst*, 84, 633 (1959).
21. British Coke Research Association, Coke Research Report 13, Chesterfield, Nov., 1961.
22. British Coke Research Association, Coke Research Report 28, Chesterfield, Sept., 1963.
23. Campbell, A. D., and M. H. G. Munro, *Anal. Chim. Acta*, 28, 574 (1963).
24. Chelishcheva, G. A., G. M. Chebysheva, and G. P. Shcherbachev, *Soviet Rubber Technol.* (*English Transl.*), 20, 19 (1961).
25. Cheng, F. W., *Microchem. J.*, 3, 537 (1959).
26. Cheng, F. W., and C. F. Smullin, *Microchem. J.*, 4, 213 (1960).
27. Cheng, F. W., and C. F. Smullin, *Microchem. J.*, 5, 43 (1961).
28. Childs, C. E., E. E. Meyers, J. Cheng, E. Laframboise, and R. B. Balodis, *Microchem. J.*, 7, 266 (1963).
29. Cohen, L. E., and F. W. Czech., *Chemist-Analyst*, 47, 86 (1958).
30. Colson, A. F., *Analyst*, 88, 26 (1963).
31. Committee on Microchemical Apparatus, Division of Anal. Chem., American Chemical Society, *Anal. Chem.*, 33, 1789 (1961).
32. Cook, W. A., *Microchem. J.*, 5, 67 (1961).

33. Corliss, J. M., and C. A. Rush, in *Microchemical Techniques*, Vol. 2 (Proc. Intern. Symp. on Microchemical Techniques, 1961), N. D. Cheronis, ed., Interscience, New York, 1962, p. 407.
34. Corner, M., *Analyst*, **84**, 41 (1959).
35. Dirscherl, A., and F. Erne, *Mikrochim. Acta*, **1960**, 775.
36. Dixon, J. P., *Analyst*, **86**, 597 (1961).
37. Dobbs, H. E., *Anal. Chem.*, **35**, 783 (1963).
38. Eder, K., *Mikrochim. Acta*, **1960**, 471.
39. Ellison, M., *Analyst*, **87**, 389 (1962).
40. Erdey, L., L. Mázor, and T. Meisel, *Mikrochim. Acta*, **1958**, 140.
41. Fabre, P., *Ann. Pharm. Franc.*, **20**, 563 (1962).
42. Farley, L. L., and A. Winkler, *Anal. Chem.*, **35**, 772 (1963).
43. Favorskaya, I. A., and V. I. Lukina, *Vestn. Leningr. Univ.*, No. 10, *Ser. Fiz. i. Khim.*, **1961**, 148.
44. Fernandopulle, M., and A. M. G. Macdonald, unpublished work.
45. Ferrari, H. J., F. C. Geronimo, and L. M. Brancome, *Microchem. J.*, **5**, 617 (1961).
46. Fleischer, K. D., B. C. Southworth, J. D. Hodecker, and M. M. Tuckerman, *Anal. Chem.*, **30**, 152 (1958).
47. Fritz, J. S., and S. S. Yamamura, *Anal. Chem.*, **27**, 1461 (1955).
48. Gedansky, S. J., J. E. Bowen, and O. I. Milner, *Anal. Chem.*, **32**, 1447 (1960).
49. Gelman, N. E., and T. M. Shanina, *Zh. Analit. Khim.*, **17**, 998 (1962).
50. Gieselmann, G., and I. Hagedorn, *Mikrochim. Acta*, **1960**, 390.
51. Gildenberg, L., *Microchem. J.*, **3**, 167 (1959).
52. Götte, H., R. Krete, and H. Baddenhausen, *Angew. Chem.*, **69**, 561 (1957).
53. Gouverneur, P., M. Sc. Thesis, Birmingham University, 1961.
54. Gouverneur, P., and C. D. F. Eerbeek, *Anal. Chim. Acta*, **27**, 303 (1962).
55. Gouverneur, P., and W. Hoedeman, *Anal. Chim. Acta*, **30**, 519 (1964).
56. Graefe, E., *Z. angew. Chem.*, **17**, 616 (1904).
57. Gubser, H., *Chimia (Aarau)*, **13**, 245 (1959).
58. Gutenmann, W. H., and D. J. Lisk, *J. Agr. Food Chem.*, **8**, 306 (1960).
59. Gutenmann, W. H., and D. J. Lisk, *J. Agr. Food Chem.*, **9**, 488, 489 (1961).
60. Gutenmann, W. H., L. E. Saint-John, D. L. Barry, E. D. Jones, and D. J. Lisk, *J. Agr. Food Chem.*, **9**, 50 (1961).
61. Haack, A., *Mikrochim. Ichnoanal. Acta*, **1963**, 201.
62. Habersbergerová-Jeničková, A., and J. Cifka, *Collection Czech. Chem. Commun.*, **24**, 3777 (1959).
63. Haslam, J., J. B. Hamilton, and D. C. M. Squirrel, *J. Appl. Chem. (London)*, **10**, 97 (1960).
64. Haslam, J., J. B. Hamilton, and D. C. M. Squirrel, *Analyst*, **85**, 556 (1960).
65. Haslam, J., J. B. Hamilton, and D. C. M. Squirrel, *Analyst*, **86**, 239 (1961).
66. Hempel, W., *Z. angew. Chem.*, **13**, 393 (1892).
67. Hennart, C., *Mikrochim. Acta*, **1961**, 543; *Talanta*, **8**, 480 (1961).
68. Ihn, W., G. Hesse, P. Neuland, *Mikrochim. Acta*, **1962**, 628.
69. Ingram, G., personal communication.
70. Ingram, G., *Analyst*, **86**, 411 (1961).

71. Johnson, C. A., and M. Leonard, *Analyst*, **86**, 101 (1961).
72. Johnson, C. A., and C. Vickers, *J. Pharm. Pharmacol.*, **11**, 218T (1959).
73. Juvet, R. S., and J. Chiu, *Anal. Chem.*, **32**, 130 (1960).
74. Kalberer, F., and J. Rutschmann, *Helv. Chim. Acta*, **44**, 1956 (1961).
75. Kelly, R. G., E. A. Peets, and D. A. Buyske, *Anal. Biochem.*, **2**, 267 (1961).
76. Kirsten, W. J., *Microchem. J.*, **4**, 3 (1960).
77. Kirsten, W. J., *Proceedings of International Symposium on Microchemistry, 1958*, Pergamon Press, London, 1960, p. 137.
78. Kirsten, W. J., *Mikrochim. Acta*, **1960**, 272.
79. Kirsten, W. J., *Microchem. J.*, **7**, 34 (1963).
80. Kirsten, W. J., K. A. Hansson, and S. K. Nilsson, *Anal. Chim. Acta*, **28**, 101, (1963).
81. Konovalov, A., *Ind. Chim. Belge*, **26**, 1257 (1961).
82. Kremsbrucker, H., *Sci. pharm.*, **27**, 294 (1959).
83. Kusenko, V. P., and M. J. Cardone, *Microchem. J.*, **6**, 605 (1962).
84. Lebedeva, A. I., N. A. Nikolaeva, and V. A. Orestova, *Zh. Analit. Khim.*, **16**, 469 (1961).
85. Lebedeva, A. I., and I. V. Novozhilova, *Zh. Analit. Khim.*, **16**, 223 (1961).
86. Lehner, H., *Chimia (Aarau)*, **13**, 248 (1959).
87. Lévy, R., and E. Debal, *Mikrochim. Acta*, **1962**, 224.
88. Liddell, C., *J. Inst. Petrol.*, **48**, 221 (1962).
88a. Lisk, D. J., *J. Agr. Food Chem.*, **8**, 119 (1960).
89. Lysyj, I., *Microchem. J.*, **3**, 529 (1959).
90. Lysyj, I., and J. E. Zarembo, *Anal. Chem.*, **20**, 428 (1958).
91. Lysyj, I., and J. E. Zarembo, *Microchem. J.*, **3**, 173 (1959).
92. Macdonald, A. M. G., *Ind. Chem.*, **35**, 33 (1959).
93. Macdonald, A. M. G., in *Comprehensive Analytical Chemistry*, Vol. IB, Wilson and Wilson, eds., Elsevier Publishing Company, Amsterdam, 1960, p. 517.
94. Macdonald, A. M. G., *Analyst*, **86**, 3 (1961).
95. Macdonald, A. M. G., M. Marks, and G. G. Turton, unpublished work.
96. Macdonald, A. M. G., and P. Sirichanya, unpublished work.
97. Macdonald, A. M. G., and W. I. Stephen, *J. Chem. Educ.*, **39**, 528 (1962).
98. Malissa, H., and L. Machherndl, *Mikrochim. Acta*, **1962**, 1089.
99. Marcusson, J., and H. Döscher, *Chemiker Ztg.*, **34**, 417 (1910).
100. Martin, A. J., and H. Deveraux, *Anal. Chem.*, **31**, 1932 (1959).
101. Mázor, L., T. Meisel, and L. Erdey, *Magy. Kém. Lapja*, **14**, 494 (1959).
102. Mázor, L., K. M. Papay, and P. Klatsmanyi, *Talanta*, **10**, 557 (1963).
103. Meier, E., *Mikrochim. Acta*, **1961**, 70.
104. Meier, E., and N. Shaltiel, *Mikrochim. Acta*, **1960**, 580.
105. Merz, W., *Mikrochim. Acta*, **1959**, 456.
106. Merz, W., *Mikrochim. Acta*, **1959**, 640.
107. Meslans, M., *Bull. soc. chim. de Paris*, **9**, 109 (1893).
108. Mikl, O., and J. Pech, *Chem. Listy*, **46**, 382 (1952); **47**, 904 (1953).
109. Mizukami, S., T. Ieki, and U. Kasugai, *Mikrochim. Acta*, **1962**, 717.
110. Nara, A., and K. Ito, *Japan Analyst*, **11**, 454 (1962).
111. Newman, D. G., and C. Tomlinson, *Mikrochim. Acta*, **1961**, 73.

112. Novikova, K. F., and N. N. Basargin, *Ref. Zh., Khim.*, **1963**, 19GDE; Abstr. 20G.141.
113. Novikova, K. F., N. N. Basargin, and M. F. Tsyganova, *Zh. Analit. Khim.*, **16**, 348 (1961).
114. Obtemperanskaya, S. I., and V. N. Likhosherstova, *Vestn. Moskov. Univ.*, (1), 57 (1960).
115. Ogg, C. L., R. B. Kelly, and J. A. Connelly, in *Microchemical Techniques*, Vol. 2 (Proc. Intern. Symp. on Microchemical Techniques, 1961) N. D. Cheronis, ed., Interscience, New York, 1962, p. 427.
116. Oliverio, V. T., C. Denham, and J. D. Davidson, *Anal. Biochem.*, **4**, 188 (1962).
117. Olson, E. C., and A. F. Krivis, *Microchem. J.*, **4**, 181 (1960).
118. Olson, E. C., and S. R. Shaw, *Microchem. J.*, **5**, 101 (1961).
119. Ottosson, R., and O. Snellman, *Acta Chem. Scand.*, **11**, 185 (1957).
120. Pražák, M., J. Benc, and Z. Bartuzek, *Chem. Průmysl*, **3**, 297 (1953).
120a. Praeger, K., and H. Fürst, *Chem. Tech. (Berlin)*, **10**, 537 (1958).
121. Püschel, R., and Z. Štefanac, *Mikrochim. Acta*, **1962**, 1108.
122. Püschel, R., and H. Wittmann, *Mikrochim. Acta*, **1960**, 670.
123. Rogers, R. N., and S. K. Yasuda, *Anal. Chem.*, **31**, 616 (1959).
124. Roth, H., *Mikrochemie ver Mikrochim. Acta*, **36/37**, 379 (1951).
125. Roth, H., and W. Beck, in Pregl-Roth, *Quantitative Organische Analyse*, 7th ed., Springer-Verlag, Wien, 1958, p. 184.
126. Ryadnina, A. M., *Zavodsk. Lab.*, **27**, 405 (1961).
127. Schöniger, W., *Mikrochim. Acta*, **1955**, 123.
128. Schöniger, W., *Mikrochim. Acta*, **1956**, 869.
129. Schöniger, W., F. and M. for Scientific Research, F. and M. Scientific Corp., Delaware, 1960.
130. Schöniger, W., *Z. Anal. Chem.*, **181**, 28 (1961).
131. Schuching, S. von, and C. W. Karickhoff, *Anal. Biochem.*, **5**, 93 (1963).
132. Senkowski, B. Z., E. G. Wollish, and E. G. E. Shafer, *Anal. Chem.*, **31**, 1575 (1959).
133. Soep, H., *Nature*, **192**, 67 (1961).
134. Soep, H., and P. Demoen, *Microchem. J.*, **4**, 77 (1960).
135. Sokolova, N. V., V. A. Orestova, and N. A. Nikolaeva, *Zh. Analit. Khim.*, **14**, 472 (1959).
136. Southworth, B. C., J. H. Hodecker, and K. D. Fleischer, *Anal. Chem.*, **30**, 1152 (1958).
137. Stefanac, Z., *Mikrochim. Acta*, **1962**, 1115.
138. Stephen, W. I., *Ind. Chemist*, **37**, 86 (1961).
139. Stephen, W. I., *Chem. Weekblad*, **57**, 273 (1961).
140. Steyermark, A., *J. Assoc. Offic. Agr. Chemists*, **43**, 683 (1960).
141. Steyermark, A., E. A. Bass, C. C. Johnston, and J. C. Dell, *Microchem. J.*, **4**, 55 (1960).
142. Steyermark, A., R. R. Kaup, D. A. Petras, and E. A. Bass, *Microchem. J.*, **3**, 523 (1959).
143. Terent'ev, A. P., S. I. Obtemperanskaya, and V. N. Likhosherstova, *Zh. Analit. Khim.*, **15**, 748 (1960).

144. Trutnovsky, H., *Mikrochim. Acta*, **1963**, 499.
145. Tuckerman, M. M., J. D. Hodecker, B. C. Southworth, and K. D. Fleischer, *Anal. Chim. Acta*, **21**, 463 (1959).
146. Ueno, K., J. Japan. Chem., **12**, 942 (1958).
147. Večeřa, M., and J. Bulušek, *Mikrochim. Acta*, **1958**, 41.
148. Vetter, G., *Chem. Tech. (Leipzig)*, **15**, 43 (1963).
149. Vickers, C., and J. V. Wilkinson, *J. Pharm. Pharmacol.*, **13**, 72 (1961).
150. Vickers, C., and J. V. Wilkinson, *J. Pharm. Pharmacol.*, **13**, 156T (1961).
151. Vieböck, F., *Ber. deut. chem. Ges.*, **65**, 496 (1932).
152. Votoček, E., *Chem. Listy*, **16**, 248 (1922).
153. Wagner, H., *Mikrochim. Acta*, **1957**, 19.
154. Weir, H. E., *Microchem. J.*, **6**, 109 (1962).
155. White, D. C., *Mikrochim. Acta*, **1959**, 254; **1960**, 282.
156. White, D. C., *Mikrochim. Acta*, **1961**, 449.
157. White, D. C., *Mikrochim. Acta*, **1962**, 807.
158. Willemart, R., and J. Robin, *Ann. Pharm. Franc.*, **21**, 423 (1963).
159. Yasuda, S. K., and R. N. Rogers, *Microchem. J.*, **4**, 155 (1960).

Manuscript received by Publisher August 31, 1964.

Phase-Solubility Techniques

TAKERU HIGUCHI AND KENNETH A. CONNORS, *School of Pharmacy,*
University of Wisconsin, Madison, Wisconsin

I. INTRODUCTION

The equilibrium solubility of a chemical substance in a given solvent, at given temperature and pressure, is a quantity characteristic of the substance, and may, therefore, be utilized as a criterion of identity and purity. The technique that has become known as phase-solubility

117

analysis is an elaboration of the notion expressed in the preceding sentence. This technique is discussed in Section III. The analytical uses of solubility phenomena, however, embrace many additional methods, some of which may be considered as classical analytical techniques. Although recent advances in such areas may have been limited, brief discussions have been given to demonstrate the essential similarity of all of these systems. Sections I, II, and III treat well-known analytical methods based on solubility phenomena. In Section IV a detailed discussion is given of some proposed new phase-solubility techniques based upon interacting multicomponent systems.

1. The Phase Rule

A *phase* is a homogeneous portion of matter (homogeneous referring to the composition and state of the matter). All portions of this matter which differ only in quantity and form are to be regarded as the same phase. Examples of phases of matter are a pure liquid, a pure solid, a solution, and a gas. The number of phases in a system is commonly represented by P.

A *component* is a constituent of a system whose concentration is capable of independent variation. This stipulation of independent variation means that the number of components may be smaller than the number of constituents, for, if two or more constituents are related by a chemical equilibrium, evidently this capability of independent variation is not possessed by all of the constituents. Consider the system composed of the substances A, B, and AB, which are related by the equilibrium $A + B \rightleftharpoons AB$. Although three constituents are present, only two of these can be independently varied, the concentration of the third being established by the equilibrium; whichever two of the constituents are selected as the components of the system is not of fundamental importance. In general the *number* of components, C (and it is only the number which is of concern) in a system is equal to the number of constituents minus the number of independent equilibrium expressions that can be written (5).

The number of *degrees of freedom* of a system, F, is the number of variable factors (temperature, pressure, and concentrations of components) which must be fixed in order that the composition and state of the system shall be perfectly defined. For example, if the system consists of a liquid in equilibrium with its own vapor, by assigning a value to *either* the temperature *or* the pressure, the condition of the system is completely defined; this system is, therefore, one of a single degree of freedom.

The numbers of phases, components, and degrees of freedom for a system are very simply related. Consider any homogeneous (that is, single phase) system of C components. A total of $C + 2$ variables may be assigned to this system. (These are the temperature, pressure and C concentrations, or alternatively, temperature, pressure, and C chemical potentials.) If, now, any system containing P phases at equilibrium is considered, then P Gibbs-Duhem relations between these same variables can be written. The number of independently variable factors (that is, the degrees of freedom, F) is equal to the total number of variables minus the available equations relating these variables, or

$$F = C - P + 2 \qquad (1)$$

Equation 1 is the *phase rule* of Gibbs (13),* which provides the theoretical basis for many analytical methods, including all of those discussed in this chapter. The monograph of Findlay et al. (8) deals with the uses of the phase rule. Case (5) has recently reviewed some of its analytical applications. Among the analytical methods and measurements based on the phase rule, but not related to solubility phenomena, are fractional distillation and crystallization, determination of melting and freezing curves, differential thermal analysis, and zone purification.

2. Solubility-Based Methods without Solubility Observations

Numerous analyses are based upon solubility phenomena at equilibrium (or near-equilibrium) conditions, but do not involve solubility measurements or even observations of solubility limits. These methods are not commonly thought of as phase-solubility techniques, but they depend upon the same principle that controls the phase-solubility systems. This principle is embodied in the phase rule. It is, of course, seldom necessary to make an explicit application of the

* It is worth pointing out that Gibb's collected papers, which have long been out of print, have recently become available in an inexpensive paperbound reprint (12).

phase rule to the analytical problem; nevertheless, confidence in some of these methods is derived from their secure foundation on the phase rule.

Classical gravimetric analysis is an example of such a method. Usually equilibrium conditions obtain. The system is composed of the homogeneous precipitate and the solution, and is, therefore, a two-phase system. Application of the phase rule to the particular system yields the number of variable factors needed to define the system perfectly, and ability to control these factors accounts for the success of this type of analysis. The convenience of any gravimetric analysis is largely dependent upon the solubility behavior of the solid phase, which is usually expressed in terms of the solubility product. Although the solubility phenomenon is of the first importance in these analyses, seldom is any observation of solubility limits or phase appearance made. Closely related to gravimetric analysis is conventional precipitation titration, which also relies on solubility behavior. Some types of precipitation titration that explicitly employ phase observations will be discussed in the next section.

Diphasic titrations similarly utilize solubility properties. A diphasic titration is one in which the titrand is contained in a two-phase system, the phases usually being an aqueous solution and an immiscible organic liquid. Such a system is employed to achieve sharper visual end points by one of two mechansims: (1) Solution of a titration reaction product which would precipitate out in one of the phases. Thus, if a sodium barbiturate is titrated in aqueous solution with standard acid the water-insoluble barbituric acid is precipitated. By adding a chloroform phase to the titration solution, the acid passes into the organic layer; (2) Concentration of an indicator substance by preferential partitioning into a small volume of the second phase; titration of iodine, with the iodine acting as its own indicator, is a familiar example. Iodine partitions into a carbon tetrachloride or carbon disulfide phase from the aqueous titration solution. The disappearance of iodine color from the organic layer marks the end point.

Solvent extraction procedures, including countercurrent distribution, are very important analytical methods based upon solubility behavior. All forms of chromatography may be included here, though the application of thermodynamic arguments to these systems is less certain because equilibrium conditions are not, in practical analytical situations, established.

II. PHASE TITRATIONS

In the sense used here, a *phase titration* may be defined as a titration whose end point is marked by the appearance or disappearance of a phase. This phase may be a solid or a liquid. (The appearance of a gaseous phase may also provide good end point detection.) Many phase titrations involve a chemical interaction as the immediate cause of the appearance or disappearance of the additional phase, but in the simplest systems the phase appearance may not be preceded by such interaction and may merely reflect solubility limits of the titrant-titrand mixture. For convenience we may classify phase titrations on this basis: if the titration behavior appears to be the result of simple solubility equilibria without reaction between components, the system is classified as a solubility titration; if the phase appearance seems to be due to micelle formation the titration is a micellar titration; if a true molecular species is formed and is responsible for the phase separation, the titration is a heterometric titration (though this term usually implies, also, a specific manner of following the titration). Obviously, it may not always be possible to classify such titrations unambiguously without a careful study of the system.

1. Solubility Titrations

Consider a system composed of two miscible organic liquids A and B, one of which (say A) is miscible with water, while B is immiscible with water. If the binary solution of A and B is titrated with water, at some volume of titrant a phase separation will (usually) occur. The volume of water required to produce phase separation depends upon the temperature, the nature of the liquids A and B, and the composition of the binary solution. Evidently, then, the technique is applicable to the analysis of such binary solutions. One simply prepares a calibration curve by titrating several A–B mixtures of known composition, and then compares the unknown titration result with this calibration curve. By conducting the known and unknown titrations under similar conditions many errors are cancelled. The technique is rapid, simple, and quite accurate for suitable mixtures.

This method of analysis is well known, but has not found wide application. Recently, Rogers and his co-workers (54–57) have reinvestigated phase titrations; they have given a theoretical analysis of the method and have applied it to many systems. Examples of such mixtures are chloroform with alcohols, benzene with dioxane, cyclohexane with acetone, etc. The average error of the method is about 0.1% absolute.

A more difficult analytical problem is the determination of binary solutions of chemically similar liquids. Rogers et al. (56) have carried out such analyses by first adding a substance soluble in both the sample and the titrant. For example, the mixture cyclohexane and benzene was analyzed by titration with water after the addition of ethanol. Again, it is necessary to conduct analyses of known mixtures under the same conditions to be used for the unknown.

It is possible to reverse the system and titrate with one of the other components. Thus, the composition of water–pyridine mixtures may be determined by titration with chloroform to the appearance of turbidity; the end point in the titration was detected photometrically (57).

2. Micellar Titrations

Micellar titrations are often employed to determine the phase diagram of a water–organic substance–surfactant system. A typical titration procedure is described by W. I. Higuchi and J. Misra (22) who titrated a hydrocarbon–surfactant solution with water to the appearance of a second phase, which was marked by a turbidity in the titration solution. The end point was reversible and reproducible (±1%). The end point turbidity was transformed, after a few minutes, into two clear liquid phases, and the volume of the aqueous phase was much greater than the volume that could be accounted for on the basis of only pure water. From such titrations it was possible to construct diagrams of the moles of water solubilized per mole of surfactant (which was Aerosol OT) vs. the per cent of surfactant in the hydrocarbon solution. It was concluded that water is solubilized by internal micellar solvation as well as by solvation of the micelle exterior, on the basis of the effect of hydrocarbon chain length on the solubilization ratio. Similar titrations were used by O'Malley et al. (48) in a study of the solubilization of peppermint oil in water by some amphiphilic agents; these authors collated the titration data in triangular phase diagrams. Hall (19) titrated solutions of polysorbate-80 solubilizer and salicylic acid with water to the turbidity end point; at this point the ratio of salicylic acid to polysorbate 80 was calculated and plotted against the per cent of water in the system. From this diagram the amount of salicylic acid solubilized by a given weight of polysorbate-80 at any water concentration can be calculated.

Examples of direct analytical use of micellar titrations have been given by Lumb and Winsor (42), who describe the course of a typical titration. A mixture of 5 ml. of n-hexane and 5 ml. of aqueous "Teepol" solution (a surfactant largely composed of sodium secondary alkyl sulfates) was titrated with n-octanol. The titration passes through several steps:

(a) Solubilization of the organic liquids in the aqueous phase, giving a clear single-phase solution (point S_1).

(b) Precipitation of a gel-like phase, finally leading to complete conversion to a gel.

(c) Re-solution of the gel to give another clear solution.

(d) Precipitation of an aqueous phase from solution c (point S_2). The location of end point S_1 (the point of complete solubilization) and of end point S_2 (the point of initial precipitation of the aqueous phase) can be accomplished with a reproducibility of 0.01 ml. of titrant.

This procedure was used to analyze binary mixtures of polar compounds, especially mixtures of isomeric alcohols. The titration is conducted as described above using as the titrant, alcohol mixtures of known composition. The end point volume S_1 or S_2 is plotted against the composition of the titrant. An unknown mixture of the same alcohols can then be analyzed by carrying out an identical titration and reading the unknown composition from the graph. The relative sensitivity of the S_1 and S_2 volumes to the titrant composition depends upon the particular substances involved.

Micellar titrations carried out as described here evidently do not achieve true equilibrium at the end point, since the titration usually takes only a few minutes to perform. Nevertheless, the results conform closely enough to those expected from equilibrium conditions that this does not seem to be a hindrance.

3. Heterometric Titrations

During the past decade, a phase-titration technique called *heterometry* has been developed and applied, largely by Bobtelsky and his co-workers (2), to the quantitative study of suspensions produced by chemical reactions. The technique involves photoelectric monitoring of a stirred titration system, the apparent absorbance of the entire system (easily obtained by vertical, rather than horizontal, orientation

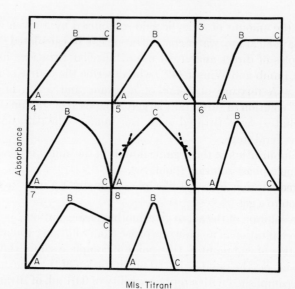

Mls. Titrant

Fig. 1. Types of heterometric titration curves, after Bobtelsky (2).

of the light beam) being measured as a function of the titrant volume. The photometric titration plot of absorbance *vs.* volume may assume several shapes, but all of these are characterized by more or less sharp breaks, or critical points, which correspond to end points of various titrant–titrand reactions. These titrations are carried out rapidly, and so they do not represent equilibrium conditions with respect to crystallization processes, but they appear to reflect accurately chemical equilibria which can lead to the appearance or disappearance of phases. Bobtelsky (2) has emphasized the transient nature of the suspensions formed, and in fact this state of physical nonequilibrium (which distinguishes heterometry from turbidimetry) during the titration is claimed to be an advantage of the procedure for detecting intermediate species in a sequence of reactions.

Heterometric titration plots, at least in the simpler systems, look like the schematic curves shown in Figure 1 (2,7). Curve 1 represents formation of a very insoluble precipitate upon addition of the titrant; the critical point *B* represents the end point of the titration with no further reaction, and, therefore, no change in absorbance beyond *B*. Curve 2 shows the initial formation of an insoluble species (complete at point *B*) followed by resolution as more titrant is added. Curve 3

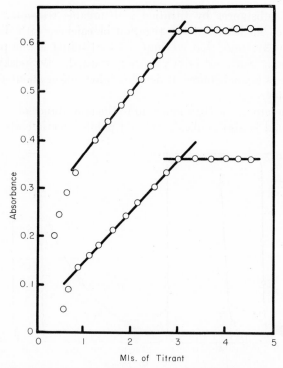

Fig. 2. Heterometric titration of calcium with $0.1M$ dipotassium phthalate in 90% alcohol. Upper curve: titration of 3 ml. $0.1M$ $Ca(NO_3)_2$ plus 7 ml. of solvent. Lower curve: titration of 3 ml. $0.1M$ $Ca(NO_3)_2$ plus 3 ml. $1M$ $MgCl_2$ plus 4 ml. solvent (3).

may be interpreted as the formation of a soluble species, this reaction being complete at point A. Next an insoluble species is formed accounting for the rise in absorbance to B. A similar curve would be observed if a slightly soluble species were formed, with A being the point at which its solubility limit is reached. Curves 4–8 show more complex systems which can, however, be interpreted in much the same way, that is, as manifestations of phase appearances or disappearances due to successive chemical reactions.

The absolute values of absorbance in heterometric titrations are not highly reproducible, but in spite of this the horizontal location of the critical points is easily reproduced, hence the practical analytical value of this technique. Most applications have been in the analysis of inorganic substances by titration with organic reagents. Figure 2 shows such an analysis, the titration of calcium with dipotassium phthalate (3); note that calcium can be titrated in the presence of magnesium. Such selectivity is not unusual. Bobtelsky's monograph (2) is a good source of detailed information about the uses of heterometry.

Most heterometric titrations lead to the appearance of solid phases. The method is also applicable to end point detection when a liquid

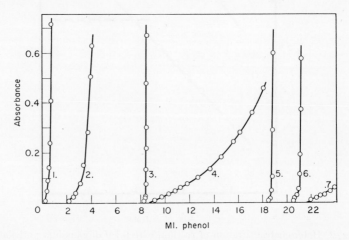

Fig. 3. Heterometric titration of some polymers in aqueous solution with 0.55M phenol: 1, polypropylene glycol (PPG) 1200; 2, PPG 750; 3, polyvinylpyrrolidone; 4, PPG 400; 5, polyethylene glycol (PEG) 6000; 6, PEG 4000; 7, PEG 1500 (16).

phase separates. Figure 3 shows heterometric curves for the titration of some polymeric substances with phenol in aqueous solution (16). The rise in absorbance is due to appearance of an oily liquid phase which appears to be a complex of the polymer with phenol. The sensitivity of the heterometric titration, even with quite dilute polymer solutions, makes it an excellent qualitative test for the presence of these polymers in solution. The inverse relationship between chain length and the concentration of phenol required to initiate separation of the second phase (Fig. 3) indicates that a titration of this nature might be of value in differentiating members of a polymer group of different molecular weights.

4. Turbidity Indicators

The preceding discussion has described some phase titrations in which a reaction between the titrant and titrand is responsible for the phase change. It is possible, also, to add an indicator substance which will signal the end point by appearing as a new phase. Though no recent work on such indicators appears to have been reported, it seems worthwhile to call attention to these novel systems (7,38).

It is possible to utilize nearly any slightly soluble acid or base as a precipitation indicator. If, for example, an insoluble weak acid of suitable pK_a is dissolved in basic solution, and the sample base is titrated with acid, then in the region of the end point the insoluble acid indicator will be precipitated. The drawback to such an indicator is that the conversion to the insoluble form, and hence the phase appearance, occurs in accordance with the usual mass action law for acid–base indicators; therefore, the precipitation process is spread over about 2 pH units, and is not particularly abrupt. This limitation was overcome by Naegeli (44), who introduced so-called turbidity indicators which function by a different mechanism from that just described. These turbidity indicators are organic acids or bases that form colloidal systems and flocculate at characteristic pH values. This process of coagulation is apparently not described by the mass action law, and the coagulation occurs over an extremely narrow pH range (usually about 0.1 pH unit). These substances are, therefore, sensitive acid–base indicators, and they were used by Naegeli and Tyabji (46) to titrate very weak acids. Most of the turbidity indicators introduced by these authors flocculate at very high pH, but it should be possible to design indicators for other pH ranges. The present widespread interest in photometric indicator titrations (7) suggests that the combination of Naegeli-type turbidity indicators with photometric detection of the phase appearance may lead to highly precise acid–base titrations.

Any of the factors that usually affect colloidal coagulation, such as the nature and concentration of salts and the presence of organic solvents, may be expected to alter in some degree the response of turbidity indicators. Table I lists some of Naegeli's indicators with their pH flocculation intervals; it will be noted that the flocculation pH varies slightly with the nature of the buffer. These indicators do not seem highly sensitive to temperature changes. All of the indi-

TABLE I

Flocculation Intervals of Some Turbidity Indicators at 18°C. (46)

Indicator	Buffer	pH Interval
Isonitrosoacetyl-*p*-aminoazobenzene	Borax	10.66–10.78
Isonitrosoacetyl-*p*-aminoazobenzene	Phosphate	10.80–10.97
p-Tolueneazoisonitrosoacetyl-*p*-toluidine	Borax	11.52–11.66
p-Tolueneazoisonitrosoacetyl-*p*-toluidine	Phosphate	11.58–11.66
m-Tolueneazoisonitrosoacetyl-*p*-toluidine	Borax	9.30–9.40
p-Tolueneazoisonitrosoacetyl-*m*-toluidine	Borax	11.55–11.64
p-Tolueneazoisonitrosoacetyl-*m*-toluidine	Phosphate	11.43–11.58
m-Tolueneazoisonitrosoacetyl-*m*-toluidine	Borax	11.07–11.38
m-Tolueneazoisonitrosoacetyl-*m*-toluidine	Phosphate	11.24–11.50
Isonitrosoacetyl-*o*-aminoazobenzene	Borax	9.00–9.23
p-Tolueneazoisonitrosoacetyl-*o*-toluidine	Borax	9.24–9.35

cators listed are isonitrosoacetanilide derivatives (45); the structure of *p*-tolueneazoisonitrosoacetyl-*m*-toluidine is given as an example:

$$CH_3\text{—}\langle\bigcirc\rangle\text{—}N{=}N\text{—}\langle\bigcirc\rangle\text{—}NHCOCH{=}NOH$$
$$CH_3$$

III. SOLUBILITY ANALYSIS WITH NON-INTERACTING COMPONENTS

The equilibrium solubility of a pure compound is a characteristic physical property just as is the melting point; in fact, the solution and fusion processes have much in common.   If a sample exhibits a solubility in excess of that expected for the pure compound, evidently the additional quantity of solute may be ascribed to the presence of a second component.   The refinement of this basic idea for the determination of purity is generally known as phase-solubility analysis. Several related techniques have been proposed, and one of these, utilizing a phase solubility diagram, has become a part of the analytical repertory.   The subject was reviewed by Mader in 1954 (43). An account will be given here primarily for the sake of completeness.

1. Phase-Solubility Diagrams

Solubility analysis as it is practiced today was introduced by Northrop and Kunitz (47), who considered two-component mixtures.

Early applications of the method to protein preparations were especially valuable (21). Thorp (61) extended the technique to multicomponent mixtures, and Willermain (63) has given a general theoretical analysis. Several authors have reviewed the method (9, 43, 62). To introduce the principle of phase-solubility analysis let us first consider the case of a pure compound. The experimental operation consists of adding successive portions of the sample to constant volumes of a solvent in which it is slightly soluble. The systems are brought to equilibrium by prolonged agitation at constant temperature. The solution phases are then analyzed for total solute content. A phase diagram is constructed by plotting the weight of solute found per unit of solution on the vertical axis against weight of sample added per unit of solvent on the horizontal axis (see Fig. 4). This diagram is readily interpreted. Along the segment AB all of the solid added to the system dissolves and is found in solution; the slope of AB is, therefore, unity.* At point B the solution becomes saturated with the compound, so further addition of sample cannot lead to an increase in solution concentration; the slope of BC is zero. Extrapolation of BC to the vertical axis yields the solubility of the compound.

Now consider the same experiment carried out on a three-component mixture. Subject to certain restrictions, to be given later, the phase diagram will take the form shown in Figure 5. As in Figure 4, the slope of AB is unity, for all solid added goes into solution. At point B the solution has become saturated with respect to one of the components. Along BC, therefore, only the remaining two components pass into solution. At C the solution reaches saturation with a second substance, so from C to D only the final component is dissolving. At D the solution is saturated with all components and the slope of DE is zero. The order in which the components reach saturation depends upon their solubilities and their concentrations in the original sample (47).

From B to C only the fraction of original sample consisting of components other than the first to reach saturation are going into solution; therefore, the slope of BC is equal to the fraction of these two components. Similarly, the slope of CD is equal to the fraction of the third

* The slope actually deviates from unity because the concentration bases are slightly different for the two axes, but if the solubility is low the deviation is negligible.

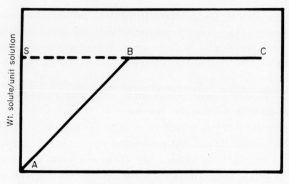

Fig. 4. Phase-solubility diagram of a pure compound.

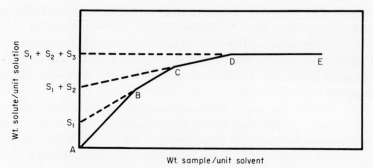

Fig. 5. Phase-solubility diagram of a three-component mixture.

component in the sample, since only this fraction of the material dissolves in this portion of the diagram. Evaluation of the slopes, therefore, leads to the fractional composition of the mixture. Extrapolation of the line segments to the vertical axis gives the solubilities of the components, with the BC intercept equalling the solubility of the first component to reach saturation, the CD intercept the sum of solubilities of the first two components to reach saturation, and the DE intercept the sum of all three solubilities. A further use of this type of experiment is in the isolation of small quantities of pure substances. Along the segment BC in Figure 5 the system contains two phases: one of these is a solution of all three components, the second is a solid phase consisting of a pure compound, that component whose solubility was reached at point B.

TABLE II
Application of the Phase Rule to Figure 5

Segment	C	P	F	Enumeration of degrees of freedom
AB	4	1	5	T, P, C_1, C_2, C_3
BC	4	2	4	T, P, C_2, C_3
CD	4	3	3	T, P, C_3
DE	4	4	2	T, P

The phase diagram of Figure 5 can be interpreted in terms of the phase rule, which gives the number of degrees of freedom at each point on the diagram. This analysis is shown in Table II. Since temperature and pressure are removed as variables by controlling the experimental conditions, the final segment DE represents an invariant system.

The limitations on the use of this solubility method are these: (1) the solubility of each component must not be affected by the presence of the other components; (2) the components must not form a solid solution; (3) the components must not be present in the sample in the ratio of their solubilities. For most mixtures only the first of these conditions is a serious drawback, and treatment of interacting components will be given in Section IV.

The selection of solvent for a solubility analysis is governed partly by the solubility of the major component—a solubility in the range 0.1–1% is convenient—and partly by the method of analysis of the solution phase. Evidently, the analysis must be general so that all components respond, so the most widely used analysis involves evaporation of the solvent and weighing the residue. The experimental details have been discussed by Mader (43).

Phase-solubility analysis has been accepted as a routine procedure for purity determination. The examples of steroid analysis given by Tarpley and Yudis are typical (60). The official U. S. P. assay of mecamylamine hydrochloride is by phase-solubility analysis (50).

2. Related Methods

Purity determination by means of solubility measurements is usually accomplished by the graphical procedure outlined in the preceding paragraphs. This technique is not the only one capable of yielding the desired result, however, and several alternate experimental designs have been suggested. One of these involves a reversal of variables. Usually temperature is maintained constant and the equilibrium solubility is measured. Reeve and Adams (52) determined the temperature at which a solid dissolves in a given amount of solvent; this quantity, which they called the solubility temperature, is characteristic of the compound. These authors give solubility temperatures for amino acids, and they used such data to analyze binary mixtures.

The conventional phase-solubility study cannot readily distinguish between a pure compound and one that contains up to about 0.5% impurity, because of the direct relationship between impurity concentration and slope of the line segment. Stenger et al. (58) proposed an extraction-solubility method designed to permit the analysis of high-purity substances. In effect, the impurities are concentrated by a Soxhlet extraction with a solvent in which the main component is but slightly soluble.

Two kinds of differential solubility methods have been used to analyze mixtures. In one of these, the mixture of unknown composition is extracted with a solvent which is saturated with one of the components of the mixture. If mutual solubilization effects are absent, evidently the remaining components of the mixture will be extracted leaving behind only the component used to saturate the extraction liquor (1). Of more general applicability is the method in which a mixture of n components is extracted with a solution saturated with respect to $n - 1$ of the components. If, again, no interaction effects are observed, only the nth component will be removed from the mixture. This technique can be repeated with n extraction solvents, each saturated with a different set of $n - 1$ components. The concentrations of the resulting solutions can be measured with any suitable means and, if calibration curves with the pure substances are first prepared, the composition of the unknown mixture can be estimated. This method has proved valuable in the analysis of organic reaction product mixtures (1,36).

IV.   SOLUBILITY ANALYSIS WITH INTERACTING COMPONENTS (COMPLEXATION SOLUBILITY ANALYSIS)

It was pointed out in Section III that conventional solubility-analytical techniques require that solubilities be additive, that is, that the solubility of each component in a mixture be uninfluenced by the presence of the other substances in the mixture. Many systems (perhaps most systems) do not exhibit such ideal behavior, and inaccuracies are thus introduced into the analytical results. From this viewpoint the solution interactions responsible for non-additive solubility behavior are unfortunate and disagreeable phenomena.

By shifting one's point of view, however, it seems reasonable to expect that such non-ideal behavior can itself be systematized, and that when this has been done, these systems will be amenable to the straightforward application of simple solubility techniques. Many such investigations have in fact been conducted, and they lead, as hoped, to at least a partial understanding of the nature of the interactions in phase-solubility systems. Although many of these studies were initiated to study the chemistry of the systems, rather than to provide analytical methods, this emphasis on the mechanism rather than the application is not important for the present purpose. Since the systems are described by the phase rule one may be confident that, within these limitations, analytical methods based upon these considerations are feasible. The general occurrence of molecular interactions in solution means that these methods should be of wide applicability.

In order to provide a suitable background for understanding solubility systems in which molecular interactions can be detected, the following pages will describe in some detail the nature of these systems and the methods used in studying them.

1. Types of Phase-Solubility Diagrams

The general experimental operation in studying molecular interactions by means of solubility measurements entails the addition of an equal weight (in considerable excess of its normal solubility) of a slightly soluble compound S (the substrate) into each of several vials or ampuls. A constant volume of solvent is added to each container. Then successively increasing portions of a relatively soluble compound L (the ligand or complexing agent) are added to these vessels, which are closed and brought to solubility equilibrium at constant temperature. The solution phases are then analyzed, by any suitable means, for their total concentration of compound S, no matter what its molecular state may be.

A phase diagram is constructed by plotting, on the vertical axis, total molar concentration of S found in the solution phase against the molar concentration of L added to the system. The phase diagrams are observed to fall into two main classes, with some variation within the classes. The terminology assigned here will be found convenient for later reference and tabulation.

A. TYPE A DIAGRAMS

Figure 6 shows one general class of phase diagram observed in these experiments. The symbol S_t represents the total molar concentration of dissolved S and L_t is the total concentration of L. The solubility of S is apparently increased by the presence of L. S_0 is the equilibrium solubility of S in the absence of L. A linear

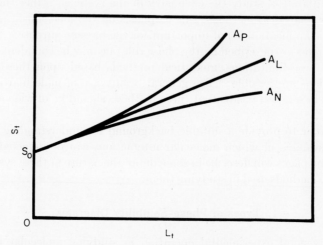

Fig. 6. Phase-solubility diagram of Type A systems showing apparent increase in solubility of S caused by component L.

increase in solubility is represented by line A_L, while positive and negative curvature in the line is indicated by A_P and A_N, respectively. The premise is made that increases (beyond a certain level; see Section IV-3-C) in solubility in these systems are due to one or more molecular interactions between S and L to form distinct chemical species which may be called complexes. In this light, then, Type A diagrams indicate the formation of soluble complexes between S and L, thereby increasing the total amount of S in solution. It should be kept in mind that a solid phase consisting of pure S is present in these systems, therefore the thermodynamic activity of dissolved S is constant, since the solution phase is in equilibrium with the solid phase. This fact will be found useful later.

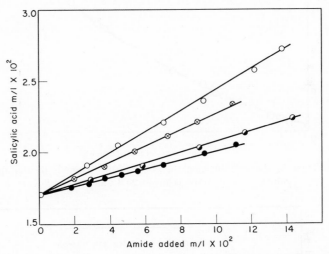

Fig. 7. Type A_L diagrams showing the apparent solubility of salicylic acid in aqueous solution at 30°C. in the presence of: O—tetramethylfumaramide; ⊗—tetramethylisophthalamide; ◑—tetramethylsuccinamide; ●—tetramethylphthalamide (39).

Some more specific statements may be made about the origin of Type A diagrams:

(a) If all complexes formed are of the first order in L, that is, they may be written SL, S_2L, S_3L, . . . , S_mL, then a Type A_L diagram will be observed. Although the reverse statement, that if a linear plot is found the complexes must be first order in L, does not necessarily follow, it is usually adopted.

(b) If complexes are present to a higher order than one in L, for example, SL_2, SL_3, . . . , SL_n, then the Type A_P diagram is produced.

(c) The origin of the Type A_N diagram is uncertain. It may be associated with an alteration in the effective nature of the solvent in the presence of large concentrations of L, thus leading to a change in the complex formation constant. Another possibility is self-associa-

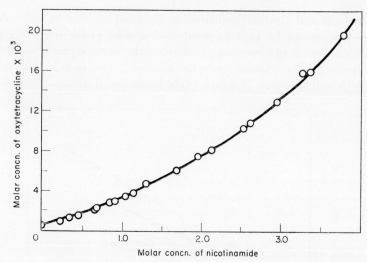

Fig. 8. Type A_P diagram showing the effect of nicotinamide on the apparent solubility of oxytetracycline at 25°C. and pH 5 (23).

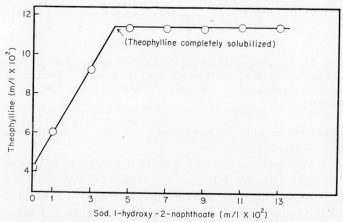

Fig. 9. Type A diagram illustrating plateau formation due to disappearance of solid S (25).

tion of L at higher concentrations; this might affect the apparent degree of complexation.

Data for the interaction between salicylic acid and several water-soluble amides are shown in Figure 7 (39). Evidently, the total con-

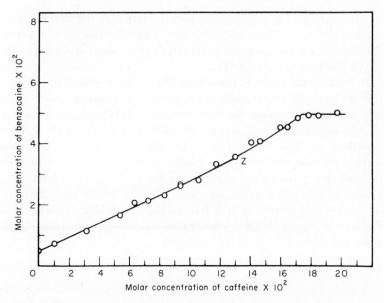

Fig. 10. Type A diagram showing invariance due to appearance of solid L (26); the system is benzocaine and caffeine at 30°C.

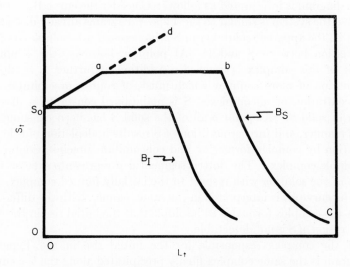

Fig. 11. Phase-solubility diagrams of Type B systems.

centration of acid in solution increases linearly with the added concentration of amide; these are, therefore, Type A_L diagrams. A Type A_P diagram, obtained for the system oxytetracycline (S)-nicotinamide-(L), is pictured in Figure 8 (23).

It may occasionally happen that the Type A plot will exhibit a plateau level of S which additional quantities of L do not alter. There are two possible reasons for this behavior: (1) The sharp break may merely represent disappearance of solid S from the system by its complete solubilization. Evidently, addition of more L cannot further increase the S concentration. Figure 9 gives an example of this behavior; the theophylline (S) in the system is completely solubilized at the point indicated (25); (2) The break may represent saturation with respect to L, if L is not highly soluble. This behavior is shown in Figure 10 (26). (Only case 2 represents invariance in the phase rule sense.)

B. TYPE B DIAGRAMS

A second major class of phase-solubility diagrams is illustrated by the curves in Figure 11. These curves, which may be labeled Type B diagrams, are observed when insoluble complexes are formed. The experimental operation is identical with that described earlier. The diagram is interpreted as follows: Consider the curve B_s. From S_0 to a the system is similar to the Type A diagrams already discussed, that is, the apparent solubility of S is increased due to soluble complex formation between S and L. At point a, however, the solubility limit of this complex is reached. Addition of further L results in formation of more complex which must, of course, precipitate; the concentration of uncomplexed S is maintained constant by dissolution of solid S. At point b all of the solid S has been consumed in this manner, and further addition of S results in depletion of S in the solution by complex formation and concomitant precipitation of the insoluble complex. The dotted segment a-d represents supersaturation of the solution with respect to the initially formed complex.

The curve B_I is interpreted in the same manner, with the difference that the complex formed is so insoluble that the initial rise in the concentration of S is not detectable.

If the complex responsible for the initial rise in the Type B_S diagram is the same complex finally precipitated along the b-c curve, evidently the increase in S concentration from S_0 to a must be equal to the final S concentration at c. This condition is not often observed, however, suggesting that often the system must involve formation of two or more distinct complexes, one of these being responsible for the initial rise in solubility while another is precipitated in the latter stages of the diagram. Another feature sometimes seen is an increase in solubility beyond point c, apparently due to formation of another complex species which is more soluble than the one responsible for the descending portion of the curve, b–c.

Figure 12 shows typical examples of Type B complexing phase diagrams (4). The two upper curves are Type B_S diagrams, the lowest curve a Type B_I diagram. Table III gives a phase-rule analysis of the

TABLE III
Application of the Phase Rule to the Type B_S Diagram

Segment (from Fig. 11)	C	P	F	Enumeration of degrees of freedom
S_0–a	3	2	3	T, P, C_L
a–b	3	3	2	T, P
b–c	3	2	3	T, P, C_S

Type B_S diagram. Application of the phase rule to the descending portion of the curve leads to an interesting result. It is evident, from a visual examination, that the system contains at least 2 phases in this region. However, since F must equal 3 here (T, P, and concentration of S, the concentration of L then being fixed by the system), the phase rule states that the number of phases is 2; in other words, there cannot be two solid phases. This means that only one complex can precipitate out at any given point on b–c, though at different points on b–c it is possible that different complexes may appear. An alternate explanation is that more than one insoluble complex is formed at a given point, but that these complexes form a solid solution, thus giving P = 2.

One type of phase diagram that fits neither the Type A nor the Type B classes as described, though it is closely related to the latter, is occasionally encountered. The plot of S_t against L_t shows an immediate and progressive decrease in the apparent concentration of S; Figure 13 is an example of such a plot (20). This behavior is at first appearance inexplicable, since it does not seem that the concentration

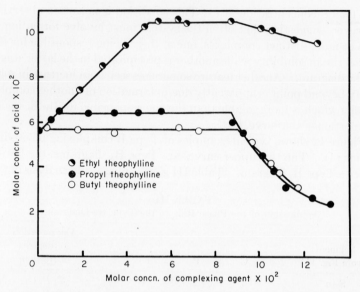

Fig. 12. Type B diagrams showing the effect of several theophylline derivatives on the apparent solubility of p-hydroxybenzoic acid in water at 30°C. (4).

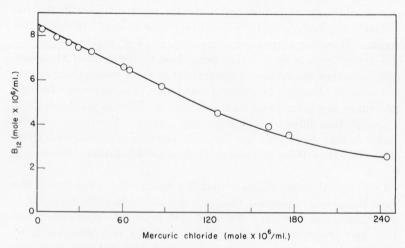

Fig. 13. Phase diagram showing the effect of mercuric chloride on the apparent solubility of cyanocobalamin in water at 25°C. (20).

of S can decrease until all of the solid S has disappeared from the system. However, application of the phase rule ($C = 3$, $F = 3$) indicates that two phases are present; since one phase is the solution, only one solid phase may be present. That is, a solid solution probably forms between the solid S and the insoluble complex. Other possible explanations have been suggested for this phase diagram (20).

2. Characterization of Complexation Phenomena

It is obviously desirable to be able to specify the extent of molecular interaction in a quantitative fashion. Knowledge of the stoichiometry and equilibrium constants for complex formation will permit such quantitative description of the solubility behavior. These quantities can often be evaluated from the phase diagram. In most instances the complexity of the chemical system precludes a complete description of the equilibria, but even in such cases it may be possible to calculate apparent stability constants on the basis of an assumed stoichiometry. From the point of view of the analytical chemist, such assumptions are not unsatisfactory if they lead to a simple and useful description of the phase diagram.

A. STOICHIOMETRY OF COMPLEXES

Let us first consider Type A phase diagrams, that is, systems in which soluble complexes are found. (Notice that the initial portion of a Type B_S diagram may be considered a Type A diagram.) The problem is to determine the stoichiometry of the complex or complexes responsible for the increase in concentration of S, or, in other words, to evaluate m and n in the general formula $S_m L_n$. First we may note that if the slope of a Type A_L line is greater than unity, then at least one species must be present in which m is greater than one, for it is obviously impossible for one mole of L to take more than one mole of S into solution if the complex is of the 1:1 type. On the other hand, a slope of less than unity with a Type A_L diagram does not necessarily mean that only a 1:1 complex is formed (though in the absence of additional information this assumption is usually made). More definite statements concerning the order with respect to S cannot usually be made from these phase diagrams since the presence of solid S is responsible for maintaining a constant activity of S in the systems. The order with respect to S, therefore, cannot be determined.

If a Type A diagram exhibits a plateau due to the appearance of a solid L phase (as discussed earlier), it is possible to calculate a stoichiometric ratio.   Figure 10 shows such a system (26).   Benzocaine is substance S and caffeine is L.   Point Z on the diagram represents the normal solubility limit of caffeine ($13.3 \times 10^{-2}M$).   The molar quantities represented by the increase in the solubilities of both components correspond to the amounts of these components entering into complex formation.   Thus, the solubility increase of caffeine is $(17.5 - 13.3) \times$

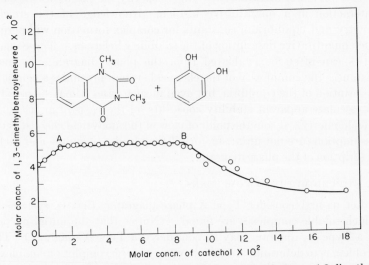

Fig. 14. Type B_S phase diagram showing the interaction between 1,3-dimethylbenzoyleneurea and catechol in carbon tetrachloride (18).

$10^{-2}M = 4.2 \times 10^{-2}M$, where 17.5×10^{-2} is the molar concentration of caffeine added to the break point in the diagram and 13.3×10^{-2} is the molar solubility of caffeine in water.   The solubility increase of benzocaine = total benzocaine − normal solubility of benzocaine = $(4.9 - 0.5) \times 10^{-2}M = 4.4 \times 10^{-2}M$.   Then the stoichiometric ratio is

$$\frac{\text{Benzocaine (S) content}}{\text{Caffeine (L) content}} = \frac{4.4 \times 10^{-2}}{4.2 \times 10^{-2}} = 1.05$$

indicating that the formula of the complex is SL.   (It is probable that a second complex is present to a minor extent, since this is really a Type A_P diagram.)

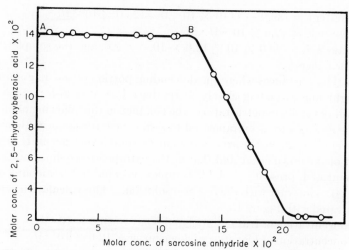

Fig. 15. Type B_I diagram showing the effect of sarcosine anhydride on the apparent solubility of 2,5-dihydroxybenzoic acid in water at 25°C. (51).

In contrast to the diagrams for soluble complexes, a stoichiometric ratio can always be evaluated from a Type B diagram (26). Whether this stoichiometry is a valid reflection of the chemistry depends upon whether one or several complexes are formed; if more than one complex is contributing to the solubility behavior at any region of the diagram, the stoichiometry that is calculated will reflect contributions from all of the complexes.

Figure 14 is a typical Type B_S diagram (18). The stoichiometric calculation is possible because the amount of L (catechol) represented by the plateau is equal to that entering into the complex in this interval, and the corresponding amount of S (dimethylbenzoyleneurea) being converted to complex is equal to that present as free undissolved S at point A. Therefore, S content of complex formed in the plateau region = Total S added to system −S in solution at point A = $(7.97 − 5.22) \times 10^{-2}M = 2.75 \times 10^{-2}M$. L content of complex in the same region = $(8.62 − 1.45) \times 10^{-2}M = 7.17 \times 10^{-2}M$. The stoichiometric ratio S/L is then $2.75 \times 10^{-2}/7.17 \times 10^{-2} = 1/2.6 = 2/5.1$, indicating that the complex probably has the formula S_2L_5.

Figure 15 is a Type B_I diagram (51). The system contained a total of $0.390M$ of 2,5-dihydroxybenzoic acid. The same type of calculation carried out on Figure 14 can be applied here:

S content $= (39.0 - 14.0) \times 10^{-2}M = 25.0 \times 10^{-2}M$.
L content $= 12.6 \times 10^{-2}M$.
Ratio S/L $= 25.0 \times 10^{-2}/12.6 \times 10^{-2} = 2.0$, and the complex has the formula S_2L.

In those instances where the descending portion of the diagram is a straight line extending closely to the base line, it is also possible to obtain the stoichiometric ratio of the complex in the following manner. If the down curve is extrapolated to zero concentration of S, then the difference between the concentration of complexing agent L at the start of the down curve and that at the extrapolated point, minus the amount of L present as soluble complex, is equal to the amount of L needed to interact with the free S in solution. This calculation can be illustrated with Figure 15.

Concentration of L at extrapolated point $= 20.2 \times 10^{-2}M$.
Concentration of L at start of downcurve $= 12.6 \times 10^{-2}M$.
Concentration of L present as soluble complex $= 0$.
Therefore, the amount of L entering into the complex along the downcurve $= (20.2 - 12.6) \times 10^{-2}M = 7.6 \times 10^{-2}M$.
Concentration of S in solution $= 14.0 \times 10^{-2}M$.
Ratio S/L $= 1.8$, indicating that the complex formula is S_2L.

These graphical methods for the evaluation of stoichiometry may be supplemented by isolation and chemical analysis of insoluble complexes (see, for example, ref. 20, 37, and 51).

B.   ESTIMATION OF EQUILIBRIUM CONSTANTS

It is the fundamental assumption of this entire treatment of the solubility behavior of systems of interacting components that the interactions can be described by mass action expressions. The molecular interaction products are discrete molecular species called complexes.*   The interpretation to be placed upon the equilibrium constants describing complex formation requires some comment. The complicated nature of these systems has already been pointed out, and the difficulty in obtaining the correct stoichiometric ratio is clear. Obviously, an unambiguous interpretation of the complex formation constant is not possible unless the stoichiometry of the reaction is known.   In most cases, therefore, we shall be content to evaluate an

* Solubilization by micelle formation is a different phenomenon (14), though some systems may exhibit characteristics of both molecular interaction and micellar solubilization.

apparent constant, based upon a reasonable stoichiometric ratio. For the purpose of indicating the extent of interaction this apparent stability constant is often satisfactory, but as a guide for sophisticated mechanistic interpretations it must be recognized as limited in its applicability. All of the constants considered here are concentration constants, with concentrations expressed in molar units and represented by parentheses. As in the earlier parts of this section, S will represent the substance in excess and L the complexing agent. The general formula for a complex is $S_m L_n$.

Let us first consider Type A systems, including the initial rising portion of Type B_S diagrams. Suppose that a single complex, $S_m L_n$, is responsible for the increase in apparent solubility of S. The complex formation (or stability) constant for this species is given by

$$K = (S_m L_n)/(S)^m (L)^n \qquad (2)$$

The concentrations can be expressed in terms of known quantities:

$$(S) = S_0 \qquad (3)$$

$$(S_m L_n) = \frac{S_t - S_0}{m} \qquad (4)$$

$$(L) = L_t - n(S_m L_n) \qquad (5)$$

where S_0 is the equilibrium solubility of S in the absence of L, S_t is the total concentration of dissolved S regardless of molecular state, and L_t is the total added concentration of L. Equations 2–5 can be combined to give an expression for K in terms of known concentrations, m, and n. A special case of this equation, that in which $n = 1$, is of great interest. In this case equation 6 can be derived.

$$S_t = \frac{mKS_0^m L_t}{1 + KS_0^m} + S_0 \qquad (6)$$

A plot of S_t against L_t for the formation of a soluble complex $S_m L$ should, therefore, yield a straight line (the Type A_L diagram). The intercept is equal to S_0 and the slope is given by

$$\text{slope} = \frac{mKS_0^m}{1 + KS_0^m} \qquad (7)$$

If m is known, equation 7 provides the basis for calculation of K from the slope of a Type A_L diagram. In the important case in which $m = 1$, equation 8 results.

$$K_{1:1} = \frac{\text{Slope}}{S_0(1 - \text{Slope})} \tag{8}$$

For this special case ($m = 1$, $n = 1$) combination of equations 2–5 gives

$$K_{1:1} = \frac{S_t - S_0}{S_0(L_t - S_t + S_0)} \tag{9}$$

Equations 8 and 9 are equivalent relations for the calculation of the stability constant on the basis of a 1:1 stoichiometric ratio. If a series of complexes of the formulas SL, S_2L, . . ., S_mL were present, a Type A_L diagram would still be observed, but this situation might not be distinguishable from that for the 1:1 complex alone. Nevertheless, an apparent constant, calculated with the assumption of only 1:1 stoichiometry, is often taken to describe the system. As pointed out earlier, if the slope of a Type A_L diagram is greater than unity, evidently the assumption of a 1:1 complex alone is untenable, and the calculation according to equation 8 is impossible. The more general expression 7 may be used in such a case by assigning a value to m. The Type A_P and A_N diagrams are frequently approximated by a straight line tangent to the curve at L = 0, the apparent stability constant then being calculated with equation 8.

A more quantitative description of the Type A_P diagram may be achieved by assuming that it results from the formation of the two complexes SL and SL_2, characterized by the constants*

$$K_{1:1} = (SL)/(S)(L) \tag{10}$$

$$K_{1:2} = (SL_2)/(SL)(L) \tag{11}$$

* Note that $K_{1:2}$ could equally well be defined $K_{1:2} = (SL_2)/(S)(L)^2$. This will not alter the form of the equations but will change the magnitude of the constant. These different formulations imply different mechanisms, but mechanistic interpretation is not intended here. It is also possible to imagine a system consisting of SL, a different 1:1 complex LS, and 1:2 complexes derived from either or both of these. Such considerations are beyond the scope of the present discussion.

The material balance equations are

$$S_t = (S) + (SL) + (SL_2) \tag{12}$$

$$(S) = S_0 \tag{13}$$

$$L_t = (L) + (SL) + 2(SL_2) \tag{14}$$

Combination of equations 10–14 gives

$$S_t = \frac{L_t[K_{1:1}S_0 + K_{1:1}K_{1:2}S_0(L)]}{1 + K_{1:1}S_0 + 2K_{1:1}K_{1:2}S_0(L)} + S_0 \tag{15}$$

which shows that a plot of S_t against L_t will have an intercept S_0 and a slope which is a function of (L); the slope will increase with (L), thus giving rise to the Type A_P diagram. A more tractable expression may be obtained by combining equations 10–13:

$$S_t = S_0 + K_{1:1}S_0(L) + K_{1:1}K_{1:2}S_0(L)^2$$

If the extent of complexation is fairly small it may be permissible to set (L) approximately equal to L_t, thus giving

$$\frac{S_t - S_0}{L_t} = K_{1:1}S_0 + K_{1:1}K_{1:2}S_0L_t \tag{16}$$

A plot of $(S_t - S_0)/L_t$ against L_t should be linear. From the slope and intercept, values for $K_{1:1}$ and $K_{1:2}$ may be estimated. Note that $(S_t - S_0)/L_t$ is the slope of the chord from S_0 to the point S_t on the Type A_P diagram. If the approximation $(L) = L_t$ is not a good one, a better approximation is achieved by combining equation 14 for (L) with equations 12 and 13. It is customary to assume either that all of the complex is in the SL form or that it is in the SL_2 form in obtaining the estimate of (L).

The more complicated system containing SL, SL_2, and SL_3 has been analyzed by a similar treatment (23).

All of the above discussion applies to the rising segment of Type B_S diagrams as well as to Type A diagrams. It is also possible to estimate stability constants from the descending portion of Type B curves (Fig. 16). It is assumed that the stoichiometry of the complex is known. The equilibrium constant is written as in equation 2. At point X equations 17 and 18 hold

$$S_X = (S) + m(S_mL_n) \tag{17}$$

$$L_X = (L) + n(S_mL_n) \tag{18}$$

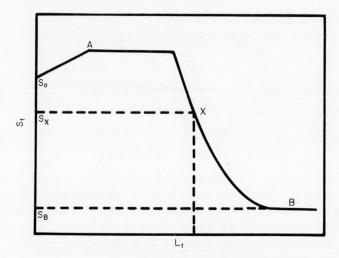

Fig. 16. Type B diagram showing calculation of the stability constant from the descending portion of the curve.

The concentration of complex is a constant throughout the down curve, since the solution is in equilibrium with solid complex. The concentration of S at point B, where all free S has been removed from solution, may, therefore, be attributed to complex in solution, this giving

$$K_{m:n} = \frac{S_B}{(S_X - mS_B)^m (L_X - nS_B)^n} \tag{19}$$

If the same complex is believed to be responsible for the behavior over the entire curve, then S_B may be replaced by the increase in solubility from S_0 to point A.

3. The Nature of Molecular Complexes

A. RESULTS OF PHASE-SOLUBILITY STUDIES

In Table IV are collected the results of solubility studies that have been carried out by Higuchi and his co-workers. This is, of course, not a complete collation of such data, but it includes enough systems to demonstrate the ubiquity of mutual solubility effects, and to allow some correlations between molecular structure and the extent of interaction to be made.

Each pair of compounds has been assigned a unique number, which is given in the first column of the table. The second column lists the S component (the substrate, or the component present in excess of its solubility) and the third column the L component (the ligand or complexing agent). The temperature and solvent are given in the next two columns. Next a value is tabulated for the equilibrium molar solubility of S (in the absence of L); in some instances this quantity was reported in the original literature, and sometimes it was estimated from the phase diagram. The seventh column gives the type of phase diagram, the symbols being those introduced in the first part of this section.

The stoichiometry and the equilibrium constants may be ambiguous quantities, as pointed out earlier. When a solid complex was isolated and analyzed its stoichiometry has been noted. In other cases a graphical estimate of the stoichiometric ratio is available. When conflicting results were obtained by these methods only one has been given; it must be kept in mind that more than one complex species is probably formed in most of these systems.

The stability constants reported in the table are defined by equations 20-22

$$K_{1:1} = (SL)/(S)(L) \tag{20}$$

$$K_{1:2} = (SL_2)/(SL)(L) \tag{21}$$

$$K_{2:1} = (S_2L)/(S)^2(L) \tag{22}$$

Even when no evidence is available to indicate that a one-to-one complex is formed, it is common practice to calculate $K_{1:1}$ for Type A and Type B_S diagrams in order to facilitate comparison of complexing tendencies. If the slope of the plot is greater than unity such a calculation is impossible, and in some such cases, whose stoichiometric ratio appeared to be $2:1$, the constant $K_{2:1}$ was tabulated. Sometimes both $K_{1:1}$ and $K_{2:1}$ are given; the diagram can be described by either one or the other of these constants, depending upon one's assumption of a stoichiometric ratio. Type A_P diagrams are sometimes represented by a value for $K_{1:1}$ obtained from the initial linear portion of the curve, sometimes by $K_{1:1}$ calculated from the best overall linear fit, and, in some cases, by both $K_{1:1}$ and $K_{1:2}$ values describing more exactly the shape of the curve. In nearly all instances the stability constants are to be regarded as empirical parameters which describe,

TABLE IV

Phase-Solubility Data From Studies of Interacting Systems

System number	S	L	t (°C)	Solvent	$10^2 S_0$ (mole/l.)	Type of diagram (S:L)	Stoichiometry (S:L)	$K_{1:1}$	$K_{1:2}$	$K_{2:1}$	Reference
1	Acetylsalicylic acid	Caffeine	15	$\mathrm{H_2O}$ $\left(\begin{array}{c}0.001N\\ \mathrm{H_2SO_4}\end{array}\right)$	1.716	A_N		19.8^b			34
1	Acetylsalicylic acid	Caffeine	30	$\mathrm{H_2O}$ $\left(\begin{array}{c}0.001N\\ \mathrm{H_2SO_4}\end{array}\right)$	2.851	A_N		17.4^b			34
2	Salicylic acid	Caffeine	15	$\mathrm{H_2O}$ $\left(\begin{array}{c}0.003N\\ \mathrm{H_2SO_4}\end{array}\right)$	1.028	B_S	$1:1^a$	40^e			29, 34
2	Salicylic acid	Caffeine	30	$\mathrm{H_2O}$ $\left(\begin{array}{c}0.003N\\ \mathrm{H_2SO_4}\end{array}\right)$	1.796	B_S	$1:1^a$	44			34
3	Caffeine	Salicylate ion	15	$\mathrm{H_2O}$	6.71	A_L^f					34
3	Caffeine	Salicylate ion	30	$\mathrm{H_2O}$	13.43	A_L^f					34
4	p-Hydroxybenzoic acid	Caffeine	15	$\mathrm{H_2O}$ $\left(\begin{array}{c}0.005N\\ \mathrm{H_2SO_4}\end{array}\right)$	2.624	B_S	$1:1^a$	100^e			34
4	p-Hydroxybenzoic acid	Caffeine	30	$\mathrm{H_2O}$ $\left(\begin{array}{c}0.005N\\ \mathrm{H_2SO_4}\end{array}\right)$	5.421	A_N		100^e			34
5	m-Hydroxybenzoic acid	Caffeine	15	$\mathrm{H_2O}$ $\left(\begin{array}{c}0.003N\\ \mathrm{H_2SO_4}\end{array}\right)$	4.477	B_S	$1:1^a$				28, 34
6	Butyl p-hydroxybenzoate	Caffeine	15	$\mathrm{H_2O}$ $\left(\begin{array}{c}0.001N\\ \mathrm{H_2SO_4}\end{array}\right)$	0.064	A_L		91			34

No.									Ref.
6	Butyl p-hydroxyben-zoate	Caffeine	30	H_2O (0.001N H_2SO_4)	0.131	A_L		50	34
7	Caffeine	Benzoate ion	0	H_2O	3.887	A_L		23.1	33
7	Caffeine	Benzoate ion	15	H_2O	6.603	A_L		16.4	33
7	Caffeine	Benzoate ion	30	H_2O	13.33	A_L		12.8	33
8	Sulfathiazole	Caffeine	30	H_2O	0.227	A_N		11.3	26
9	Sulfadiazine	Caffeine	30	H_2O	0.036	A_P		6.9	26
10	p-Aminobenzoic acid	Caffeine	30	H_2O	4.579	B_S	1:1[a]	48	26,28
11	Ethyl p-aminoben-zoate	Caffeine	30	H_2O	0.515	A_P	1:1	59.1	26
12	Barbital	Caffeine	15	H_2O	3.187	B_S	2:1[a]		26
12	Barbital	Caffeine	30	H_2O	4.408	B_S	2:1[a]		26
13	Phenobarbital	Caffeine	15	H_2O	0.398	B_S	1:1[a]		26
13	Phenobarbital	Caffeine	30	H_2O	0.631	B_S	2:1[a]		26
14	Phenobarbital	Polyethylene glycol 4000	30	H_2O	0.92[a]	B_I	1:2[h]		27
14	Phenobarbital	Polyethylene glycol 4000	40	H_2O		B_I	1:2[h]		
15	Phenobarbital	Polyethylene glycol 6000	30	H_2O	0.92[a]	B_I			27
15	Phenobarbital	Polyethylene glycol 6000	40	H_2O	0.92[a]	B_I			27
16	Barbital	Polyethylene glycol 4000	30	H_2O		A_L[d]		0	27
17	Pentobarbital	Polyethylene glycol 4000	30	H_2O	0.7[a]	A_L[d]		0	27
18	m-Hydroxybenzoic acid	Polyethylene glycol 4000	30	H_2O (0.003N H_2SO_4)	8.7[a]	A_L			27

(continued)

TABLE IV (continued)

System number	S	L	t (°C)	Solvent	$10^2 S_0$ (Mole/L.)	Type of diagram	Stoichiometry (S:L)	$K_{1:1}$	$K_{1:2}$	$K_{2:1}$	Reference
19	p-Hydroxybenzoic acid	Polyethylene glycol 4000	30	H₂O (0.003N H₂SO₄)		A_L					27
20	o-Phthalic acid	Polyethylene glycol 4000	30	H₂O (0.003N H₂SO₄)	4.9^g	A_L					27
21	Salicylic acid	Polyethylene glycol 4000	30	H₂O (0.003N H₂SO₄)		A_L					27
22	Picric acid	Caffeine	30	H₂O	6.2^a	B_S	$1:1^a$	8			28
23	o-Phthalic acid	Caffeine	30	H₂O	2.8^g	A_N		14			28
24	Suberic acid	Caffeine	30	H₂O (0.003N H₂SO₄)	1.75^g	A_N		3			28
25	p-Aminobenzoic acid	Theophylline	30	H₂O		B_S	1:1	31			29
26	p-Aminobenzoic acid	Theobromine	30	H₂O		A_L					29
27	Salicylic acid	Theophylline	30	H₂O		B_S	$1:1^a$	40^e			29
28	Salicylic acid	Theobromine	30	H₂O (0.003N H₂SO₄)		B_S	$1:1^a$	40^e			29
29	Acetylsalicylic acid	Theophylline	30	H₂O (0.003N H₂SO₄)		A_N		8.5			29

30	Acetylsalicylic acid	Theobromine	30	H_2O ($0.003N$ H_2SO_4)	A_N			29
31	p-Hydroxybenzoic acid	Theophylline	30	H_2O ($0.003N$ H_2SO_4)	B_S	$1{:}1^a$	14^e	29
32	p-Hydroxybenzoic acid	Theobromine	30	H_2O ($0.003N$ H_2SO_4)	B_S	$2{:}1^a$		29
33	p-Hydroxybenzoic acid	N,N,N',N'-tetramethylisophthalamide	30	H_2O ($0.005N$ H_2SO_4)	A_L		5.7	39
34	p-Hydroxybenzoic acid	N,N,N',N'-tetramethylphthalamide	30	H_2O ($0.005N$ H_2SO_4)	B_S	$4{:}1^a$	4.0	39
35	p-Hydroxybenzoic acid	N,N,N',N'-tetramethylterephthalamide	30	H_2O ($0.005N$ H_2SO_4)	B_S	$2{:}1^a$	3.7	39
36	p-Hydroxybenzoic acid	N,N,N',N'-tetramethylfumaramide	30	H_2O ($0.005N$ H_2SO_4)	B_S	$3{:}1^a$	5.9	39
37	p-Hydroxybenzoic acid	N,N,N',N'-tetramethylsuccinamide	30	H_2O ($0.005N$ H_2SO_4)	B_S	$2{:}1^a$	4.5	39
38	Salicylic acid	N,N,N',N'-tetramethylterephthalamide	30	H_2O ($0.005N$ H_2SO_4)	B_S	$3{:}1^a$	2.6	39
39	Salicylic acid	N,N,N',N'-tetramethylfumaramide	30	H_2O ($0.005N$ H_2SO_4)	A_L		4.7	39

(continued)

TABLE IV (continued)

System number	S	L	t (°C)	Solvent	$10^2 S_0$ (Mole/L.)	Type of diagram	Stoichiometry (S:L)	$K_{1:1}$	$K_{1:2}$	$K_{2:1}$	Reference
40	Salicylic acid	N,N,N',N'-tetramethylisophthalamide	30	H_2O $\left(\begin{array}{c}0.005N\\H_2SO_4\end{array}\right)$		A_L		3.5			39
41	Salicylic acid	N,N,N',N'-tetramethylsuccinamide	30	H_2O $\left(\begin{array}{c}0.005N\\H_2SO_4\end{array}\right)$		A_L		2.2			39
42	Salicylic acid	N,N,N',N'-tetramethylphthalamide	30	H_2O $\left(\begin{array}{c}0.005N\\H_2SO_4\end{array}\right)$		A_L		2.0			39
43	Chloramphenicol	N,N,N',N'-tetramethylisophthalamide	30	H_2O	1.37^g	A_L		2.7			39
44	Chloramphenicol	N,N,N',N'-tetramethylterephthalamide	30	H_2O		A_L		2.4			39
45	Chloramphenicol	N,N,N',N'-tetramethylphthalamide	30	H_2O		A_L		1.6			39
46	p-Hydroxybenzoic acid	N,N,N',N'-tetraethylfumaramide	30	H_2O $\left(\begin{array}{c}0.005N\\H_2SO_4\end{array}\right)$		B_S	$6:1^a$	1.1			40
47	p-Hydroxybenzoic acid	N,N,N',N'-tetraethylisophthalamide	30	H_2O $\left(\begin{array}{c}0.005N\\H_2SO_4\end{array}\right)$		B_I	1:1				40
48	p-Hydroxybenzoic acid	N,N,N',N'-tetraethylterephthalamide	30	H_2O $\left(\begin{array}{c}0.005N\\H_2SO_5\end{array}\right)$		B_I	$1:1^e$				40

49	Salicylic acid	N,N,N',N'-tetraethylfumaramide	30	H_2O $\left(\begin{matrix}0.005N\\H_2SO_5\end{matrix}\right)$	B_S	3:1	4.5	40
50	Salicylic acid	N,N,N',N'-tetraethylisophthalamide	30	H_2O $\left(\begin{matrix}0.005N\\H_2SO_5\end{matrix}\right)$	B_S	2:1	4.5	40
51	Salicylic acid	N,N,N',N'-tetraethyl terephthalamide	30	H_2O $\left(\begin{matrix}0.005N\\H_2SO_4\end{matrix}\right)$	B_I	2:1[a]		40
52	Chloramphenicol	N,N,N',N'-tetraethylisophthalamide	30	H_2O	A_L		3.5	40
53	Chloramphenicol	N,N,N',N'-tetraethyl terephthalamide	30	H_2O	A_L		3.5	40
54	p-Hydroxybenzoic acid	Ethyl theophylline	30	H_2O $\left(\begin{matrix}0.005N\\H_2SO_4\end{matrix}\right)$	B_S	1:1[a]		4
55	p-Hydroxybenzoic acid	Propyl theophylline	30	H_2O $\left(\begin{matrix}0.005N\\H_2SO_4\end{matrix}\right)$	B_S	1:1[a]		4
56	p-Hydroxybenzoic acid	Butyl theophylline	30	H_2O $\left(\begin{matrix}0.005N\\H_2SO_4\end{matrix}\right)$	B_S	1:1[a]		4
57	p-Hydroxybenzoic acid	Ethyl theobromine	30	H_2O $\left(\begin{matrix}0.005N\\H_2SO_4\end{matrix}\right)$	B_S	1:1[a]		4
58	p-Hydroxybenzoic acid	Propyl theobromine	30	H_2O $\left(\begin{matrix}0.005N\\H_2SO_5\end{matrix}\right)$	B_S	1:1[a]		4

(continued)

TABLE IV (continued)

System number	S	L	t (°C)	Solvent	$10^2 S_0$ (Mole/L.)	Type of diagram	Stoichiometry (S:L)	$K_{1:1}$	$K_{1:2}$	$K_{2:1}$	Reference
59	p-Hydroxybenzoic acid	Butyl theobromine	30	H₂O (0.005N H₂SO₅)		B_S	1:1[a]				4
60	Ethyl p-amino-benzoate	1-Ethyl theobromine	30	H₂O		B_S	2:1				17
61	Tetracycline	Caffeine	25	H₂O (pH 5.0)	0.052[a]	A_N					10
62	Oxytetracycline	Caffeine	25	H₂O (pH 5.0)	0.048[a]	A_N					10
63	Tetracycline	γ-Butyrolactone	25	CCl₄	0.125	B_S	1:1[a]				11
64	p-Aminosalicylic acid	Isoniazid	30	H₂O	1.0[a]	B_S	1:1				53
65	Oxytetracycline	Phenol	25	H₂O (pH 5.0)		A_L		2.4			23
66	Oxytetracycline	Aniline	25	H₂O (pH 5.0)		A_L		1.2			23
67	Oxytetracycline	Benzoic acid	25	H₂O (pH 5.0)		A_L		3.2			23
68	Oxytetracycline	Pyridine	25	H₂O (pH 5.0)		A_P		1.2	0.85		23
69	Oxytetracycline	Resorcinol	25	H₂O (pH 5.0)		A_P		4.5	1.00[c]		23
70	Oxytetracycline	Catechol	25	H₂O (pH 5.0)		A_P		3.2	1.32[c]		23
71	Oxytetracycline	Hydroquinone	25	H₂O (pH 5.0)		A_L		4.0			23

No.	Drug	Complexing agent	Temp.	Solvent	Type			
72	Oxytetracycline	p-Aminophenol	25	H_2O (pH 5.0)	A_L	2.0		23
73	Oxytetracycline	o-Aminophenol	25	H_2O (pH 5.0)	A_L	1.4		23
74	Oxytetracycline	m-Aminophenol	25	H_2O (pH 5.0)	A_L	2.6		23
75	Oxytetracycline	Salicylic acid	25	H_2O (pH 5.0)	A_P	6.4[c]		23
76	Oxytetracycline	p-Hydroxybenzoic acid	25	H_2O (pH 5.0)	A_L	5.6		23
77	Oxytetracycline	m-Hydroxybenzoic acid	25	H_2O (pH 5.0)	A_P	5.6[c]		23
78	Oxytetracycline	2,4-Dihydroxybenzoic acid	25	H_2O (pH 5.0)	A_P	11.2	0.45	23
79	Oxytetracycline	2,5-Dihydroxybenzoic acid	25	H_2O (pH 5.0)	A_L	10.0		23
80	Oxytetracycline	2,5-Dihydroxybenzoic ethanolamide	25	H_2O (pH 5.0)	A_L	10.8		23
81	Oxytetracycline	3,4-Dihydroxybenzoic acid	25	H_2O (pH 5.0)	A_P	8.2	0.70	23
82	Oxytetracycline	3,5-Dihydroxybenzoic acid	25	H_2O (pH 5.0)	A_L	8.8		23
83	Oxytetracycline	p-Aminobenzoic acid	25	H_2O (pH 5.0)	A_L	3.6		23
84	Oxytetracycline	o-Aminobenzoic acid	25	H_2O (pH 5.0)	A_L	4.4		23
85	Oxytetracycline	m-Aminobenzoic acid	25	H_2O (pH 5.0)	A_L	3.4		23
86	Oxytetracycline	Nicotinic acid	25	H_2O (pH 5.0)	A_L	3.9		23

(continued)

TABLE IV (continued)

System number	S	L	t (°C)	Solvent	$10^2 S_0$ (Mole/L.)	Type of diagram	Stoichiometry (S:L)	$K_{1:1}$	$K_{1:2}$	$K_{2:1}$	Reference
87	Oxytetracycline	Nicotinamide	25	H₂O (pH 5.0)		A_P		4.1	0.34		23
88	Oxytetracycline	Isonicotinic acid	25	H₂O (pH 5.0)		A_L		3.1			23
89	Oxytetracycline	Picolinic acid	25	H₂O (pH 5.0)		A_P		2.6	0.31		23
90	Oxytetracycline	Benzaldehyde	25	H₂O (pH 5.0)		A_L		2.8			23
91	Oxytetracycline	m-Hydroxybenzaldehyde	25	H₂O (pH 5.0)		A_L		5.2			23
92	Oxytetracycline	Salicylaldehyde	25	H₂O (pH 5.0)		A_L		2.8			23
93	Oxytetracycline	Ethyl theophylline	25	H₂O (pH 0.5)		A_L		14.8			23
94	Oxytetracycline	Gallic acid	25	H₂O (pH 5.0)		A_L		9.2			23
95	Oxytetracycline	2,3-Diketo-1,2,3,4-tetrahydroxyquinoxaline	25	H₂O (pH 5.0)		A_L		8.8			23
96	Oxytetracycline	Apresoline hydrochloride	25	H₂O (pH 5.0)		A_L		8.0			23
97	Oxytetracycline	p-Aminosalicylic acid	25	H₂O (pH 5.0)		A_L		7.8			23
98	Oxytetracycline	Melamine	25	H₂O (pH 5.0)		A_L		6.4			23

99	Oxytetracycline	Quinoline-8-carboxylic acid	25	H$_2$O (pH 5.0)	A_L	5.4		23
100	Oxytetracycline	Polyethylene glycol 4000	25	H$_2$O (pH 5.0)	A_L	5.2		23
101	Oxytetracycline	Pyrogallol	25	H$_2$O (pH 5.0)	A_P	4.4^c		23
102	Oxytetracycline	Maleic hydrazide	25	H$_2$O (pH 5.0)	A_L	3.8		23
103	Oxytetracycline	8-Hydroxyquinoline	25	H$_2$O (pH 5.0)	A_L	3.6		23
104	Oxytetracycline	Antipyrine	25	H$_2$O (pH 5.0)	A_P	3.4	0.36	23
105	Oxytetracycline	o-Phthalic acid	25	H$_2$O (pH 5.0)	A_L	2.8		23
106	Oxytetracycline	Monomethyloldimethylhydantoin	25	H$_2$O (pH 5.0)	A_P	1.9	0.37	23
107	Oxytetracycline	Pyridazine	25	H$_2$O (pH 5.0)	A_L	1.8		23
108	Oxytetracycline	Dimethylhydantion	25	H$_2$O (pH 5.0)	A_P	1.4	0.43	23
109	Oxytetracycline	Oxazolidone	25	H$_2$O (pH 5.0)	A_P	1.2	0.19^c	23
110	Oxytetracycline	Barbital	25	H$_2$O (pH 5.0)	A_L	1.2		23
111	Oxytetracycline	Polyethylene glycol 1500 w.	25	H$_2$O (pH 5.0)	A_L	1.2		23
112	Oxytetracycline	3-Hydroxy-3-methyl-2-butanone	25	H$_2$O (pH 5.0)	A_P	0.24	1.2	23

(continued)

TABLE IV (*continued*)

System number	S	L	t (°C)	Solvent	$10^2 S_0$ (Mole/L.)	Type of diagram	Stoichiometry (S:L)	$K_{1:1}$	$K_{1:2}$	$K_{2:1}$	Reference
113	Oxytetracycline	Malonic acid	25	H₂O (pH 5.0)		A_L		0.2			23
114	Oxytetracycline	Riboflavin-5-phosphate sodium	25	H₂O (pH 5.0)		A_L		25.6			23
115	Oxytetracycline	Desoxyribonucleic acid	25	H₂O (pH 5.0)		A_L		23.0			23
116	Oxytetracycline	Adenylic acid	25	H₂O (pH 5.0)		A_L		10.0			23
117	Oxytetracycline	Thymine	25	H₂O (pH 5.0)		A_L		6.2			23
118	Oxytetracycline	Uracil	25	H₂O (pH 5.0)		A_L		5.0			23
119	Oxytetracycline	Pyridoxine hydrochloride	25	H₂O (pH 5.0)		A_P		4.6	0.26[c]		23
120	Oxytetracycline	Dimethyluracil	25	H₂O (pH 5.0)		A_P		4.0	0.5		23
121	Oxytetracycline	Alloxan	25	H₂O (pH 5.0)		A_L		5.0			23
122	Oxytetracycline	Thiamine hydrochloride	25	H₂O (pH 5.0)		A_P		4.5	0.6[c]		23
123	Oxytetracycline	Tryptophan	25	H₂O (pH 5.0)		A_L		4.0			23
124	Oxytetracycline	Cytosine	25	H₂O (pH 5.0)		A_L		3.0			23
125	Oxytetracycline	Creatinine	25	H₂O (pH 5.0)		A_P		2.6	0.35		23

No.	Compound	Component	Temp	Solvent	Value	Type	Ratio			Ref
126	Oxytetracycline	l-Histidine hydrochloride	25	H_2O (pH 5.0)		A_P		1.4	0.45	23
127	Oxytetracycline	Ascorbic acid	25	H_2O (pH 5.0)		A_L		1.2		23
128	Oxytetracycline	Urea	25	H_2O (pH 5.0)		A_P		0.4	0.52	23
129	Cyanocobalamin	Sodium silico-12-molybdate	25	H_2O	0.85[a]	A_L				20
130	Cyanocobalamin	Sodium 2-phospho-18-molybdate	25	H_2O		A_L				20
131	Cyanocobalamin	Sodium phospho-12-molybdate	25	H_2O		B_S	1:1[a]			20
132	Cyanocobalamin	Manganese phospho-12-molybdate	25	H_2O		B_S	6:1[a]			20
133	Cyanocobalamin	Nickel phospho-12-molybdate	25	H_2O		B_S	5:2[a]			20
134	Cyanocobalamin	Phosphotungstic acid	25	H_2O		B_S	4:1[a]			20
135	Cyanocobalamin	Phosphomolybdic acid	25	H_2O		B_S	2:1			20
136	Cyanocobalamin	Potassium gold chloride	25	H_2O		B_S	1:2			20
137	Cyanocobalamin	Palladium chloride	25	H_2O		B_S	1:1			20
138	Cyanocobalamin	Platinum chloride	25	H_2O		B_S	2:3[a]			20
139	Cyanocobalamin	Gold chloride	25	H_2O		B_S	1:1			20
140	Cyanocobalamin	Mercuric chloride	25	H_2O		B_I^i				20
141	p-Hydrobenzoic acid	Sarcosine anhydride	25	$\left(\dfrac{0.001N}{H_2SO_4}\right)$	4.31	B_S	2:1		54	51

(continued)

TABLE IV (continued)

System number	S	L	t (°C)	Solvent	$10^2 S_0$ (mole/L.)	Type of diagram	Stoichiometry (S:L)	$K_{1:1}$	$K_{1:2}$	$K_{2:1}$	Reference
142	o-Hydroxybenzoic acid	Sarcosine anhydride	25	H_2O $\left(\begin{array}{c}0.001N\\H_2SO_4\end{array}\right)$	1.75	A_L	2:1				150	51
143	m-Hydroxybenzoic	Sarcosine anhydride	25	H_2O $\left(\begin{array}{c}0.001N\\H_2SO_4\end{array}\right)$	5.85	B_S	2:1				27	51
144	p-Aminobenzoc aicid	Sarcosine anhydride	25	H_2O $\left(\begin{array}{c}0.001N\\H_2SO_4\end{array}\right)$	4.03	A_L		4.2			49	51
145	m-Aminobenzoic acid	Sarcosine anhydride	25	H_2O $\left(\begin{array}{c}0.001N\\H_2SO_4\end{array}\right)$	5.63	A_L		1.1			10	51
146	o-Aminobenzoic acid	Sarcosine anhydride	25	H_2O $\left(\begin{array}{c}0.001N\\H_2SO_4\end{array}\right)$	3.73	A_L		2.6			34	51
147	Isonicotinic acid	Sarcosine anhydride	25	H_2O $\left(\begin{array}{c}0.001N\\H_2SO_4\end{array}\right)$	4.73	$A_L{}^d$		0			0	51
148	Benzoic acid	Sarcosine anhydride	25	H_2O $\left(\begin{array}{c}0.001N\\H_2SO_4\end{array}\right)$	2.85			2.9			50	51
149	Acetylsalicylic acid	Sarcosine anhydride	25	H_2O $\left(\begin{array}{c}0.001N\\H_2SO_4\end{array}\right)$	2.27			3.1			65	51
150	o-Phthalic acid	Sarcosine anhydride	25	H_2O $\left(\begin{array}{c}0.001N\\H_2SO_4\end{array}\right)$	3.90			2.2			29	51

151	p-Aminosalicylic acid	Sarcosine anhydride	25	H_2O $\left(\begin{array}{c}0.001N\\H_2SO_4\end{array}\right)$	1.00			5.1	250	51
152	2,4-Dihydroxybenzoic acid	Sarcosine anhydride	25	H_2O $\left(\begin{array}{c}0.001N\\H_2SO_4\end{array}\right)$	3.75	B_S	2:1		63	51
153	3,4-Dihydroxybenzoic acid	Sarcosine anhydride	25	H_2O $\left(\begin{array}{c}0.001N\\H_2SO_4\end{array}\right)$	8.92	B_S	2:1		38	51
154	2,5-Dihydroxybenzoic acid	Sarcosine anhydride	25	H_2O $\left(\begin{array}{c}0.001N\\H_2SO_4\end{array}\right)$	13.6	B_I	2:1			51
155	3,5-Dihydroxybenzoic acid	Sarcosine anhydride	25	H_2O $\left(\begin{array}{c}0.001N\\H_2SO_3\end{array}\right)$	66.0	B_I	6:1			51
156	Gallic acid	Sarcosine anhydride	25	H_2O $\left(\begin{array}{c}0.001N\\H_2SO_4\end{array}\right)$	7.78	B_S	6:1	64		51
157	8-Hydroxyquinoline	Sarcosine anhydride	25	H_2O	0.41	A_L		8.2	1000	51
158	Galloacetophenone	Sarcosine anhydride	25	H_2O	3.38	A_L		8.3	120	51
159	Phloroglucinol	Sarcosine anhydride	25	H_2O	16.5	A_L		12	18	51
160	2,5-Dihydroxybenz-oic acid ethanol-amide	Sarcosine anhydride	25	H_2O	28.6			39	10	51
161	2,3-Dihydroxyquin-oxaline	Sarcosine anhydride	25	H_2O	0.15			2.5	800	51

(continued)

TABLE IV (*continued*)

System number	S	L	t (°C)	Solvent	$10^2 S_0$ (mole/l.)	Type of diagram	Stoichiometry (S:L)	$K_{1:1}$	$K_{1:2}$	$K_{2:1}$	Reference
162	o-Aminophenol	Sarcosine anhydride	25	H_2O	2.96			2.3		37	51
163	p-Aminophenol	Sarcosine anhydride	25	H_2O	5.03			1.9		18	51
164	m-Aminophenol	Sarcosine anhydride	25	H_2O	28.5			5.6		5.6	51
165	Salicylamide	Sarcosine anhydride	25	H_2O	1.82			3.9		110	51
166	Salicyl alcohol	Sarcosine anhydride	25	H_2O	59.5	$A_L{}^f$				2.9	51
167	Salicylamine	Sarcosine anhydride	25	H_2O	7.80			0.8		4.8	51
168	1,5-Naphthalenediol	Sarcosine anhydride	25	H_2O	0.15	B_S	$1:1^a$	23			51
169	2,7-Naphthalenediol	Sarcosine anhydride	25	H_2O	2.55	B_I	$3:1^a$				51
170	Hydroquinone	Sarcosine anhydride	25	H_2O	63.5	B_I	$2:1^a$				51
171	2,6-Dihydroxytoluene	Sarcosine anhydride	25	H_2O	212	B_I	$2:1^a$				51
172	m-Xylylene glycol	Sarcosine anhydride	25	H_2O (20% NaCl)	58.5	$A_L{}^f$				5.2	51
173	o-Xylylene glycol	Sarcosine anhydride	25	H_2O	114	$A_L{}^f$				5.9	51

174	p-Xylylene glycol	Sarcosine anhydride	25	H_2O	41.1			1.4	0.1	51
175	Suberic acid	Sarcosine anhydride	25	H_2O $\left(\begin{array}{c}0.001N\\H_2SO_4\end{array}\right)$	0.82	A_L		2.2	120	51
176	Pimelic acid	Sarcosine anhydride	25	H_2O $\left(\begin{array}{c}0.001N\\H_2SO_4\end{array}\right)$	28.5	A_L		1.4	1.9	51
177	Adipic acid	Sarcosine anhydride	25	H_2O $\left(\begin{array}{c}0.001N\\H_2SO_4\end{array}\right)$	14.8	A_L		0.5	1.7	51
178	Rutin	Sarcosine anhydride	25	H_2O	0.0055	A_L		11.3	10^6	51
179	Oxytetracycline	Sarcosine anhydride	25	H_2O	0.04	A_L		2.5	2600	51
180	Melamine	Sarcosine anhydride	25	H_2O	4.20	A_L		2.0	23	51
181	Chloramphenicol	Sarcosine anhydride	25	H_2O	1.21	A_L		1.7	68	51
182	Quinine hydrochloride	Sarcosine anhydride	25	H_2O	13.3	A_L		1.4	4.9	51
183	Picric acid	Sarcosine anhydride	25	H_2O	5.50	A_L		1.5	13	51
184	Phenobarbital	Sarcosine anhydride	25	H_2O	0.55	A_L		1.8	170	51
185	L-Tyrosine	Sarcosine anhydride	25	H_2O	0.31	A_L		1.4	220	51
186	1,3-Dimethyl-benzoylene urea	Catechol	30	CCl_4	4.1[a]	B_S	2:5			18

(continued)

TABLE IV (continued)

System number	S	L	t (°C)	Solvent	$10^2 S_0$ (Mole/L.)	Type of diagram	Stoichiometry (S:L)	$K_{1:1}$	$K_{1:2}$	$K_{2:1}$	Reference
187	1,3-Dimethyl-benzoylene urea	Resorcinol	30	CCl₄		B_S	1:4				18
188	1,3-Dimethyl-benzoylene urea	Hydroquinone	30	CCl₄		B_I					18
189	1,3-Dimethyl-benzoylene urea	Phenol	30	CCl₄		A_L		2.44			18
190	2,3-Diketo-1,4-dimethylquinoxaline	Resorcinol	30	CCl₄	0.1^a	A_L					18
191	2,3-Diketo-1,4-dimethylquinoxaline	Hydroquinone	30	CCl₄		$A_L{}^d$		0			18
192	2,3-Diketo-1,4-dimethylquinoxaline	Phenol	30	CCl₄		A^i					18
193	2,3-Dimethyl-phthalylhydrazide	Phenol	30	CCl₄	2.3^a	A_L					18
194	2,3-Diketo-1,2,3,4-tetrahydroquinoxaline	Hydroquinone	30	H₂O	0.21^a	B_I	$2:1^a$				32
195	2,3-Diketo-1,2,3,4-tetrahydroquinoxaline	Resorcinol	30	H₂O		B_S	$2:1^a$	4.16			32
196	2,3-Diketo-1,2,3,4-tetrahydroquinoxaline	Catechol	30	H₂O		B_S	$2:1^a$	3.8			32
197	2,3-Diketo-1,2,3,4-tetrahydroquinoxaline	Phenol	30	H₂O		B_S	$2:1^a$	1.6			32

	Compound	Temp	Solvent		Type	Ratio	Value	Ref
198	1,4-Dimethyl-2,3-d'keto-1,2,3,4-tetrahydroquinoxaline	30	H_2O	1.90	B_S	2:1[a]	4.9	32
199	1,4-Dimethyl-2,3-diketo-1,2,3,4-tetrahydroquinoxaline	30	H_2O		B_S	2:1[a]	14.2	32
200	1,4-Dimethyl-2,3-diketo-1,2,3,4-tetrahydroquinoxaline	30	H_2O		B_S	2:1[a]	8.3	32
201	1,4-Dimethyl-2,3-diketo-1,2,3,4-tetrahydroquinoxaline	30	H_2O		B_S	2:1[a]	5.9	32
202	1-Methyl-2,3-diketo-1,2,3,4-tetrahydroquinoxaline	30	H_2O	0.75[g]	A_P		6.4[b]	32
203	1-Methyl-2,3-diketo-1,2,3,4-tetrahydroquinoxaline	30	H_2O		B_S	2:1[a]	8.6	32
204	1-Methyl-2,3-diketo-1,2,3,4-tetrahydroquinoxaline	30	H_2O		A_L		6.1	32
205	1-Methyl-2,3-diketo-1,2,3,4-tetrahydroquinoxaline	30	H_2O		A_P		4.7[b]	32

(continued)

TABLE IV (*continued*)

System number	S	L	t (°C)	Solvent	$10^2 S_0$ (Mole/L.)	Type of diagram	Stoichiometry (S:L)	$K_{1:1}$	$K_{1:2}$	$K_{2:1}$	Reference
206	1-Methyl-2-keto-3-methoxy-1,2-dihydroquinoxaline	Hydroquinone	30	H_2O	0.6[a]	B_S	2:1[a]	14.6			32
207	1-Methyl-2-keto-3-methoxy-1,2-dihydroquinoxaline	Resorcinol	30	H_2O		A_P		12.4[b]			32
208	1-Methyl-2-keto-3-methoxy-1,2-dihydroquinoxaline	Catechol	30	H_2O		A_P		8.1[b]			32
209	1-Methyl-2-keto-3-methoxy-1,2-dihydroquinoxaline	Phenol	30	H_2O		B_S	2:1[a]	7.3			32
210	2,3-Dimethoxyquinoxaline	Hydroquinone	30	H_2O	0.44[a]	A_P		7.4[b]			32
211	2,3-Dimethoxyquinoxaline	Resorcinol	30	H_2O		A_P		7.3[b]			32
212	2,3-Dimethoxyquinoxaline	Catechol	30	H_2O		A_P		5.9[b]			32
213	2,3-Dimethoxyquinoxaline	Phenol	30	H_2O		A_P		4.9			32
214	2,4-Diketo-1,2,3,4-tetrahydroquinazoline	Hydroquinone	30	H_2O	0.95[a]	A_N		17.5[b]			32
215	2,4-Diketo-1,2,3,4-tetrahydroquinazoline	Resorcinol	30	H_2O		A_L		6.0			32

216	2,4-Diketo-1,2,3,4-tetrahydroquinazoline	Catechol	30	H_2O		A_N		32
217	2,4-Diketo-1,2,3,4-tetrahydroquinazoline	Phenol	30	H_2O		A_L	3.8	32
218	1,3-Dimethyl-2,4-diketo-1,2,3,4-tetrahydroquinazoline	Hydroquinone	30	H_2O	0.22[a]	A_L	12.2	32
219	1,3-Dimethyl-2,4-diketo-1,2,3,4-tetrahydroquinazoline	Resorcinol	30	H_2O		A_P	11.3[b]	32
220	1,3-Dimethyl-2,4-diketo-1,2,3,4-tetrahydroquinazoline	Catechol	30	H_2O		A_L	10.5	32
221	1,3-Dimethyl-2,4-diketo-1,2,3,4-tetrahydroquinazoline	Phenol	30	H_2O		A_P	5.8[b]	32
222	1,4-Diketo-1,2,3,4-tetrahydrophthalazine	Hydroquinone	30	H_2O	0.18[a]	A_L	7.2	32
223	1,4-Diketo-1,2,3,4-tetrahydrophthalazine	Resorcinol	30	H_2O		A_L	4.8	32
224	1,4-Diketo-1,2,3,4-tetrahydrophthalazine	Catechol	30	H_2O		A_L	4.9	32

(continued)

TABLE IV (continued)

System number	S	L	t (°C)	Solvent	$10^2 S_0$ (Mole/l.)	Type of diagram	Stoichiometry (S:L)	$K_{1:1}$	$K_{1:2}$	$K_{2:1}$	Reference
225	1,4-Diketo-1,2,3,4-tetrahydrophthalazine	Phenol	30	H_2O		A_L		3.4			32
226	1,4-Diketo-2,3-dimethyl-1,2,3,4-tetrahydrophthalazine	Hydroquinone	30	H_2O	7^a	B_S		18.4			32
227	1,4-Diketo-2,3-dimethyl-1,2,3,4-tetrahydrophthalazine	Resorcinol	30	H_2O		B_S	$2.5:1^a$	47.6			32
228	1,4-Diketo-2,3-dimethyl-1,2,3,4-tetrahydrophthalazine	Catechol	30	H_2O		B_S	$1:1^a$	13.2			32
229	1,4-Diketo-2,3-dimethyl-1,2,3,4-tetrahydrophthalazine	Phenol	30	H_2O		A_L		16.6			32
230	1-keto-2-methyl-4-methoxy-1,2-dihydrophthalazine	Hydroquinone	30	H_2O	0.9^a	B_I	$3:1^a$				32
231	1-keto-2-methyl-4-methoxy-1,2-dihydrophthalazine	Resorcinol	30	H_2O		B_S	$2:1^a$	8.1			32

232	1-keto-2-methyl-4-methoxy-1,2-dihydrophthalazine	Catechol	30	H_2O		B_S	3:2^a	6.9	32
233	1-keto-methyl-4-methoxy-1,2-dihydrophthalazine	Phenol	30	H_2O		B_S	2:1^a	4.1	32
234	1-keto-4-methoxy-2,3-dihydrophthalazine	Hydroquinone	30	H_2O	0.28^a	A_L		7.7	32
235	1-keto-4-methoxy-2,3-dihydrophthalazine	Resorcinol	30	H_2O		A_L		7.4	32
236	1-keto-4-methoxy-2,3-dihydrophthalazine	Catechol	30	H_2O		A_L		5.3	32
237	1-keto-4-methoxy-2,3-dihydrophthalazine	Phenol	30	H_2O		A_L		4.9	32
238	Theophylline	Benzoate ion	30	H_2O	4.2^a			5.3	25
239	Theophylline	o-Hydroxybenzoate ion	30	H_2O		A_L		20	25
240	Theophylline	m-Hydroxybenzoate ion	30	H_2O		A_L		11	25
241	Theophylline	p-Hydroxybenzoate ion	30	H_2O		A_L		12	25
242	Theophylline	2,4-Dihydroxybenzoate ion	30	H_2O		A_L		58	25
243	Theophylline	2,5-Dihydroxybenzoate ion	30	H_2O		A_P		43^j	25
244	Theophylline	2,6-Dihydroxybenzoate ion	30	H_2O		A_L		300	25

(continued)

TABLE IV (*continued*)

System number	S	L	t (°C)	Solvent	$10^2 S_0$ (mole/l.)	Type of diagram	Stoichiometry (S:L)	$K_{1:1}$	$K_{1:2}$	$K_{2:1}$	Reference
245	Theophylline	3,4-Dihydroxybenzoate ion	30	H_2O		A_L		14			25
246	Theophylline	3,5-Dihydroxybenzoate ion	30	H_2O		A_L		20			25
247	Theophylline	3,4,5-Trihydroxybenzoate ion	30	H_2O		A_P		22^j			25
248	Theophylline	1-Naphthoate ion	30	H_2O		A_L^f		38			25
249	Theophylline	2-Naphthoate ion	30	H_2O		A_L^f					25
250	Theophylline	2-Hydroxy-1-naphthoate ion	30	H_2O		A_L^f					25
251	Theophylline	1-Hydroxy-2-naphthoate ion	30	H_2O		A_L^f					25
252	Theophylline	3-Hydroxy-2-naphthoate ion	30	H_2O		A_L^f					25
253	Hydrocortisone	Benzoate ion	30	H_2O		A_L		2.9			25
254	Hydrocortisone	o-Hydroxybenzoate ion	30	H_2O		A_L		7.2			25
255	Hydrocortisone	m-Hydroxybenzoate ion	30	H_2O		A_L		4.9			25
256	Hydrocortisone	p-Hydroxybenzoate ion	30	H_2O		A_L		4.1			25
257	Hydrocortisone	2,4-Dihydroxybenzoate ion	30	H_2O		A_L		13			25
258	Hydrocortisone	2,5-Dihydroxybenzoate ion	30	H_2O		A_P		10^j			25

259	Hydrocortisone	2,6-Dihydroxybenzoate ion	30	H_2O		A_P	13^j	25
260	Hydrocortisone	3,4-Dihydroxybenzoate ion	30	H_2O		A_L	6.8	25
261	Hydrocortisone	3,5-Dihydroxybenzoate ion	30	H_2O		A_P	6.0^i	25
262	Hydrocortisone	3,4,5-Trihydroxybenzoate ion	30	H_2O		A_L	7.3	25
263	Prednisolone	Benzoate ion	30	H_2O	0.07^a	A_L	3.7	25
264	Prednisolone	o-Hydroxybenzoate	30	H_2O		A_L	7.3	25
265	Prednisolone	m-Hydroxybenzoate ion	30	H_2O		A_L	6.1	25
266	Prednisolone	p-Hydroxybenzoate ion	30	H_2O		A_L	5	25
267	Prednisolone	2,4-Dihydroxybenzoate ion	30	H_2O		A_L	12	25
268	Prednisolone	2,5-Dihydroxybenzoate ion	30	H_2O		A_L	12	25
269	Prednisolone	2,6-Dihydroxybenzoate ion	30	H_2O		A_P	10^i	25
270	Prednisolone	3,4-Dihydroxybenzoate ion	30	H_2O		A_L	6.5	25
271	Prednisolone	3,5-Dihydroxybenzoate ion	30	H_2O		A_L	6.5	25
272	Prednisolone	3,4,5-Trihydroxybenzoate ion	30	H_2O		A_P	6.2^j	25
273	Acetophenetidin	Benzoate ion	30	H_2O		A_L	1.0	25
274	Acetophenetidin	o-Hydroxybenzoate ion	30	H_2O		A_L	1.9	25
275	Acetophenetidin	m-Hydroxybenzoate ion	30	H_2O		A_L	1.1	25

(continued)

TABLE IV (continued)

System number	S	L	t (°C)	Solvent	$10^2 S_0$ (Mole/L.)	Type of diagram	Stoichiometry (S:L)	$K_{1:1}$	$K_{1:2}$	$K_{2:1}$	Reference
276	Acetophenetidin	p-Hydroxybenzoate ion	30	H_2O		A_L		1.2			25
277	Acetophenetidin	2,4-Dihydroxybenzoate ion	30	H_2O		A_L		2.4			25
278	Acetophenetidin	2,5-Dihydroxybenzoate	30	H_2O		A_L		2.4			25
279	Acetophenetidin	2,6-Dihydroxybenzoate ion	30	H_2O		A_L		3.3			25
280	Acetophenetidin	3,4-Dihydroxybenzoate ion	30	H_2O		A_L		1.5			25
281	Acetophenetidin	3,5-Dihydroxybenzoate ion	30	H_2O		A_L		2.0			25
282	Acetophenetidin	3,4,5-Trihydroxybenzoate ion	30	H_2O		A_L		2.1			25
283	Acetophenetidin	1-Naphthoate ion	30	H_2O		A_L		2.5			25
284	Acetophenetidin	2-Naphthoate ion	30	H_2O		A_P		5.8[j]			25
285	Acetophenetidin	2-Hydroxy-1-naphthoate ion	30	H_2O		A_P		6.6[j]			25
286	Acetophenetidin	1-Hydroxy-2-naphthoate ion	30	H_2O		A_P		7.0[j]			25
287	Acetophenetidin	3-Hydroxy-2-naphthoate ion	30	H_2O		A_L		6.3			25
288	Hydrocortisone	1-Naphthoate ion	30	H_2O		A_P		8.2[j]			25
289	Hydrocortisone	2-Naphthoate ion	30	H_2O		A_P		19[j]			25
290	Hydrocortisone	2-Hydroxy-1-naphthoate ion	30	H_2O		A_P		21[j]			25

291	Hydrocortisone	1-Hydroxy-2-naphthoate ion	30	H_2O	A_P	35^j	25
292	Hydrocortisone	3-Hydroxy-2-naphthoate ion	30	H_2O	A_L	32	25
293	Prednisolone	1-Naphthoate ion	30	H_2O	A_P	8.0^j	25
294	Prednisolone	2-Naphthoate ion	30	H_2O	A_P	20^j	25
295	Prednisolone	2-Hydroxy-1-naphthoate ion	30	H_2O	A_P	23^j	25
296	Prednisolone	1-Hydroxy-2-naphthoate ion	30	H_2O	A_P	35^j	25
297	Prednisolone	3-Hydroxy-2-naphthoate ion	30	H_2O	A_L	39	25
298	Hydrocortisone	Benzoic acid	30	H_2O (0.005N H_2SO_4)	A_L	12	25
299	Hydrocortisone	o-Hydroxybenzoic acid	30	H_2O (0.005N H_2SO_4)	A_L	12	25
300	Hydrocortisone	m-Hydroxybenzoic acid	30	H_2O (0.005N H_2SO_4)	A_L	13	25
301	Hydrocortisone	p-Hydroxybenzoic acid	30	H_2O (0.005N H_2SO_4)	A_P	10^j	25
302	Hydrocortisone	2,4-Dihydroxybenzoic acid	30	H_2O (0.005N H_2SO_4)	A_P	12^j	25
303	Hydrocortisone	2,5-Dihydroxybenzoic acid	30	H_2O (0.005N H_2SO_4)	A_L	16	25

(continued)

TABLE IV (continued)

System number	S	L	t (°C)	Solvent	$10^2 S_0$ (Mole/L.)	Type of diagram	Stoichiometry (S:L)	$K_{1:1}$	$K_{1:2}$	$K_{2:1}$	Reference
304	Hydrocortisone	2,6-Dihydroxy-benzoic acid	30	H_2O $\left(\begin{array}{c}0.005N\\H_2SO_4\end{array}\right)$		A_P		12^j			25
305	Hydrocortisone	3,4-Dihydroxy-benzoic acid	30	H_2O $\left(\begin{array}{c}0.005N\\H_2SO_4\end{array}\right)$		A_L		12			25
306	Hydrocortisone	3,5-Dihydroxy-benzoic acid	30	H_2O $\left(\begin{array}{c}0.005N\\H_2SO_4\end{array}\right)$		A_P		18^j			25
307	Hydrocortisone	3,4,5-Trihydroxy-benzoic acid	30	H_2O $\left(\begin{array}{c}0.005N\\H_2SO_4\end{array}\right)$		A_P		19^j			25
308	Prednisolone	Benzoic Acid	30	H_2O $\left(\begin{array}{c}0.005N\\H_2SO_4\end{array}\right)$		A_L		11			25
309	Prednisolone	o-Hydroxybenzoic acid	30	H_2O $\left(\begin{array}{c}0.005N\\H_2SO_4\end{array}\right)$		A_L		10			25
310	Prednisolone	m-Hydroxybenzoic acid	30	H_2O $\left(\begin{array}{c}0.005N\\H_2SO_4\end{array}\right)$		A_L		12			25
311	Prednisolone	p-Hydroxybenzoic acid	30	H_2O $\left(\begin{array}{c}0.005N\\H_2SO_4\end{array}\right)$		A_P		11^j			25
312	Prednisolone	2,4-Dihydroxy-benzoic acid	30	H_2O $\left(\begin{array}{c}0.005N\\H_2SO_4\end{array}\right)$		A_L		15			25

No.	Compound	Acid		Solvent	Type	Value	Temp
313	Prednisolone	2,5-Dihydroxybenzoic acid	30	H_2O $\left(\begin{array}{c}0.005N\\ H_2SO_4\end{array}\right)$	A_P	15[j]	25
314	Prednisolone	2,6-Dihydroxybenzoic acid	30	H_2O $\left(\begin{array}{c}0.005N\\ H_2SO_4\end{array}\right)$	A_L	13	25
315	Prednisolone	3,4-Dihydroxybenzoic acid	30	H_2O $\left(\begin{array}{c}0.005N\\ H_2SO_4\end{array}\right)$	A_P	14[j]	25
316	Prednisolone	3,5-Dihydroxybenzoic acid	30	H_2O $\left(\begin{array}{c}0.005N\\ H_2SO_4\end{array}\right)$	A_P	17[j]	25
317	Prednisolone	3,4,5-Trihydroxybenzoic acid	30	H_2O $\left(\begin{array}{c}0.005N\\ H_2SO_4\end{array}\right)$	A_P	6.2[j]	25
318	Acetophenetidin	Benzoic acid	30	H_2O $\left(\begin{array}{c}0.005N\\ H_2SO_4\end{array}\right)$	A_L	2.6	25
319	Acetophenetidin	o-Hydroxybenzoic	30	H_2O $\left(\begin{array}{c}0.005N\\ H_2SO_4\end{array}\right)$	A_L	5.4	25
320	Acetophenetidin	m-Hydroxybenzoic acid	30	H_2O $\left(\begin{array}{c}0.005N\\ H_2SO_4\end{array}\right)$	A_L	3.9	25
321	Acetophenetidin	p-Hydroxybenzoic acid	30	H_2O $\left(\begin{array}{c}0.005N\\ H_2SO_4\end{array}\right)$	A_L	4.0	25
322	Acetophenetidin	2,4-Dihydroxybenzoic acid	30	H_2O $\left(\begin{array}{c}0.005N\\ H_2SO_4\end{array}\right)$	A_L	4.5	25

(continued)

TABLE IV (continued)

System number	S	L	t (°C)	Solvent	$10^3 S_0$ (Mole/L.)	Type of diagram (S:L)	$K_{1:1}$	$K_{1:2}$	$K_{2:1}$	Reference
323	Acetophenetidin	2,5-Dihydroxybenzoic acid	30	H_2O (0.005N H_2SO_4)		A_L	4.6			25
324	Acetophenetidin	2,6-Dihydroxybenzoic acid	30	H_2O (0.005N H_2SO_4)		A_L	4.5			25
325	Acetophenetidin	3,4-Dihydroxybenzoic acid	30	H_2O (0.005N H_2SO_4)		A_L	4.3			25
326	Acetophenetidin	3,5-Dihydroxybenzoic acid	30	H_2O (0.005N H_2SO_4)		A_L	4.9			25
327	Acetophenetidin	3,4,5-Trihydroxybenzoic acid	30 30	H_2O (0.005N H_2SO_4)		A_L	5.3			25
328	Acetophenetidin	4-Chlorobenzoate ion	30	H_2O (0.1M $NaHCO_3$)		A_L	2.1			31
329	Acetophenetidin	4-Bromobenzoate ion	30	H_2O (0.1M $NaHCO_3$)		A_L	2.7			31
330	Acetophenetidin	4-Iodobenzoate ion	30	H_2O (0.1M $NaHCO_3$)		A_L	3.4			31
331	Acetophenetidin	4-Methylbenzoate ion	30	H_2O (0.1M $NaHCO_3$)		A_L	1.3			31

332	Acetophenetidin	4-Nitrobenzoate ion	30	H_2O $\left(\dfrac{0.1M}{NaHCO_3}\right)$	A_L	3.3	31
333	Acetophenetidin	Terephthalate ion	30	H_2O $\left(\dfrac{0.1M}{NaHCO_3}\right)$	A_L	0.42	31
334	Acetophenetidin	3,4-Dimethyl-benzoate ion	30	H_2O $\left(\dfrac{0.1M}{NaHCO_3}\right)$	A_L	2.6	31
335	Acetophenetidin	3,4-Dichloro-benzoate ion	30	H_2O $\left(\dfrac{0.1M}{NaHCO_3}\right)$	A_L	4.3	31
336	Acetophenetidin	4-Hydroxy-3-chlorobenzoate ion	30	H_2O $\left(\dfrac{0.1M}{NaHCO_3}\right)$	A_L	2.7	31
337	Acetophenetidin	2-Chlorobenzoate ion	30	H_2O $\left(\dfrac{0.1M}{NaHCO_3}\right)$	A_L	0.85	31
338	Acetophenetidin	Biphthalate ion	30	H_2O $\left(\dfrac{0.1M}{NaHCO_3}\right)$	A_L	1.4	31
339	Acetophenetidin	Isophthalate ion	30	H_2O $\left(\dfrac{0.1M}{NaHCO_3}\right)$	A_L	0.27	31
340	Acetophenetidin	5-Iodosalicylate ion	30	H_2O $\left(\dfrac{0.1M}{NaHCO_3}\right)$	A_L	5.8	31
341	Acetophenetidin	3,5-Diiodosalicylate ion	30	H_2O $\left(\dfrac{0.1M}{NaHCO_3}\right)$	A_L	12	31

(continued)

TABLE IV (continued)

System number	S	L	t (°C)	Solvent	$10^2 S_0$ (Mole/l.)	Type of diagram	Stoichiometry (S:L)	$K_{1:1}$	$K_{1:2}$	$K_{2:1}$	Reference
342	Acetophenetidin	4-Aminosalicylate ion	30	$\mathrm{H_2O}$ $\left(\begin{array}{c}0.1M\\ \mathrm{NaHCO_3}\end{array}\right)$		A_L		1.9			31
343	Acetophenetidin	5,5′-Methylenedisalicylate ion	30	$\mathrm{H_2O}$ $\left(\begin{array}{c}0.1M\\ \mathrm{NaHCO_3}\end{array}\right)$		A_L		12			31
344	Acetophenetidin	2,3-Dihydroxyterephthalate ion	30	$\mathrm{H_2O}$ $\left(\begin{array}{c}0.1M\\ \mathrm{NaHCO_3}\end{array}\right)$		A_L		3.9			31
345	Acetophenetidin	4,6-Dihydroxy isophthalate ion	30	$\mathrm{H_2O}$ $\left(\begin{array}{c}0.1M\\ \mathrm{NaHCO_3}\end{array}\right)$		A_L		5.3			31
346	Acetophenetidin	2,5-Dihydroxyterephthalate ion	30	$\mathrm{H_2O}$ $\left(\begin{array}{c}0.1M\\ \mathrm{NaHCO_3}\end{array}\right)$		A_L		5.3			31
347	Acetophenetidin	3,5-Dihydroxy-2-naphthoate ion	30	$\mathrm{H_2O}$ $\left(\begin{array}{c}0.1M\\ \mathrm{NaHCO_3}\end{array}\right)$		A_L		11			31
348	Acetophenetidin	1,3-Dihydroxy-2-naphthoate ion	30	$\mathrm{H_2O}$ $\left(\begin{array}{c}0.1M\\ \mathrm{NaHCO_3}\end{array}\right)$		A_L		7.6			31
349	Acetophenetidin	3,6-Dihydroxy-2-naphthoate ion	30	$\mathrm{H_2O}$ $\left(\begin{array}{c}0.1M\\ \mathrm{NaHCO_3}\end{array}\right)$		A_L		7.5			31
350	Acetophenetidin	1-Hydroxy-4-bromo-2-naphthoate ion	30	$\mathrm{H_2O}$ $\left(\begin{array}{c}0.1M\\ \mathrm{NaHCO_3}\end{array}\right)$		A_L		12			31

351	Acetophenetidin	3-Hydroxy-4-iodo-2-naphthoate ion	30	H_2O / $0.1M$ $NaHCO_3$	A_L	17	31
352	Acetophenetidin	Naphthalene-2,3-dicarboxylate ion	30	H_2O / $0.1M$ $NaHCO_3$	A_L	1.1	31
353	Acetophenetidin	Pamoate ion	30	H_2O / $0.1M$ $NaHCO_3$	A_L	33	31
354	Theophylline	4-Chlorobenzoate ion	30	H_2O / $0.1M$ $NaHCO_3$	A_L	14	31
355	Theophylline	4-Bromobenzoate ion	30	H_2O / $0.1M$ $NaHCO_3$	A_L	16	31
356	Theophylline	4-Iodobenzoate ion	30	H_2O / $0.1M$ $NaHCO_3$	A_L	23	31
357	Theophylline	4-Methylbenzoate ion	30	H_2O / $0.1M$ $NaHCO_3$	A_L	7.7	31
358	Theophylline	4-Nitrobenzoate ion	30	H_2O / $0.1M$ $NaHCO_3$	A_L	9.0	31
359	Theophylline	Terephthalate ion	30	H_2O / $0.1M$ $NaHCO_3$	A_L	3.9	31
360	Theophylline	3,4-Dimethyl-benzoate ion	30	H_2O / $0.1M$ $NaCHO_3$	A_L	16	31

(continued)

TABLE IV (continued)

System number	S	L	t (°C)	Solvent	$10^2 S_0$ (Mole/l.)	Type of diagram	Stoichiometry (S:L)	$K_{1:1}$	$K_{1:2}$	$K_{2:1}$	Reference
361	Theophylline	3,4-Dichlorobenzoate ion	30	H$_2$O $\left(\begin{smallmatrix} 0.1M \\ NaHCO_3 \end{smallmatrix} \right)$		A_L		52			31
362	Theophylline	4-Hydroxy-3-chlorobenzoate ion	30	H$_2$O $\left(\begin{smallmatrix} 0.1M \\ NaHCO_3 \end{smallmatrix} \right)$		A_L		34			31
363	Theophylline	2-Chlorobenzoate ion	30	H$_2$O $\left(\begin{smallmatrix} 0.1M \\ NaHCO_3 \end{smallmatrix} \right)$		A_L		1.6			31
364	Theophylline	Biphthalate ion	30	H$_2$O $\left(\begin{smallmatrix} 0.1M \\ NaHCO_3 \end{smallmatrix} \right)$		A_L		12			31
365	Theophylline	Isophthalate ion	30	H$_2$O $\left(\begin{smallmatrix} 0.1M \\ NaCHO_3 \end{smallmatrix} \right)$		A_L		1.9			31
366	Theophylline	5-Iodosalicylate ion	30	H$_2$O $\left(\begin{smallmatrix} 0.1M \\ NaHCO_3 \end{smallmatrix} \right)$		A_L^f					31
367	Theophylline	3,5-Diiodosalicylate ion	30	H$_2$O $\left(\begin{smallmatrix} 0.1M \\ NaHCO_3 \end{smallmatrix} \right)$		A_L^f					31
368	Theophylline	4-Aminosalicylate ion	30	H$_2$O $\left(\begin{smallmatrix} 0.1M \\ NaHCO_3 \end{smallmatrix} \right)$		A_L		20			31
369	Theophylline	5,5'-Methylenedisalicylate ion	30	H$_2$O $\left(\begin{smallmatrix} 0.1M \\ NaHCO_3 \end{smallmatrix} \right)$		A_L^f					31

No.	Compound	Ligand		Solvent	Type		Ref.
370	Theophylline	2,3-Dihydroxyisophthalate ion	30	$\left(\begin{array}{c}H_2O\\0.1M\\NaHCO_3\end{array}\right)$	A_L	107	31
371	Theophylline	4,6-Dihydroxyisophthalate ion	30	$\left(\begin{array}{c}H_2O\\0.1M\\NaHCO_3\end{array}\right)$	A_L	110	31
372	Theophylline	2,5-Dihydroxyterephthalate ion	30	$\left(\begin{array}{c}H_2O\\0.1M\\NaHCO_3\end{array}\right)$	A_L	166	31
373	Theophylline	3,5-Dihydroxy-2-naphthoate ion	30	$\left(\begin{array}{c}H_2O\\0.1M\\NaHCO_3\end{array}\right)$	A_L^f		31
374	Theophylline	1-Hydroxy-4-bromo-2-naphthoate ion	30	$\left(\begin{array}{c}H_2O\\0.1M\\NaHCO_3\end{array}\right)$	A_L^f		31
375	Theophylline	3-Hydroxy-4-iodo-2-naphthoate ion	30	$\left(\begin{array}{c}H_2O\\0.1M\\NaHCO_3\end{array}\right)$	A_L^f		31
376	Theophylline	Naphthalene-2,3-dicarboxylate ion	30	$\left(\begin{array}{c}H_2O\\0.1M\\NaHCO_3\end{array}\right)$	A_L	37	31
377	Theophylline	Pamoate ion	30	$\left(\begin{array}{c}H_2O\\0.1M\\NaHCO_3\end{array}\right)$	A_L^f		31
378	Prednisolone	5-Iodosalicylate ion	30	$\left(\begin{array}{c}H_2O\\0.1M\\NaHCO_3\end{array}\right)$	A_L	27	31
379	Prednisolone	3,5-Diiodosalicylate ion	30	$\left(\begin{array}{c}H_2O\\0.1M\\NaHCO_3\end{array}\right)$	A_L	58	31

(continued)

TABLE IV (continued)

System number	S	L	t (°C)	Solvent	$10^3 S_0$ (Mole/L.)	Type of diagram	Stoichiometry (S:L)	$K_{1:1}$	$K_{1:2}$	$K_{2:1}$	Reference
380	Prednisolone	5,5'-Methylenedisalicylate ion	30	H₂O (0.1M NaHCO₃)		A_L		62			31
381	Prednisolone	2,3-Dihydroxyterephthalate ion	30	H₂O (0.1M NaHCO₃)		A_L		18			31
382	Prednisolone	4,6-Dihydroxyisophthalate ion	30	H₂O (0.1M NaHCO₃)		A_L		22			31
383	Prednisolone	1,3-Dihydroxy-2-naphthoate ion	30	H₂O (0.1M NaHCO₃)		A_L		100			31
384	Prednisolone	3,6-Dihydroxy-2-naphthoate ion	30	H₂O (0.1M NaHCO₃)		A_L		97			31
385	Prednisolone	1-Hydroxy-4-bromo-2-naphthoate ion	30	H₂O (0.1M NaHCO₃)		A_L		64			31
386	Prednisolone	Pamoate ion	30	H₂O (0.1M NaHCO₃)		A_L		160			31
387	Salicylic acid	Methanol	30	CCl₄	3.53	A_L		16.5			24
388	Salicylic acid	Ethanol	30	CCl₄		A_L		19.4			24
389	Salicylic acid	n-Butanol	30	CCl₄		A_L		19.2			24
390	Salicylic acid	n-Octanol	30	CCl₄		A_L		19.4			24

391	Salicylic acid	n-Dodecanol	30	CCl$_4$		A_L	18.8		24
392	Salicylic acid	iso-Butyl alcohol	30	CCl$_4$		A_L	17.5		24
393	Salicylic acid	sec-Butyl alcohol	30	CCl$_4$		A_L	20.3		24
394	Salicylic acid	tert-Butyl alcohol	30	CCl$_4$		A_L	23.7		24
395	Salicylic acid	Cyclohexanol	30	CCl$_4$		A_L	22.2		24
396	Salicylic acid	Benzyl alcohol	30	CCl$_4$		A_L	11.5		24
397	Salicylic acid	Phenol	30	CCl$_4$		A_L	0.26		24
398	Catechol	Methanol	30	CCl$_4$	1.97	A_P	16.3	14.1	24
399	Catechol	Ethanol	30	CCl$_4$		A_P	14.2	29.3	24
400	Catechol	n-Propanol	30	CCl$_4$		A_P	20.8	12.7	24
401	Catechol	n-Butanol	30	CCl$_4$		A_P	19.8	15.4	24
402	Catechol	n-Octanol	30	CCl$_4$		A_P	22.4	14.1	24
403	Catechol	iso-Butyl alcohol	30	CCl$_4$		A_P	16.8	10.3	24
404	Catechol	sec-Butyl alcohol	30	CCl$_4$		A_P	26.9	10.2	24
405	Catechol	tert-Butyl alcohol	30	CCl$_4$		A_P	40.2	5.0	24
406	Catechol	Cyclohexanol	30	CCl$_4$		A_P	22.8	22.0	24
407	Catechol	Benzyl alcohol	30	CCl$_4$		A_P	11.7	14.8	24
408	Catechol	1,4-Dioxane	30	CCl$_4$		A_P	20.8	2.9	24
409	Catechol	β-Propiolactone	30	CCl$_4$		A_P	9.8	15.3	24
410	Catechol	γ-Butyrolactone	30	CCl$_4$		A_P	51	12.6	24
411	p-Phenylphenol	Methanol	30	CCl$_4$	1.67	A_P	9.0	3.8	24
412	p-Phenylphenol	Ethanol	30	CCl$_4$		A_P	11.4	3.3	24
412	p-Phenylphenol	Ethanol	30	Cyclo-hexane	0.354	A_P	9.9	31	24
413	p-Phenylphenol	n-Propanol	30	CCl$_4$		A_P	9.6	5.4	24
413	p-Phenylphenol	n-Propanol	30	Cyclo-hexane		A_P	9.6	28	24
414	p-Phenylphenol	n-Butanol	30	CCl$_4$		A_P	9.6	5.6	24
414	p-Phenylphenol	n-Butanol	30	Cyclo-hexane		A_P	12.1	21	24

(continued)

TABLE IV (continued)

System number	S	L	t (°C)	Solvent	$10^2 S_0$ (Mole/l.)	Type of diagram	Stoichiometry (S:L)	$K_{1:1}$	$K_{1:2}$	$K_{2:1}$	Reference
414	p-Phenylphenol	n-Butanol	30	Heptane	0.223	A_P		13.0	17.2		24
415	p-Phenylphenol	n-Octanol	30	CCl₄		A_P		10.2	5.3		24
415	p-Phenylphenol	n-Octanol	30	Cyclo-hexane		A_P		13.0	21		24
415	p-Phenylphenol	n-Octanol	30	Heptane		A_P		15.3	19		24
416	p-Phenylphenol	iso-Butyl alcohol	30	CCl₄		A_P		10.2	2.2		24
416	p-Phenylphenol	iso-Butyl alcohol	30	Cyclo-hexane		A_P		11.0	14.6		24
417	p-Phenylphenol	sec-Butyl alcohol	30	CCl₄		A_P		12.0	3.0		24
417	p-Phenylphenol	sec-Butyl alcohol	30	Cyclo-hexane		A_P		12.1	19		24
418	p-Phenylphenol	tert-Butyl alcohol	30	CCl₄		A_L		13.2			24
418	p-Phenylphenol	tert-Butyl alcohol	30	Cyclo-hexane		A_P		20.3	7.8		24
419	p-Phenylphenol	Cyclohexanol	30	CCl₄		A_P		12.6	8.2		24
419	p-Phenylphenol	Cyclohexanol	30	Cyclo-hexane		A_P		16.1	18		24
420	p-Phenylphenol	Benzyl alcohol	30	CCl₄		A_P		7.2	3.3		24
420	p-Phenylphenol	Benzyl alcohol	30	Cyclo-hexane		A_P		9.6	29		24
421	p-Phenylphenol	n-Butyraldehyde	30	CCl₄		A_L		6.6			24
421	p-Phenylphenol	n-Butyraldehyde	30	Cyclo-hexane		A_L		8.8			24
422	p-Phenylphenol	n-Heptaldehyde	30	CCl₄		A_L		6.6			24
422	p-Phenylphenol	n-Heptaldehyde	30	Cyclo-hexane		A_P		5.7	7.0		24

423	p-Phenylphenol	β-Propiolactone	30	CCl₄		A_P	5.9	6.1	24
424	p-Phenylphenol	γ-Butyrolactone	30	CCl₄		A_P	19.2	4.7	24
425	p-Phenylphenol	N,N-Dimethyl-myristamide	30	CCl₄		A_P	240	9.4	24
425	p-Phenylphenol	N,N-Dimethyl-myristamide	30	Cyclo-hexane		A_P	396	21	24
426	p-Phenylphenol	Diethyl succinate	30	CCl₄		A_L	18.0		24
426	p-Phenylphenol	Diethyl succinate	30	Cyclo-hexane		A_P	24.8	2.4	24
427	p-Phenylphenol	4-Heptanone	30	CCl₄		A_L	12.0		24
427	p-Phenylphenol	4-Heptanone	30	Cyclo-hexane		A_P	8.5	13.3	24
428	p-Phenylphenol	Cyclohexanone	30	CCl₄		A_L	21.6		24
428	p-Phenylphenol	Cyclohexanone	30	Cyclo-hexane		A_P	25.4	4.4	24
429	Salicylic acid	Ethyl acetate	30	CCl₄	3.53	A_L	4.8		24
429	Salicylic acid	Ethyl acetate	30	Cyclo-hexane	0.503	A_L	17.7		24
429	Salicylic acid	Ethyl acetate	30	Heptane	0.412	A_L	15.9		24
430	Salicylic acid	n-Propyl propion-ate	30	CCl₄		A_L	3.8		24
430	Salicylic acid	n-Propyl propion-ate	30	Cyclo-hexane		A_L	15.1		24
430	Salicylic acid	n-Propyl propion-ate	30	Heptane		A_L	12.2		24
431	Salicylic acid	n-Butyl-n-butyrate	30	CCl₄		A_L	3.9		24
431	Salicylic acid	n-Butyl-n-butyrate	30	Cyclo-hexane		A_L	17.1		24
431	Salicylic acid	n-Butyl-n-butyrate	30	Heptane		A_L	15.7		24
432	Salicylic acid	iso-Butyl-iso-butyrate	30	CCl₄		A_L	3.3		24

(continued)

TABLE IV (*continued*)

System number	S	L	t (°C)	Solvent	$10^2 S_0$ (Mole/L)	Type of diagram	Stoichiometry (S:L)	$K_{1:1}$	$K_{1:2}$	$K_{2:1}$	Reference
433	Salicylic acid	Diethyl ether	30	CCl₄		A_L		7.4			24
434	Salicylic acid	n-Propyl ether	30	CCl₄		A_L		5.3			24
435	Salicylic acid	iso-Propyl ether	30	CCl₄		A_L		6.8			24
436	Salicylic acid	n-Butyl ether	30	CCl₄		A_L		5.2			24
437	Catechol	Ethyl acetate	30	CCl₄	1.97	A_L		24.5			24
438	Catechol	n-Propyl-propionate	30	CCl₄		A_L		20.6			24
439	Catechol	iso-Butyl iso-butyrate	30	CCl₄		A_L		21.7			24
440	Catechol	Diethyl ether	30	CCl₄		A_L		22.2			24
441	Catechol	n-Propyl ether	30	CCl₄		A_L		14.8			24
442	Catechol	iso-Propyl ether	30	CCl₄		A_L		24.0			24
443	Catechol	n-Butyl ether	30	CCl₄		A_L		14.8			24
444	p-Phenylphenol	Ethyl acetate	30	CCl₄	1.67	A_L		10.4			24
444	p-Phenylphenol	Ethyl acetate	30	Cyclohexane	0.354	A_L		16.4			24
445	p-Phenylphenol	n-Propyl propionate	30	CCl₄		A_L		9.9			24
445	p-Phenylphenol	n-Propyl propionate	30	Cyclohexane		A_L		16.4			24
446	p-Phenylphenol	iso-Butyl iso-butyrate	30	CCl₄		A_L		9.2			24
446	p-Phenylphenol	iso-Butyl iso-butyrate	30	Cyclohexane		A_L		16.4			24
447	p-Phenylphenol	Diethyl ether	30	CCl₄		A_P		6.4	10.6		24

No.			Temp			Type			Ref.
447	p-Phenylphenol	Diethyl ether	30	Cyclohexane		A_L	12.7		24
448	p-Phenylphenol	n-Propyl ether	30	CCl$_4$		A_L	6.4		24
448	p-Phenylphenol	n-Propyl ether	30	Cyclohexane		A_L	7.9		24
449	p-Phenylphenol	iso-Propyl ether	30	CCl$_4$		A_L	9.4		24
449	p-Phenylphenol	iso-Propyl ether	30	Cyclohexane		A_L	12.7		24
450	p-Phenylphenol	n-Butyl ether	30	CCl$_4$		A_L	6.3		24
450	p-Phenylphenol	n-Butyl ether	30	Cyclohexane		A_L	7.9		24
451	Hydroquinone	Ethyl acetate	30	CCl$_4$	0.040	A_P	10.3	4.4	24
452	Hydroquinone	n-Propyl propionate	30	CCl$_4$		A_P	10.3	3.4	24
453	Hydroquinone	n-Butyl n-butyrate	30	CCl$_4$		A_P	6.8	13.7	24
454	p-Nitrophenol	n-Butanol	30	CCl$_4$	0.717	A_P	46	20	24
454	p-Nitrophenol	n-Butanol	30	Cyclohexane	0.103	A_P	87	26	24
454	p-Nitrophenol	n-Butanol	30	Heptane	0.073	A_P	105	28	24
455	p-Nitrophenol	n-Octanol	30	CCl$_4$		A_P	57	15.3	24
455	p-Nitrophenol	n-Octanol	30	Cyclohexane		A_P	78	46	24
455	p-Nitrophenol	n-Octanol	30	Heptane		A_P	58	55	24
456	p-Nitrophenol	N,N-Dimethyl-myristamide	30	CCl$_4$		$A_L,^f$			24
456	p-Nitrophenol	N,N-Dimethyl-myristamide	30	Cyclohexane		A_P	4300	61	24
456	p-Nitrophenol	N,N-Dimethyl-myristamide	30	Heptane		A_P	4500	49	24
457	p-Nitrophenol	Ethyl acetate	30	CCl$_4$		A_L	59		24

(continued)

TABLE IV (continued)

System number	S	L	t (°C)	Solvent	$10^2 S_0$ (Mole/L.)	Type of diagram	Stoichiometry (S:L)	$K_{1:1}$	$K_{1:2}$	$K_{2:1}$	Reference
457	p-Nitrophenol	Ethyl acetate	30	Cyclohexane		A_L		126			24
457	p-Nitrophenol	Ethyl acetate	30	Heptane		A_L		138			24
458	p-Nitrophenol	n-Propyl propionate	30	CCl₄		A_L		59			24
458	p-Nitrophenol	n-Propyl propionate	30	Cyclohexane		A_L		126			24
458	p-Nitrophenol	n-Propyl propionate	30	Heptane		A_L		138			24
459	p-Nitrophenol	n-Butyl n-butyrate	30	CCl₄		A_L		59			24
459	p-Nitrophenol	n-Butyl n-butyrate	30	Cyclohexane		A_L		126			24
459	p-Nitrophenol	n-Butyl n-butyrate	30	Heptane		A_L		152			24
460	Salicylic acid	Dimethyl oxalate	30	CCl₄		A_L		2.2			24
461	Salicylic acid	Dimethyl malonate	30	CCl₄		A_L		4.3			24
462	Salicylic acid	Dimethyl succinate	30	CCl₄		A_L		5.4			24
463	Salicylic acid	Dimethyl glutarate	30	CCl₄		A_L		6.5			24
464	Salicylic acid	Dimethyl adipate	30	CCl₄		A_L		8.0			24
465	Salicylic acid	Dimethyl pimelate	30	CCl₄		A_L		8.1			24
466	Salicylic acid	Dimethyl suberate	30	CCl₄		A_L		7.8			24
467	Salicylic acid	Dimethyl azelate	30	CCl₄		A_L		7.9			24
468	Salicylic acid	Dimethyl sebacate	30	CCl₄		A_L		7.9			24
469	Salicylic acid	Dimethyl dodecanedioate	30	CCl₄		A_L		7.5			24
470	Salicylic acid	Diethyl oxalate	30	CCl₄		A_L		2.2			24

No.								
471	Salicylic acid	Diethyl malonate	30	CCl_4	A_L	5.5		24
472	Salicylic acid	Diethyl ethyl-pentylmalonate	30	CCl_4	A_L	2.4		24
473	Salicylic acid	Diethyl succinate	30	CCl_4	A_L	6.0		24
474	Salicylic acid	Diethyl glutarate	30	CCl_4	A_L	7.4		24
475	Salicylic acid	Diacetoxy ethane	30	CCl_4	A_L	7.0		24
476	Salicylic acid	Diacetoxy butane	30	CCl_4	A_L	9.6		24
477	Salicylic acid	Diacetoxy hexane	30	CCl_4	A_L	11.0		24
478	Salicylic acid	Dimethoxy ethane	30	CCl_4	A_L	13.5		24
479	Salicylic acid	Dimethoxy octane	30	CCl_4	A_L	18.0		24
480	Catechol	Dimethyl oxalate	30	CCl_4	A_P	7.1	10.0	24
481	Catechol	Dimethyl malonate	30	CCl_4	A_P	18.8	7.6	24
482	Catechol	Dimethyl succinate	30	CCl_4	A_P	29	6	24
483	Catechol	Dimethyl glutarate	30	CCl_4	A_P	28	16	24
484	Catechol	Dimethyl adipate	30	CCl_4	A_P	41	14	24
485	Catechol	Dimethyl pimelate	30	CCl_4	A_P	48	12	24
486	Catechol	Dimethyl suberate	30	CCl_4	A_P	53	13	24
487	Catechol	Dimethyl azelate	30	CCl_4	A_P	59	7.2	24
488	Catechol	Dimethyl sebacate	30	CCl_4	A_P	52	15	24
489	Catechol	Dimethyl dodecanedioate	30	CCl_4	A_P	52	6.1	24
490	Catechol	Diethyl oxalate	30	CCl_4	A_P	15.2	2.4	24
491	Catechol	Diethyl malonate	30	CCl_4	A_P	24	6.5	24
492	Catechol	Diethyl ethyl-pentylmalonate	30	CCl_4	A_P	33	11	24
493	Catechol	Diacetoxy ethane	30	CCl_4	A_P	27	10	24
494	Catechol	Diacetoxy butane	30	CCl_4	A_P	56	14	24
495	Catechol	Diacetoxy hexane	30	CCl_4	A_P	51	41	24
496	Catechol	Acetal	30	CCl_4	A_L	20.4		24

continued

TABLE IV (*continued*)

System number	S	L	t (°C)	Solvent	$10^2 S_0$ (Mole/L.)	Type of diagram	Stoichiometry (S:L)	$K_{1:1}$	$K_{1:2}$	$K_{2:1}$	Reference
497	Catechol	Dimethoxy ethane	30	CCl₄		A_L		67			24
498	Catechol	Dimethoxy octane	30	CCl₄		A_L		62			24
499	Hydroquinone	Dimethyl oxalate	30	CCl₄		A_P		1.5	30		24
500	Hydroquinone	Dimethyl malonate	30	CCl₄		A_P		8.5	9.4		24
501	Hydroquinone	Dimethyl succinate	30	CCl₄		A_P		10.5	12		24
502	Hydroquinone	Dimethyl adipate	30	CCl₄		A_P		16.3	8.5		24
503	Hydroquinone	Dimethyl pimelate	30	CCl₄		A_P		17.0	7.5		24
504	Hydroquinone	Dimethyl suberate	30	CCl₄		A_P		20.3	6.7		24
505	Hydroquinone	Dimethyl azelate	30	CCl₄		A_P		24	4.9		24
506	Hydroquinone	Dimethyl sebacate	30	CCl₄		A_P		24	6.6		24
507	Hydroquinone	Dimethyl dodecanedioate	30	CCl₄		A_P		3.0	1.5		24
508	Hydroquinone	Diethyl oxalate	30	CCl₄		A_P		6.3	7.2		24
509	Hydroquinone	Diethyl malonate	30	CCl₄		A_P		12.8	4.3		24
510	Hydroquinone	Diethyl succinate	30	CCl₄		A_P		15.8	4.6		24
511	Hydroquinone	Diacetoxy ethane	30	CCl₄		A_P		12.5	7.8		24
512	Salicylic acid	Triethyl phosphate	30	CCl₄		A_L		790			24
513	Catechol	Triethyl phosphate	30	CCl₄		A_L^f					24
514	p-Phenylphenol	Triethyl phosphate	30	CCl₄		A_L^f					24
515	Salicylic acid	Acetic acid	30	CCl₄		A_L		340			24
516	Salicylic acid	Monochloroacetic acid	30	CCl₄		A_L		161			24
517	Salicylic acid	n-Butyraldehyde	30	CCl₄		A_L		8.1			24
518	Salicylic acid	n-Heptaldehyde	30	CCl₄		A_L		7.6			24

No.	Solute	Ligand	Temp	Solvent	Type			Ref.
519	Salicylic acid	N,N-Dimethyl-myristamide	30	CCl₄	A_L	107		24
520	Salicylic acid	1,4-Dioxane	30	CCl₄	A_L	9.4		24
521	Salicylic acid	3-Pentanone	30	CCl₄	A_L	5.3		24
522	Salicylic acid	4-Heptanone	30	CCl₄	A_L	4.6		24
523	Salicylic acid	Cyclohexanone	30	CCl₄	A_L	9.7		24
524	Salicylic acid	β-Propiolactone	30	CCl₄	A_L	2.7		24
525	Salicylic acid	γ-Butyrolactone	30	CCl₄	A_L	8.5		24
526	Hydroquinone	Ethanol	30	CCl₄	A_P	7.3	28	24
527	Hydroquinone	n-Propanol	30	CCl₄	A_P	5.3	37	24
528	Hydroquinone	n-Butanol	30	CCl₄	A_P	5.5	34	24
529	Hydroquinone	iso-Butanol	30	CCl₄	A_P	1.8	96	24
530	Hydroquinone	sec-Butanol	30	CCl₄	A_P	7.5	28	24
531	Hydroquinone	tert-Butanol	30	CCl₄	A_P	7.8	29	24
532	Hydroquinone	n-Octanol	30	CCl₄	A_P	6.3	32	24
533	Hydroquinone	Cyclohexanol	30	CCl₄	A_P	10.0	21	24
534	Hydroquinone	Methanol	30	CCl₄	A_P	0[e]	$10^{3.6}$	24
535	Theophylline	3,4,5-Trimethoxy-benzoate ion	30	H₂O	A_L	23		25

[a] Stoichiometry of isolable solid complex.
[b] Based on initial linear portion of curve.
[c] A value for $K_{1:3}$ was also estimated.
[d] No detectable change in solubility (slope = 0).
[e] Approximate value.
[f] Slope equal to or greater than one.
[g] Estimated from phase diagram.
[h] With respect to functional units (not moles) of the polymer.
[i] Anomalous.
[j] Best fit linear constant.

approximately, the increase in apparent solubility of S in the presence of L. Often a more precise interpretation may be made by reference to the original literature. One important piece of information, not included in Table IV, which may sometimes be found in the original papers is the approximate solubility of complexes formed in Type B systems.

The order in which the systems are tabulated is chronological, though some exceptions have occurred.

B. FORCES OF MOLECULAR INTERACTION

The interactions responsible for complex formation as manifested by the solubility effects apparent in Table IV are not chemical (covalent) bonds. Much weaker forces are responsible, and a summary of the several types of molecular attractive forces will be useful in the later discussion. All of these forces may be broadly classified as long-range forces. They may be discussed under three categories: electrostatic, induction, and dispersion contributions to the intermolecular potential energy (35).

Electrostatic forces operate between polar molecules. The molecule may carry a charge, or it may possess a dipole or quadrupole. The force of intermolecular attraction varies with the intermolecular distance, and the form of the function depends upon the nature of the interacting molecules. Thus, the force between two charges (ions) is inversely proportional to the square of the intermolecular distance; for an ion–dipole interaction the force varies with the inverse fifth power of the distance; for an ion–quadrupole interaction, with the inverse seventh power; for a dipole–dipole interaction, also with the inverse seventh power of the distance; and for a dipole–quadrupole interaction, with the inverse ninth power. All of these forces, with the exception of those associated with ion–ion interactions, are temperature dependent.

Induction forces are responsible for attraction between a polar and a nonpolar molecule. The polar molecule (either an ion or a dipole) may induce a dipole in a nonpolar molecule, which leads to interaction between the two molecules. The force of the interaction varies with the inverse fifth power of the intermolecular distance for an ion-induced dipole interaction, and with the inverse seventh power of the distance for a dipole-induced dipole interaction. The potential energy of this interaction is directly dependent upon the polarizability of the nonpolar molecule.

Dispersion forces (London forces) account for attraction between two nonpolar molecules. At any given instant the electronic configuration of one molecule will create an instantaneous dipole moment for the molecule. This induces a dipole in the second molecule, which interacts with the instantaneous dipole in the first molecule, to produce an attractive force. This induced dipole-induced dipole interaction force varies with the inverse seventh power of the intermolecular distance, and it depends upon the polarizabilities of the two molecules.

In chemical terms, the interactions responsible for complex formation are: hydrogen bonds, charge-transfer forces, and other interactions which may be characterized as electrostatic in nature; inductive forces between, for example, an ion and an isolated double bond; and the so-called hydrophobic bonding between hydrocarbons, which arises partly from dispersion interactions and partly from the disruption of solvent structure. Hydrogen bonding is one of the most important of the interactions responsible for the solubility effects noted in these systems, and the solubility technique provides one way to study the efficacy of the H—bond in forming molecular species. A few important properties of this bond should be pointed out (49): (1) With very few exceptions, a hydrogen atom bonds only two other atoms together; that is, the hydrogen bond can be represented as A—H $\cdots$ B, in which the A—H bond is a covalent bond and the H $\cdots$ B bond a dipole-dipole interaction; (2) The strength of the H—bond increases with the electronegativity of the atoms A and B. It is found that only the very electronegative atoms are involved in such bonding; fluorine, oxygen, and nitrogen are most commonly encountered as the atoms bound by a hydrogen bond, with the strength of the bond decreasing in the order F, O, N; (3) The A—H $\cdots$ B bond is approximately linear.

Charge-transfer complexes may be present in many of the systems listed in Table IV. Electron transfer from one molecule to another results in an electrostatic attractive force. Such a profound alteration in the electronic configurations of the molecules may be expected to be manifested by changes in their electronic absorption spectra, and spectroscopic measurements have been the preferred means for studying charge-transfer complexation. It is less easily employed in the systems considered here, however, for the degree of complexation is rather small and relatively high concentrations are required to obtain measurable interaction, thus yielding inconveniently high absorbances. Nevertheless, some spectral evidence has been obtained indicating that charge-transfer phenomena are important contributors to the overall solubility effect in systems (usually aromatic) capable of entering into these interactions (31).

Hydrophobic bonding is a term applied to attractive forces between nonpolar (usually hydrocarbon) molecules or portions of molecules. Although these forces are small, they are relatively enhanced, when the molecules are in a very polar medium such as water, by the high solvent–solvent intermolecular attractive forces. Thus, the hydrophobic units are, in a sense, "squeezed out" of the polar phase by its high internal pressure, leading to an appreciable degree of interaction between the nonpolar molecules (27).

The observed overall effect (an alteration in solubility in the cases being considered here) may evidently be the resultant of more than one type of interaction. This is both an advantage and a disadvantage of the solubility technique for studying molecular interactions. But it may be expected that the solubility method employed in conjunction with more specific investigational tools (spectroscopy in particular) should provide a powerful approach for the separation of types of molecular interactions in these systems. The investigation of molecular interactions as a function of structure is a mechanistic approach, and an understanding of the mechanism of molecular complex formation is, of course, the goal of such studies. It is also possible to adopt a thermodynamic point of view in which the results, but not the specific natures, of the interactions are recognized. In general, complex formation is a resultant of competitions among several reactants. Thus, the interaction between the substrate S and the ligand L is modified by the attraction of each of these molecules for the solvent, which in turn is influenced by the solvent–solvent interaction. The situation is further complicated by possibilities of intramolecular interactions of S and L, and by intermolecular associations of (for example) L molecules to form dimers, trimers, etc. All of these possibilities combine to produce the observed effect. By studying related systems with many experimental factors held constant within a series, one attempts to minimize alterations in some of these interactions, thus exposing the effects of the changing contributors.

C. STRUCTURE–REACTIVITY RELATIONSHIPS

A complex may be considered to have formed when in the immediate vicinity of one molecular species, say S, more molecules of L are found than would be expected on a purely statistical basis. An approximate calculation may be made of this statistical association and its effect on the observed solubility. Consider the case in which the complexing agent L is sarcosine anhydride (51). In chemical terms an absence of complex formation means that the substrate S has no greater tendency to associate with sarcosine anhydride than with the solvent. If this were the case, an S–L association would result only from a chance nonspecific contact of S molecules with sarcosine anhydride. It was determined from density measurements that a 1% (w./v.) solution of sarcosine anhydride in water corresponds to a volume fraction of 0.008. There is, therefore, a rough probability of 8/1000 that a sarcosine anhydride molecule may be a neighbor of an S molecule. If we assume, very crudely, that each S molecule has about ten neighboring molecules, this probability is increased about ten times to 0.08. If such contacting S–L pairs are assumed to be a separate species, an increase in the original solubility of S of about 8% may be expected in a 1% sarcosine anhydride solution, even in the absence of specific complex formation. Any substantially greater increase in solubility may be ascribed to a specific interaction to form a discrete molecular species.

Although more than one complex species may be formed in a system, one may expect that some valid correlations between structure and extent of complexation may emerge from studies of the type described. Although many of the data of Table IV were not gathered with a systematic investigation of structure–reactivity relationships as the major intent, yet it is possible to make some limited correlations and to indicate directions in which further work may lead to fruitful results. The mechanisms of molecular complex formation would provide the most satisfactory classification basis for a discussion of these systems if our knowledge were more detailed and extensive. At our present stage of understanding, however, the discussion may profitably be based upon the structural features of the reactants (and the solvent). (This will inevitably involve some overlapping in the categories.) More detailed discussions will be found in many of the original papers.

(1) **Hydroxy Compounds.** Hydrogen bonding appears to be the most important type of interaction observed in systems containing

alcohols and phenols as one or both of the reactions (S or L). Such interaction is sensitive to the nature of the solvent, and is most readily observed in nonpolar, nonhydroxylic solvents which do not themselves present much competition for the reactant species. Since the H—bond is a dipole–dipole interaction it is reasonable to expect that variable polar (inductive) effects will be manifested by corresponding changes in extent of complex formation. Thus, the 1:1 stability constants describing the solubility increase of salicylic acid in carbon tetrachloride in the presence of various alcohols (Systems 387–396, Table IV) can be reasonably correlated with equation 23.

$$\log\left(K_{1:1}/K_{1:1}{}^{n\text{-BuOH}}\right) = -0.4(\sigma^* + 0.13) \qquad (23)$$

$K_{1:1}$ is the complex stability constant, $K_{1:1}{}^{n\text{-BuOH}}$ is the stability constant for the n-butanol–salicylic acid system, σ^* is the Taft polar substituent constant for the R group in the alcohol ROH, and -0.4 is the value of the reaction parameter ρ^* describing the susceptibility of the reaction to polar effects (59). The n-butanol reaction has been selected as the reference because it is a better behaved member of the series than the methanol reaction. Whatever the theoretical significance of equation (23) may be, it can be regarded as an empirical relationship permitting one to estimate reasonably accurate values for stability constants between salicylic acid and alcohols in this solvent.

It is of interest to inquire whether salicylic acid or the alcohol is the proton donor in this reaction. A comparison of the complexing tendencies of the salicylic acid–acetic acid and salicylic acid–chloroacetic acid systems (515 and 516, Table IV) indicates that, for these reactions at least, salicylic acid is the hydrogen donor. Since chloroacetic acid is a stronger acid than acetic acid, its smaller stability constant is most easily rationalized by supposing that salicylic acid provides the proton in the hydrogen bond. The sign of ρ^* in equation 23 supports this conclusion. A negative rho value indicates that the reaction is facilitated by electron release, which is consistent with the proposition that the alcohol in this system is the hydrogen acceptor. The carboxylic proton of salicylic acid must be the one forming the hydrogen bond to the alcohol, for the phenolic proton is tied up in an intramolecular H—bond.

A more complicated problem is presented by the catechol–ROH systems in carbon tetrachloride (24), which appear to lead to both

1:1 and 1:2 complexes. Three reasonable assumptions concerning the mechanism of this interaction provide a satisfactory correlation of the data: (a) the 1:1 interaction is assumed to be affected by polar properties but not by steric effects; (b) the 1:2 interaction is considered to have the same susceptibility to polar effects as does the 1:1 complexation; (c) the 1:2 interaction is assumed to be affected by the steric nature of the alcohol. The linear free-energy relationships (24) and (25) can be developed from the available data (398–406 in Table IV).

$$\log(K_{1:1}/K_{1:1}{}^{n\text{-BuOH}}) = -1.8(\sigma^* + 0.13) \tag{24}$$

$$\log(K_{1:2}/K_{1:2}{}^{n\text{-BuOH}}) = -1.8(\sigma^* + 0.13) + 0.7(E_s + 0.39) \tag{25}$$

where E_s is the steric constant of Taft (59) and 0.7 is the value of δ, a constant describing the sensitivity of the reaction to steric effects. Plots of these equations are shown in Figures 17 and 18. Table V

TABLE V

Comparison of Observed and Calculated Stability Constants for the Salicylic Acid–Aliphatic Alcohol Interaction (24)

R in ROH	$K_{1:1}$ Obsd.	Calcd.[a]	$K_{1:2}$ Obsd.	Calcd.[b]
Me	16.3	11.6	14.1	17.0
Et	14.2	17.5	29.3	22.8
n-Pr	20.8	19.3	12.7	15.4
n-Bu	19.8	19.8	15.4	15.4
i-Bu	16.8	16.1	10.3	5.3
s-Bu	26.9	27.6	10.2	6.6
tert-Bu	40.2	40.1	5.0	5.1
Cyclo-C_6H_{11}	22.8	21.5	22.0	8.9

[a] With equation 24.
[b] With equation 25.

gives the experimental values of the stability constants and the estimates calculated with equations 24 and 25. Except for methanol and ethanol, the $K_{1:1}$ values are reproduced satisfactorily. Greater deviation is encountered in the $K_{1:2}$ series, but even here the only serious deviation is with cyclohexanol. The data do not warrant a more refined treatment.

The much greater susceptibility of the catechol–ROH reaction to polar effects compared with the salicylic acid–ROH reaction ($\rho^* =$

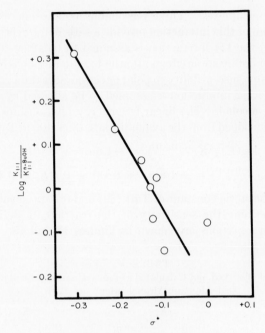

Fig. 17. Correlation of $K_{1:1}$ for the catechol–ROH system in CCl_4 at 30°C. with the Taft polar substituent constants.

−1.8 compared with −0.4) may reflect the greater acidity of salicylic acid. That is, the acidity of salicylic acid (its greater proton donor ability) has a swamping effect on the susceptibility of the reaction to the alcohol polar properties.

The hydroquinone–alcohol interaction (526–534, Table IV) presents a remarkable contrast to the corresponding reaction with catechol. It would have seemed reasonable to expect both the 1:1 and 1:2 interactions to be controlled largely by polar effects, with little steric hindrance. In fact, the data are not susceptible to such an analysis. Instead, a good linear correlation exists between $K_{1:1}$ and the reciprocal of $K_{1:2}$, the equation of the line being

$$(K_{1:1})(K_{1:2}) = 2 \times 10^2 \qquad (26)$$

These data are less accurate than the catechol results, largely because of the very low solubility of hydroquinone. Nevertheless, the correlation suggests a markedly different situation from that obtaining in

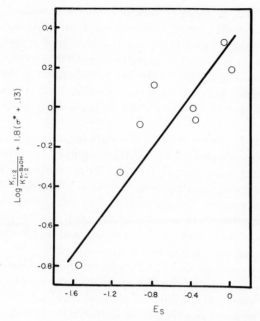

Fig. 18. Correlation of $K_{1:2}$ for the catechol–ROH system in CCl_4 at 30°C. with the Taft steric substituent constants.

the catechol systems. Equation 26 implies a mutually exclusive relationship between first and second-order complexation. Such a condition might hold if, for example, 1:1 and 1:2 complex formation proceeded by different mechanisms, and the structural features conducive to one of these mechanisms were inimical to the operation of the other. It is interesting, though perhaps not pertinent, that a linear relationship exists between $K_{1:1}$ and the number of hydrogens on one of the beta carbons of the alcohol. Even the peculiar behavior of methanol and of *iso*-butanol conform to this observation.

(2) **Carboxylic Acids and Salts.** The complexing behavior of salicylic acid with alcohols in carbon tetrachloride has already been discussed. Table IV lists many systems which include a carboxylic acid or its salt as a reactant; most of these are in aqueous solution. For some series (e.g., theophylline with carboxylate salts, Systems 238, 354–358 in Table IV) a rough correlation may be noted between the polar nature of the substituent and the extent of complex

formation. None of these correlations can be expressed quantitatively (as a Hammett-type plot, for example), probably because more than one mechanism is operative, even within such a limited series. These data for the salts are less amenable to such treatment than would be the corresponding results for the free acids because of the incursion of resonance effects between the polar substituent and the carboxylate ion; the *para*-nitro derivative should be particularly subject to this effect.

A remarkable feature of the extensive data for carboxylic compounds with several complicated molecules (theophylline, prednisolone, and acetophenetidin) is the general nature of the interaction. The apparent 1:1 stability constants between the carboxylates and these compounds are, in general, linearly related (31), suggesting that a very specific "lock-and-key" fit is not a requirement for complexing with these systems. Both hydrophobic bonding and dipole–dipole interactions involving the nucleus of the aromatic carboxylates appear to contribute to the complexation. Part of the theophylline interaction seems to be due to charge-transfer complexing, as shown by spectroscopic observations (31). With all of these substrates complexation is augmented by increasing the planar surface of the acid salt. Hydrogen bonding is probably not an important contributor to complexing in these aqueous solutions, as indicated by the same value of the stability constants for the theophylline–trihydroxybenzoate and theophylline–trimethoxybenzoate systems (Systems 247 and 535, Table IV).

A comparison of the results obtained for dihydroxybenzoates with those of the monohydroxybenzoates indicates that the additional hydroxy group intensifies the interaction (25). The total effect that additional groups may have on the binding ability may be of two types: (*1*) if the added group enhances the strength of the interaction by forming a complex with essentially the same structure as the monofunctional compound, then the *energies* of interaction should be approximately additive; (*2*) if the new group leads to formation of a new complex of different structure, the *extents* of interaction should be roughly additive. In the present case let A and B represent different monohydroxy benzoates, D the corresponding dihydroxy benzoate, and O the unsubstituted benzoate. Then the first case described can be represented by

$$\Delta G_D = \Delta G_A + \Delta G_B - \Delta G_O$$

where ΔG_O is subtracted from the sum because D possesses just a single aromatic ring and carboxylate group. This equation leads to equation 27.

$$K_D = K_A K_B / K_O \tag{27}$$

The second possibility above may be approximately expressed by equation 28.

$$K_D = K_A + K_B - K_O \tag{28}$$

In the present systems, equation 27 appears to be reasonably applicable as shown by the comparisons in Table VI (25).

TABLE VI
Comparison of Observed and Calculated Stability Constants for
Dihydroxybenzoates (25) [a,b]

Dihy-droxy-benzoate	Theo-phylline		Hydro-cortisone		Predni-solone		Aceto-phenetidin	
	Obsd.	Calcd.	Obsd.	Calcd.	Obsd.	Calcd.	Obsd.	Calcd.
2,4	56	45	13	10	12	10	2.4	2.3
2,5	43	42	10	12	12	12	2.4	2.1
2,6	300	75	13	18	11	14	3.3	3.6
3,4	14	25	6.8	6.9	6.4	8.4	1.5	1.3
3,5	20	23	5.6	8.3	6.5	10	2.0	1.2

[a] In water at 30°C.
[b] Calculated with equation 27.

(3) **Esters.** Esters interact with many types of compounds. The ester group itself must be involved intimately in this interaction as evidenced by the resistance to hydrolysis of certain ester–xanthine complexes (30,41). In nonpolar solvents the interaction between phenols or acids and esters is largely of the hydrogen-bond type, with the ester of course acting as the acceptor. Table IV includes some systematic studies of such systems. Salicylic acid, catechol, or hydroquinone is the acidic compound in these investigations of complexing behavior with diesters of straight-chain dicarboxylic acids (Systems 460–511, Table IV); some studies with diacyl glycols are also reported. It can be seen that the $K_{1:1}$ value within a series increases with the chain length until it reaches a limiting value. This increase may be accounted for by supposing that the acid or phenol

can interact with only a single ester group. Those diesters in which the ester functions are not widely separated will be no more conducive to interaction than is a monoester; but a diester with widely separated ester groups provides twice the probability of independent interaction with the acid or phenol. One would, therefore, predict that the maximum limiting value of $K_{1:1}$ for diesters should be twice the value for a similar monoester. For the dimethyl esters studied here a suitable comparison compound might be methyl n-octanoate. Ethyl acetate, which has been reported, may be taken as a substitute. Table VII shows the stability constants and the ratio of the limiting

TABLE VII

Statistical Effect on the Apparent Stability Constants of
Difunctional Esters (24)[a]

Item	Salicylic acid	Catechol	Hydroquinone
1 Ethyl acetate ($K_{1:1}$)	4.8	25	10.3
2 Dimethyl ester limiting value ($K_{1:1}$)	8.0	53	24
3 Ratio 2/1	1.8	2.1	2.3
4 Diacetyl glycol limiting value ($K_{1:1}$)	11.0	51	—
5 Ratio 4/1	2.3	2.0	—
6 Dimethyl ester limiting value ($K_{1:2}$)	—	12	6.8
7 Ratio 2/6	—	4.4	3.5

[a] In carbon tetrachloride at 30°C; data from Table IV, Systems 460–511.

value to the constant for ethyl acetate; it is reasonably close to two in each case. The same argument may be applied to the limiting value for the diacetylglycols; here again the observed ratio is about two (Table VII, item 5).

The values for $K_{1:2}$ in these systems are undoubtedly influenced by steric effects when the chain length is small. The limiting value of $K_{1:2}$, however, though affected by the sizes and shapes of the reactants, may be expected to be less susceptible to such effects than when the ester functions are closely spaced. Statistical arguments suggest that the limit of $K_{1:2}$ should be $K_{1:1}/4$: first, $K_{1:1}$ should be twice as large as $K_{1:2}$ because the formation of the 1:1 complex is statistically favored by the availability of twice as many ester groups; second, $K_{1:2}$ should be one-half as large as $K_{1:1}$ because the dissociation of the 1:2 complex is favored by a factor of two compared with the dissociation of the 1:1 complex. The total statistical effect leads to the relation $K_{1:1} = 4K_{1:2}$. The observed ratios (item 7 in Table VII) are close to this estimate.

(4) **Ethers.** Although ethers are usually considered to be relatively unreactive, these compounds appear to participate in complex formation with numerous substances. Polyethylene glycol, a polyether, has been shown to form insoluble complexes in iodine–iodide solutions (15). Ethers probably function as hydrogen-bond acceptors in nonpolar solvents. Table IV (Systems 433–436, 440–443, 447–450) lists stability constants for ether complexes with salicylic acid, catechol, and p-phenylphenol (24). Plots of log $K_{1:1}$ against the Taft polar substituent constants gave similar curves for all of these series. The shapes of these curves suggested steric hindrance to the reaction, with this effect being partially overcome by the inductive effect of electron release. The four parameter Taft equation was, therefore, fitted to the data, with the steric reaction parameter, δ, arbitrarily taken as unity in the absence of any independent estimate. It is remarkable that the fifteen constants describing the 1:1 interactions of four ethers with three substrates in two solvents are all correlated reasonably well by a single equation:

$$\log(K_{1:1}/K_{1:1}{}^{n\text{-Bu ether}}) = -4.6(\sigma^* + 0.13) + (E_s + 0.39) \quad (29)$$

The reaction is extremely sensitive to polar effects, as shown by the large value of rho (ρ^*).

(5) **Amines and Heterocyclic Compounds.** The amine group is highly polar and should enter into dipole–dipole interactions, especially the hydrogen-bond type of interaction. Systematic studies of amine structure–reactivity relationships have not yet been carried out. Table IV lists many systems involving amine reactants, however. The complexing abilities of the xanthines (caffeine, theophylline, and theobromine) and their derivatives are particularly noteworthy. Many biochemical entities are chemically similar to the xanthines and probably interact similarly. These relatively weak interactions could mediate and modify biochemical reactions in important ways.

(6) **Amides.** Amides are known to participate in hydrogen bonding (49), and complex formation by these compounds is to be expected. The amide function is a good electron donor, and the hydrogens of unsubstituted amides are available for bonding. These

features are responsible for the strong amide–amide interactions which lead to the relatively high melting points of amides. If the nitrogen is fully substituted this self-attraction due to hydrogen bonding is eliminated, and the interaction between the amide and other substances can be readily demonstrated. Thus, a series of tetramethylamides of dicarboxylic acids was shown to form complexes with some acidic compounds (39). The tetraethyl amides of the same acids were found to undergo complex formation to a greater extent than the tetramethyl compounds; this increase was partly ascribed to the squeezing out effect of water on the less-soluble diethylamides (40).

(7) **Effect of Reactant Solubility.** The solubility of a compound is closely related to the possibilities for molecular interaction possessed by the substance. The phenomenon of equilibrium solubility reflects a competition between solute–solute and solute–solvent interactions. The lower the solubility of a compound, the more favored is the solute–solute interaction.

Consider a solute in a solvent which is chemically quite dissimilar. Suppose a second substance is added which is chemically similar to the first solute and quite unlike the solvent. If the first solute is not very soluble in this solvent, then there is a high probability that the two solutes will interact (since they are chemically alike and the low solubility of the first solute indicates that interaction between such species is favored). That is, complex formation is probable in such a system. If the first solute is highly soluble, its interaction with the second substance is less likely, since the solute–solvent interaction is the more favored process. Therefore, as a rough generalization among similar systems of this type, extent of complex formation should be inversely related to reactant solubility. Within the very general terms of this discussion, this paragraph has considered two of eight possible situations. Table VIII lists all of these hypothetical cases with the conclusions, where it is possible to make a conclusion about the extent of complexation as a function of the solubility of the solute. Some of the cases are not particularly realistic in the sense that it is difficult to provide examples of them, and some would require specific structural information to make a prediction. It is nevertheless clear that the extent of intermolecular interaction may be an increasing or a decreasing function of reactant solubility. The eight cases of Table VIII represent the extremes of four possible complexation situations.

Table IV contains some good examples of the Type A class as

TABLE VIII

Predicted Effect of Reactant Solubility on Extent of Complexation

Case	Chemical nature compared with first solute		Solubility of first solute	Relative extent of complexation
	Second solute	Solvent		
A1	Similar	Dissimilar	Low	High
A2	Similar	Dissimilar	High	Low
B1	Dissimilar	Dissimilar	Low	Low
B2	Dissimilar	Dissimilar	High	High
C1	Similar	Similar	Low	?
C2	Similar	Similar	High	?
D1	Dissimilar	Similar	Low	?
D2	Dissimilar	Similar	High	Low

grouped in Table VIII. The extent of complexation of p-nitrophenol with alcohols and esters in three nonpolar solvents is listed under Systems 454–459. Most of these apparent stability constants can be correlated with equations 30–33.

$$K_{1:1} = 0.046/S_0 + 39 \ (L = n\text{-butanol}) \tag{30}$$

$$K_{1:2} = 0.006/S_0 + 19 \ (L = n\text{-butanol}) \tag{31}$$

$$K_{1:2} = 0.032/S_0 + 12 \ (L = n\text{-octanol}) \tag{32}$$

$$K_{1:1} = 0.065/S_0 + 55 \ (L = \text{ethyl acetate, } n\text{-propyl} \tag{33}$$
$$\text{propionate, } n\text{-butyl}$$
$$n\text{-butyrate}$$

The solvents were carbon tetrachloride, cyclohexane, and heptane. Because only three points were available, the quantitative validity of these correlations may not be secure, but they illustrate the phenomenon being considered. The significance of the intercept seems to be that it is a limiting value of the constant below which the constant cannot be expected to fall as long as the system belongs to the Case A class. The 1:1 stability constants for p-phenylphenol with alcohols also can be expressed as reciprocal functions of solubility:

$$K_{1:1} = 0.013/S_0 + 9.3 \ (L = n\text{-octanol}) \tag{34}$$

$$K_{1:1} = 0.009/S_0 + 9.3 \ (L = n\text{-butanol}) \tag{35}$$

Although *a priori* statements about Type C and D behavior (Table VIII) cannot be made (it probably depends intimately on the chemical nature of the three components), Table IV contains extensive data for these classes. Systems 141–185, the sarcosine anhydride systems, belong in one of these groups. Very roughly it may be said that the extent of complexation varies inversely with the solubility of S.

A Type B system would be interesting, but it is not easy to devise such a combination of reactants. The complexation behavior of *p*-hydroxybenzoic acid with some tetraalkylamides in aqueous solution may be such a system; the apparent stability constants increase with the solubility of the amide (40). Salicylic acid, however, shows no correlation with the solubility of the amide.

Notice that it is possible to study the effect of solubility on complexation by varying S, L, or the solvent within a series. The above discussion has given examples of each type of variation.

4. Analytical Applications

The preceding discussion of interacting component systems (mutual solubility effects) has been presented not because it forms the basis for many accepted analytical procedures, but simply as a background for some proposed methods of analysis. Very little actual assay development work has been done with these systems, but it seems likely that they could be usefully applied to solve specific and difficult analytical problems. Their systematic exploitation does not seem feasible at the present time because of our limited understanding of the nature of the interaction phenomena.

A. TYPE A SYSTEMS

The interaction of two solutes to form one or more soluble complexes leads to the Type A phase diagram (Fig. 6) and to the initial portion of the Type B_S diagram (Fig. 11). Such systems provide a suitable basis for the analysis of component L. Having available the phase diagram, or the apparent stability constant (that is, knowing the equation or graph of the phase solubility behavior), one can analyze for L in a solution, or in a solid sample, by equilibration with an excess of pure solid S. The total amount of dissolved S is then determined. From the phase diagram, or from the equation, the corresponding amount of L which must be present may be read.

The A_L diagram is evidently most convenient, for much of the necessary information can be stored as a single equilibrium constant. The A_P and A_L diagrams require polynomials for their complete description, though it probably would be simpler to employ the graphical methods for such diagrams.

A major advantage of such an assay is that it is a one-point assay: only a single determination need be made on the phase diagram. It is not necessary to have available an analytical method specific for L, the unknown, since it is S, the known component which may be selected nearly at will, which is analyzed for. The selection of S will depend, of course, upon the nature of L. A considerable degree of interaction is desired in order to achieve high sensitivity. The analysis of S is a consideration. The specificity of the method depends upon the nature of the inpurities in the sample of L, and the extent to which these impurities may interact with S. For this reason the absence of complexation is important analytical information.

Bennett (1) in 1948 reported the analysis of a binary nitration mixture by a solubility technique similar to the above method. Table IV lists many Type A systems which would be amenable to analytical uses.

Besides its application as a quantitative technique for purity determination, the proposed procedure might be valuable as a tool for characterization. Several types of information might be obtained from the phase diagram of an unknown compound. The type of diagram, solubility, stoichiometry, equilibrium constant, and equivalent weight could in suitable instances be criteria for identification. (This is a nondestructive method of analysis, which is advantageous in such work.) Some very closely related compounds might be differentiated in this way. The application of correlation equations like those discussed earlier might be useful in this connection.

An indirect analytical use of these solubility effects might be made in chromatography and solvent extraction; it should be possible to alter the solubility and reactivity of a substance by incorporating a suitable agent which complexes with it. This procedure (called masking) is commonly employed in inorganic analysis (6), but has not been widely used with organics.

B. TYPE B SYSTEMS

When an insoluble complex is formed, leading to Type B phase diagrams, different methods of analysis may be possible. One of these is based upon essentially quantitative precipitation of an insoluble complex of known stoichiometry by means of excess L. followed by determination of the excess L. This is, of course, a common analytical technique, especially for inorganic substances, but the data of Table IV suggest that it may be much more widely applicable. One possibility is the determination of polyethylene glycols by the formation of an insoluble iodine-PEG complex; the excess iodine is then titrated (15). The stoichiometry of the iodine-PEG complex is reproducible. The analysis of vitamin B_{12} (cyanocobalamin) precipitation with phosphomolybdate is another example suggested by Table IV. These analytical methods are one-point assays. They do not require an analytical procedure for the sample compound, and considerable specificity may sometimes be possible.

Another procedure utilizing Type B systems requires evaluation of the entire phase diagram. The sample to be analyzed, which plays the role of L, is coupled with a suitable S component. A known excess of S is taken, and the phase diagram is evaluated. The diagram is constructed by plotting S concentration in moles per liter vs. apparent L concentration in any convenient units, such as grams per liter. The calculation is based on the same arguments used in the evaluation of the stoichiometric ratio (Section IV-2-A). The amount of S entering into the complex in the plateau region is equal to the undissolved S at the start of the plateau. This is evaluated from the phase diagram. The amount of L consumed in the plateau region then can be directly related to the moles of S consumed in the plateau if the stoichiometry is known.

It would be interesting to carry out heterometric titrations (see Section II-2) on these totally organic Type B systems. Although equilibrium certainly would not be attained in these titrations, it is possible that valid analytical results may be observed.

References

1. Bennet, G. M., *Analyst*, **73**, 191 (1948).
2. Bobtelsky, M., *Heterometry*, Elsevier, New York, 1960.
3. Bobtelsky, M., and I. Bar-Gadda, *Anal. Chim. Acta*, **9**, 168 (1953).
4. Bolton, S., D. Guttman, and T. Higuchi, *J. Am. Pharm. Assoc.*, **46**, 38 (1957).
5. Case, L. O., in *Treatise on Analytical Chemistry*, Part I, Vol. 2, Interscience New York, 1961, Chap. 23.
6. Cheng, K. L., *Anal. Chem.*, **33**, 783 (1961).
7. Eriksen, S. P. and K. A. Connors, *J. Pharm. Sci.*, **53**, 465 (1964).

8. Findlay, A., A. N. Campbell, and N. O. Smith, *The Phase Rule and Its Applications*, 9th ed., Dover, New York, 1951.
9. Frediani, H. A., *Ann. Chim. (Rome)*, **42**, 692 (1952).
10. Gans, E. H. and T. Higuchi, *J. Am. Pharm. Assoc.*, **46**, 458 (1957).
11. Gans, E. and T. Higuchi, ibid., **46**, 587 (1957).
12. Gibbs, J. W., *The Scientific Papers of J. Willard Gibbs*, in two volumes, Dover, New York, 1961.
13. Gibbs, J. W., Ref. 12, Vol. I, p. 96.
14. Goodhart, F. W., and A. N. Martin, *J. Pharm. Sci.*, **51**, 50 (1962).
15. Guttman, D. E. and T. Higuchi, *J. Am. Pharm. Assoc.*, **44**, 668 (1955).
16. Guttman, D., and T. Higuchi, ibid., **45**, 659 (1956).
17. Lachman, L., D. Guttman, and T. Higuchi, Ref. 15, **46**, 37 (1957).
18. Haddad, A. F., B. J. Sciarrone, and T. Higuchi, Ref. 15, **48**, 588 (1959).
19. Hall, N. A., *J. Pharm. Sci.*, **52**, 189 (1963).
20. Havemeyer, R. N., and T. Higuchi, *J. Am. Pharm. Assoc.*, **49**, 356 (1960).
21. Herriott, R. M., *Chem. Rev.*, **30**, 413 (1942).
22. Higuchi, W. I. and J. Misra, *J. Pharm. Sci.*, **51**, 455 (1962).
23. Higuchi, T., and S. Bolton, *J. Am. Pharm. Assoc.*, **48**, 557 (1959).
24. Higuchi, T. and S. Chulkaratana, unpublished results.
25. Higuchi, T. and A. Drubulis, *J. Pharm. Sci.*, **50**, 905 (1961).
26. Higuchi, T., and J. L. Lach, *J. Am. Pharm. Assoc.*, **43**, 349 (1954).
27. Higuchi, T. and J. L. Lach, ibid., **43**, 465 (1954).
28. Higuchi, T. and J. L. Lach, ibid., **43**, 524 (1954).
29. Higuchi, T. and J. L. Lach, ibid., **43**, 527 (1954).
30. Higuchi, T. and L. Lachman, ibid., **44**, 521 (1955).
31. Higuchi, T. and F. D. Pisano, *J. Pharm. Sci.* **53**, 644 (1964).
32. Higuchi, T., B. J. Sciarrone, and A. F. Haddad, *J. Med. Pharm. Chem.*, **3**, 195 (1961).
33. Higuchi, T. and D. A. Zuck, *J. Am. Pharm. Assoc.*, **42**, 132 (1953).
34. Higuchi, T. and D. A. Zuck, ibid., **42**, 138 (1953).
35. Hirschfelder, J. O., C. F. Curtiss, and R. B. Bird, *Molecular Theory of Gases and Liquids*, Wiley, New York, 1954, pp. 22–31.
36. Holleman, A. F. and B. R. deBruyn, *Rec. Trav. Chim.*, **19**, 79 (1900).
37. Kennon, L. and K.-S. Chen, *J. Pharm. Sci.*, **51**, 1149 (1962).
38. Kolthoff, I. M., and V. A. Stenger, *Volumetric Analysis*, Vol. II, 2nd ed., Interscience, New York, 1947, pp. 49–52.
39. Kostenbauder, H. B. and T. Higuchi, *J. Am. Pharm. Assoc.*, **45**, 518 (1956).
40. Kostenbauder, H. B. and T. Higuchi, ibid., **45**, 810 (1956).
41. Lachman, L., L. J. Ravin, and T. Higuchi, Ref. 39, **45**, 290 (1956).
42. Lumb, E. C., and P. A. Winsor, *Analyst*, **77**, 1012 (1952).
43. Mader, W. J., in *Organic Analysis*, Vol. 2, Interscience, New York, 1954, p. 253.
44. Naegeli, C., *Kolloid.-Beih.*, **21**, 305 (1925).
45. Naegeli, C. and A. Tyabji, *Helv. Chim. Acta*, **15**, 403 (1932).
46. Naegeli, C. and A. Tyabji, ibid., **15**, 758 (1932).
47. Northrop, J. H. and M. Kunitz, *J. Gen. Physiol.*, **13**, 781 (1929).
48. O'Malley, W. J., L. Pennati, and A. N. Martin, *J. Am. Pharm. Assoc.*, **47**, 334 (1958).

49. Pauling, L., *The Nature of the Chemical Bond*, 3rd ed., Cornell University Press, Ithaca, New York, 1960, Chap. 12.
50. *Pharmacopia of the United States of America*, 16th rev., Mack Publishing Co., Easton, Pa., 1960, pp. 392–393.
51. Poole, J. W. and T. Higuchi, *J. Am. Pharm. Assoc.*, **48**, 592 (1959).
52. Reeve, W. and R. Adams, *Anal. Chem.*, **22**, 755 (1950).
53. Reinstein, J. A. and T. Higuchi, *J. Am. Pharm. Assoc.*, **47**, 749 (1958).
54. Rogers, D. W., *Talanta*, **9**, 733 (1962).
55. Rogers, D. W., and A. Özsoğomonyan, ibid., **10**, 633 (1963).
56. Rogers, D. W., A. Özsoğomonyan, and Sümer, A., Ref. 54, **11**, 507 (1964).
57. Rogers, D. W., and A. Özsoğomonyan, ibid., **11**, 652 (1964).
58. Stenger, V. A., W. B. Crummett, and W. R. Kramer, *Anal. Chem.*, **25**, 974 (1953).
59. Taft, R. W., Jr., in M. S. Newman, ed., *Steric Effects in Organic Chemistry*, Wiley, New York, 1956, Chap. 13.
60. Tarpley, W. and M. Yudis, *Anal. Chem.*, **25**, 121 (1953).
61. Thorp, D., *J. Soc. Chem. Ind. (London)*, **65**, 414 (1946).
62. Webb, T. J., *Anal. Chem.*, **20**, 100 (1948).
63. Willermain, M., *Anal. Chim. Acta*, **3**, 206 (1949).

Manuscript received by Publisher July 13, 1964.

The Electrochemistry of Cation-Sensitive Glass Electrodes*

GEORGE EISENMAN, *University of Utah College of Medicine, Salt Lake City, Utah*

* Most of the work reported in Section III has been carried out under the support of National Science Foundation Grant GB-40.

I. INTRODUCTION

When a thin membrane of glass is interposed between two solutions, an electric potential difference is observed across the glass, which depends on the ions present in the solutions in a simple and reproducible manner. Depending on the composition of the glass, the response may be to H^+ ion chiefly, or it may be to other cations such as Li^+, Na^+, K^+, Rb^+, Cs^+, NH_4^+, Ag^+, Tl^+, Mg^{2+}, Ca^{2+}, Sr^{2+}, Ba^{2+}, or even to organic cations. The selective response of certain glass compositions to H^+ has led to the development of pH-responsive glass electrodes (the essential components of which are oxides of silicon and of an alkali metal). Such pH-glass electrodes have become common laboratory tools following their discovery by Cremer in 1906 (18) and characterization by Haber and Klemensiewicz in 1909 (64), and a number of texts are concerned with their properties (4,26,117). On the other hand, modification of the glass composition has led to the development of electrodes selective for a variety of cations other than H^+ (32,36–38,40,54,92,131,132,134,164,165,167, 176); and it is with the sensitivity to such other cations that this monograph principally deals.

The present chapter extends considerably the empirical description (32) of electrode properties in solutions of the group Ia cations. It also includes a description of the electrode responses to Ag^+, Tl^+, NH_4^+, Mg^{2+}, Ca^{2+}, Sr^{2+}, Ba^{2+}, and certain organic cations. The factors involved in the origin of the potential of the glass electrode are analyzed from both a theoretical and experimental point of view and shown to depend on equilibrium ion exchange and also upon non-equilibrium diffusion processes. The origin of the equilibrium aspects of ion exchange specificity is analyzed theoretically. This analysis provides the basis for explicit rules which relate ionic specificity to glass composition. The chapter concludes with a brief review of the rapidly expanding literature on cation-sensitive glass electrodes and a comprehensive bibliography.

1. The Origin of the Glass Electrode Potential

At the outset, it is helpful to consider briefly the origin of the glass electrode potential, a subject examined in considerably greater detail in Section III. All usual glass electrodes are made from mixtures of oxides of elements of valence $3+$ or greater, with oxides of elements of valence $1+$ or $2+$. When melted and subsequently cooled, these form a three-dimensional glass in which the only significantly movable ionic species are the cations of charge $1+$ [and, considerably less easily, the cations of charge $2+$ (3)]. A membrane made of glass is, therefore, permeable almost solely to cations and functions as a cation exchanger, with the result that if such a membrane separates two solutions of a single salt (or acid) at two different concentrations, a Nernst potential is observed:

$$V = \frac{RT}{F} \ln \frac{a_i'}{a_i''} \tag{1}$$

where a_i' and a_i'' represent the activities of the cation I^+ (which can be H^+) in the two solutions, R is the gas constant, T is the absolute temperature, and F is the Faraday constant. If an electrode is constructed by filling a thin-walled glass bulb with a solution of a salt or acid which will remain unchanged in composition because of the low ion and water permeability of the glass, the electric potentials measured depend only on the activity of I^+ in the external solution $(')$ and can be written:

$$V = \text{const.} + \frac{RT}{F} \ln a_i' \tag{2}$$

this provides a means of measuring the activity of cation I^+ in different solutions, provided an appropriate reference electrode is used to complete the electric circuit.

If a number of cations, $I^+ = 1, \ldots, N$ are present simultaneously, it has been found experimentally that the electrode response depends on the summed contributions of each cation to the transference of electricity so that, for singly charged cationic species equation 2 becomes approximately

$$V = \text{const.} + \frac{RT}{F} \ln \sum_{i=1}^{N} K_{1i}^{\text{pot}} a_i \qquad (3)$$

or

$$V = \text{const.} + \frac{RT}{F} \ln \sum_{i=1}^{N} \frac{P_i}{P_1} a_i \qquad (4)$$

where K_{1i}^{pot} is an empirical constant describing the relative selectivity of the membrane with regard to cation i vs. cation 1 (cf. ref. 32, eq. 1) and P_i/P_1 is the ratio of permeabilities of the ith and 1st cations (58,71). In equations 3 and 4, K_{1i}^{pot}, the potential selectivity constant, is formally identical to the permeability ratio, and these terms will be used interchangeably throughout the text.

Following the pioneering work of Teorell (188–192) and of Meyer and Sievers (119–121), it has become clear that in a cation exchange membrane such as glass, the potential selectivity constant (or its equivalent permeability ratio) can be analyzed (16,17,34,39,67, 82,105) in terms of the ion-exchange equilibrium constant of the membrane–solution interfaces, K, and the mobility ratio of the ions within the membrane, u_i/u_j, as

$$K_{ij}^{\text{pot}} = \frac{P_j}{P_i} = K \frac{u_j}{u_i} \qquad (5)$$

where I^+ and J^+ represent any two singly charged cations. (For simplicity, only the case of "ideal" membrane behavior is outlined here. Section III presents the results more generally.) This means that both diffusion and boundary processes are involved in the origin of the glass-electrode potential, their magnitudes depending on the particular values of K and u_j/u_i.

K and u_j/u_i are susceptible to separate experimental measurement; and the method of doing so is outlined in Section III. From a theoretical point of view, K depends on equilibrium factors only. Its origin is analyzed in Section IV. On the other hand, the mobility ratio should depend on additional, non-equilibrium factors. Its origin will not be examined theoretically in this chapter. Thus, the considerations of the origin of specificity in equilibrium systems of Section IV relate only to that portion of the permeability due to the ion exchange equilibrium constant, K.

2. History

The historical development of the concepts which are central to those sections of the present chapter other than Sections III and IV are outlined below. The history relevant to Sections III and IV is given there.

A. H$^+$ RESPONSE OF GLASS

In 1906, Cremer (18) first observed that an electrode made from a glass bulb changed its potential when immersed in solutions having different hydrogen ion contents. Three years later, Haber and Klemensiewicz (64) demonstrated that this response was in fact that of a hydrogen electrode according to the Nernst equation

$$V = \text{const.} + \frac{RT}{F} \ln C_{H^+} \tag{6}$$

where C_{H^+} is the H$^+$ concentration or, more precisely, the H$^+$ activity.

B. "ALKALINE ERROR"

Thirteen years later, Hughes (74) observed that equation 6 was not precise in that in alkaline solutions a deviation or "alkaline error" was present. The H$^+$ response of a typical pH glass electrode (Corning 015 glass, a glass composed of Na$_2$O, CaO, and SiO$_2$) and its "alkaline errors" in 0.1N solutions of Na$^+$, Li$^+$, and K$^+$ are illustrated in the upper portion of Figure 1.

C. ENHANCEMENT OF "ALKALINE ERROR"

It was noted quite early that small amounts of Al$_2$O$_3$ or B$_2$O$_3$ increased the "alkaline error." Thus, Horovitz (72,73) and Schiller (159) showed that the introduction of B$_2$O$_3$ caused glass electrodes to become nearly as sensitive to Na$^+$ as to H$^+$; and Hughes (74) noted

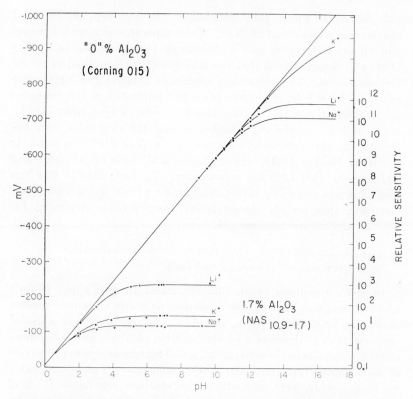

Fig. 1. Effect of Al_2O_3 on glass electrode potentials.   Glass electrode potentials, measured in reference to a saturated KCl–calomel half cell, are plotted as a function of pH in $0.1N$ solutions of the indicated cations.   The upper data points are observed in a sodium silicate glass containing no Al_2O_3, while the lower data are from a sodium silicate glass containing 1.7% Al_2O_3.   The curves are drawn according to equation 9.

that the less Al_2O_3 the glass contained, the better it was for measuring H^+.   These observations were extended by Lengyel and Blum (92), who conclusively demonstrated that the introduction of Al_2O_3 or B_2O_3 (or both) into the glass caused its potential to become strongly dependent upon Na^+, as well as H^+.   These authors were the first to show that one could thereby obtain a Nernst response to Na^+ ion, but concluded incorrectly that further variation of glass composition beyond introducing 10% Al_2O_3 or B_2O_3 had no important effects. They also reported that in such electrodes K^+ and Li^+ had a variable influence which they concluded was less reproducible and characteristic than that of Na^+. Contemporaneously with Lengyel and Blum, Evstrop'ev and Suikovskaya (40) according to Shul'ts (164) also demonstrated that the addition of B_2O_3 resulted in cation responsiveness. The pioneering studies of Lengyel and Blum were extended by others, who were primarily interested in the existence of Na^+ sensitivity *per se* (i.e., the Na^+ selectivity relative to H^+ only) and in establishing whether or not the electrodes were reversible in the thermodynamic sense. A review of this work is given by Shul'ts (164), whose studies and those of Nicolskii and Tolmacheva (131,132) are noteworthy. In fact, Shul'ts was the first to demonstrate, by direct comparison with a sodium amalgam electrode, that certain glasses behave as reversible electrodes for Na^+ at neutral and alkaline pH.

D. THE DEVELOPMENT OF GLASS COMPOSITIONS SPECIFICALLY
   SELECTIVE FOR SUCH IONS AS Na^+ OR K^+

In 1957, Eisenman et al. (36) confirmed Lengyel's and Blum's observations and showed, by a systematic study of simple glasses containing only Na_2O, Al_2O_3, and SiO_2, that not only was a useful response to Na^+ developed by the addition of Al_2O_3, but that reproducible responses to the other alkali metal cations were also properties of such glasses. In particular, they found that all glass electrodes containing Al_2O_3 were markedly cation sensitive relative to H^+ and that the "relative sensitivity" for the different cations to one another was a systematic and reproducible function of glass composition. This realization served to characterize various glass compositions, some of which had sufficiently high selectivities for Na^+ or K^+, to be of practical use for the measurement of Na^+ on the one hand or K^+ on the other. This work was considerably extended by Eisenman et al. (32,37,38) and by Nicolskii et al. (6,133–136,139, 167–172), and was the starting point for present studies on glass electrodes selective for particular cations.

To enable the reader to visualize the relationship between glasses selective for cations and the usual pH-responsive glass electrodes, the lower portion of Figure 1 illustrates the effect of adding a small amount of Al_2O_3 to a typical pH glass. The addition of Al_2O_3 enhances the "alkaline error" markedly, so that while the Al_2O_3-free glass is a good H^+ electrode over a wide pH range, the response of the

Al_2O_3-containing glass is independent of pH, except for the most acid values, and is entirely determined by the concentration of alkali metal cations over most of the pH range.

E. THE DEVELOPMENT OF EQUATIONS DESCRIBING GLASS ELECTRODE POTENTIALS

To describe the properties of glass electrodes further, it is necessary to have a quantitative description of the electrode potential and a definition of the "relative sensitivities" or "selectivities" to the various ions to which the electrodes respond.

Nicolskii (130) gave the first equation for the glass electrode which was capable of describing not only the H^+ response and the initial portions of the cation errors but also the Na^+ response of glass electrodes in the region when the electrodes were responding essentially to Na^+ alone. His equation was of the form:

$$V = E_0 + \frac{RT}{F} \ln (a_{H^+} + K^{pot}a_{Na^+}) \tag{7}$$

Nicolskii deduced equation 7 theoretically, assuming that an ion exchange of Na^+ and H^+ takes place between the solution and the

$$Na^+ + H^+ \text{ (glass)} \rightleftharpoons H^+ + Na^+ \text{ (glass)} \tag{8}$$

glass, that the same number of sites are available to each exchanging cation, that the activities of Na^+ and H^+ in the glass are proportional to their mole fractions in the glass, and that the observed glass-electrode potential represents the sum of the phase-boundary potentials (neglecting the possibility of a diffusion potential within the membrane).

Eisenman et al. (36) confirmed empirically the essential correctness of Nicolskii's equation, but found that in order to describe a wider range of data, the equation had to be elaborated to the form:

$$V = \text{const.} + \frac{nRT}{F} \ln [a_i^{1/n} + (K_{ij}^{pot}a_j)^{1/n}] \tag{9}$$

in which an additional parameter, n (which is a constant specific for a given glass and pair of cations), had to be introduced. These authors also found that equation 9 not only described the potential in H^+-cation mixtures, but that it described the potential for mixtures of two alkali metal cations at constant pH. In the case of Na^+–K^+ mixtures, n was usually 1. For these ions, equations 9 and 3 are identical, with K_{NaK}^{pot} corresponding to P_K/P_{Na}.

While equation 9 was presented initially only as a general empirical description of the electrode potential, a theoretical derivation was accomplished subsequently for the phase-boundary contribution by Eisenman (32, appendix) and also for the diffusion-potential contribution by Karreman and Eisenman (82) with the finding that the total potential is also described theoretically by an equation of the form of equation 9. This analysis, which will be discussed in Section III, was based upon the insight of Teorell (188–192) that the total potential of a membrane electrode (such as the glass electrode) should be regarded as the sum of contributions due to diffusion processes in the membrane interior and equilibrium processes at the membrane boundaries.

The "relative sensitivity" of glass to various cations is defined by K_{ij}^{pot} of equation 9. The effect of varying glass composition on relative sensitivities to various ions is illustrated in Figure 2, where the selectivities of the indicated cations relative to H^+ are plotted as a function of the aluminum content of sodium silicate glasses. At the extreme left, where the aluminum content is zero, a preference in excess of 10^{10} in favor of H^+ is seen; but, with the addition of aluminum, an abrupt enhancement of the sensitivity to the other cations occurs. Not only do the sensitivities relative to H^+ change with composition, but in addition the relative sensitivities among the alkali cations can be seen to vary systematically.

II. GENERAL CHARACTERISTICS OF THE ELECTRODE POTENTIALS OF CATION-SENSITIVE GLASSES

1. Experimental Methods

The experimental methods of making and studying cation-sensitive glass electrodes were similar to those used with H^+ selective glasses (4,26,117). However, some additional details are given here as representative of methods adequate for the preparation and general characterization of the glass electrodes for various cations. Important contributions to the techniques of electrode fabrication and use for high precision measurement are reviewed in Section V.

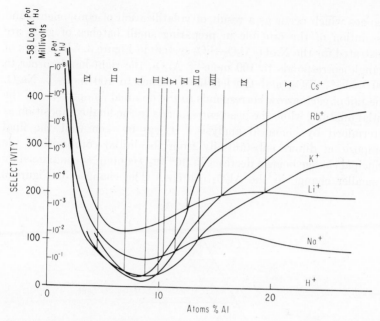

Fig. 2. Selectivity of glass electrodes to H, Li, Na, K, Rb, and Cs as a function of at-% Aluminum. (Redrawn, with permission of the *Biophysical Journal*, after Fig. 6 of Ref. 32.) The abscissa represents x, the at-% Al, in glasses of composition $(Na_2O)_{50-x} (Al_2O_3)_x (SiO_2)_{50}$. The ordinate gives the value of the sensitivity of the cation J^+ relative to H^+, K_{HJ}^{pot}.

A. MANUFACTURE OF GLASS

In the initial series of experiments, 50 g. quantities of the glasses were melted for 2–4 hr. at temperatures 1300–1600°C. in a dental furnace heated with two blast burners operating with oxygen-illuminating gas. Denver fire clay or alumina crucibles were used. SiO_2 was added as Pennsylvania glass sand, Na_2O as the carbonate, and Al_2O_3 as the hydroxide (both as analytical grade reagents). Because it was found that significant composition changes occurred with melting, all glasses were analyzed by wet analysis for major constituents, as well as spectrophotometrically for trace impurities. The compositions of the glasses of these experiments are designated as "F" for final (chemically analyzed) and "N" for nominal (i.e., calculated for the batch) composition.

To help readers who wish to prepare their own glasses, composition changes which occur as a result of volatilization of components and dissolution of the crucible in preparing small batches of glass are illustrated for the $Na_2O–Al_2O_3–SiO_2$ system in Figure 3. The apex of triangle corresponds to 100 mole-% Al_2O_3, the right-hand corner to 100 mole-% SiO_2, and the left-hand corner to 100 mole-% Na_2O. The tail of each arrow corresponds to the nominal composition of the initial mixture, while the head corresponds to the final composition as determined by chemical analysis. It can be seen that the final composition differs substantially from the initial composition, the principal change being a decrease in the Na_2O content accompanied by a smaller change in the Al_2O_3 content. The changes of Figure 3

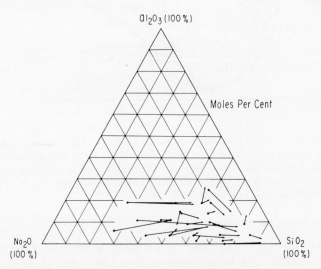

Fig. 3. Composition changes occurring when melting small batches of Na_2O–Al_2O_3–SiO_2 glasses. The coordinates are in mole-% (at 10% intervals) of the oxides in the glass. The tails of the arrows represent the "batch" compositions, while the arrowheads represent the "final" compositions.

become less important, the larger the batch of glass melted and the lower the melting temperature. This is illustrated by more recent experiments where glasses have been prepared in platinum crucibles, and usually in larger quantities, by the Research Division of the Corning Glass Works. Corning's analyses of representative glasses indicate that the final composition is close to that calculated for the batch composition in these glasses. The composition of these glasses are given in terms of batch compositions, symbolized by the letter "B".

Compositions are usually described as mole-% of the oxides. A glass whose final composition is 20 mole-% Na_2O, 10 mole-% Al_2O_3, and 70 mole-% SiO_2 has the formula $(Na_2O)_{20}(Al_2O_3)_{10}(SiO_2)_{70}$, and is designated for brevity as NAS 20-10F. Since it is sometimes appropriate to express the composition of glass in atomic per cent (at.-%) of the constituent cations, an example will clarify the relationship between mole-% and at.-% compositions. The above glass has Na, Al, and Si atoms present in the ratio 40:20:70 (multiplying the number of moles of sodium oxide by the number of atoms of sodium per mole, etc.). Since the sum of the atoms is 130, the at.-% values for Na, Al, and Si are given by multiplying the ratios 40/130, 20/130, and 70/130 by 100% to yield a composition (in at.-%) of: Na, 30.77; Al, 15.38; and Si, 53.85. Note that the ratio of Na_2O to Al_2O_3 (in mole-%) is the same as the ratio of Na to Al (in at.-%), since there are two sodium atoms as well as two aluminum atoms per molecule of Na_2O or Al_2O_3.

B. FABRICATION OF ELECTRODES

When surveying a large number of glasses of diverse compositions, it is usually least time consuming to make electrodes by drawing tubing for electrode stems from the cation-sensitive composition to be studied and then either blowing thin-walled bulbs on these stems or fusing thin membranes to them to make the "active" portions of lower electrical resistance. The use of the same glass for stem and active portion of the electrode circumvents the difficulty of matching electrode glass and stem glass softening points and thermal expansion properties. However, if one is dealing with only a few compositions, it is better to find and use a commercially available stem glass of high electrical resistance. For the Na-selective NAS 11-18B or NAS 11-18F glass, Corning type 7510 tubing (or the slightly harder type 7800) can be used. Similarly, the usual K-selective glasses (whether sodium aluminosilicates or potassium aluminosilicates) can be fused directly to Corning type 0120 glass.

Tubing is made by blowing a bubble of glass and elongating it. This is conveniently done by using a pea-sized glass fragment and a stainless steel blow-pipe ($1/4$ in. O.D.). After softening the glass, a bubble is started, which requires a great deal of blowing force. Once the bubble has been started, the glass is reheated and the bubble expanded to about $^3/_8$ in. diameter with much more gentle blowing. A second steel blowpipe, previously "tinned" with glass and kept hot, is then touched to the end of the bubble, and the bubble stretched into tubing without further blowing.

C. ELECTRODE INSULATION AND DESIGN

To establish electrical contact with the inside of the electrode, the usual procedure has been to fill the active portion of the electrode with a suitable electrolyte (such as $0.1N$ NaCl) and introduce into this a chlorided Ag wire. The principal concern in electrode construction is to provide adequate insulation to prevent the potential between the two sides of the relatively high-resistance glass from being "short circuited." The volume resistivities of "dry" glass are of the order of 10^9–10^{10} ohm cm., and typical electrode resistances vary from 10^6 to 10^{10} ohms, depending upon the electrode dimensions and the glass used.

In insulating, it is not only necessary to guard against the obvious possibility of leaks at the junction between the active portion of the electrode and the stem, but also against "surface conduction" along the inner and outer surface of the stem. In addition, it is often desirable to localize the responsive region to a particular place on the electrode (for example, to the tip of a microelectrode which must pass through a conducting medium). Most methods useful in making electrodes of pH-selective glass are directly applicable to cation-responsive glasses, whose specific resistivity is usually lower than the common pH-responsive glasses. An *external* insulation, such as paraffin or silicone, is adequate; however, a simpler, and generally more versatile, method is to insulate the electrode *internally* by layering a nonconducting fluid (e.g., benzene or silicone oil) over the electrolyte-filled region from which one wishes to localize the response. Contact with the electrolyte in this region is then easily made by a saline-filled glass micropipet or by the exposed tip of an otherwise insulated Ag wire.

D. GENERAL METHODS OF STUDY

Only routine methods are indicated here, particular methods being given where appropriate to the text. Almost all of the observations were made on bulb electrodes dipped into the solution being studied, although flow-through electrodes were also used on occasion, with identical general results but with a higher level of precision. It has been found convenient to make simultaneous observations on six glass electrodes all referred to a saturated KCl–calomel reference half cell of the asbestos fiber type. It is usually convenient to use a pH glass electrode as one of the electrodes and sometimes desirable to replace another of the glass electrodes by an Ag–AgCl electrode. Unless otherwise noted, all results were obtained on electrodes which were well aged in aqueous solutions at room temperature for a period ranging from several days (for highly Na-selective compositions) to several months (for highly K-selective compositions). Such aging is necessary because the electrode selectivity changes over the initial period of hydration of the glass. Changes with aging are minimal for Na-selective compositions which have nearly constant properties from the first hours of study to periods in excess of several years; but K-selective compositions show a tendency for the electrode selectivity to change with time. This change is most marked during the first few weeks and, fortunately, is always in the direction of an improving selectivity of K relative to Na. This is usually not of practical importance after the first week of aging, and after several months, the selectivities of most K-selective compositions are completely constant.

The experiments were designed so that changes in liquid junction potentials contributed no important errors to the results. This was accomplished either by using dilute solutions (of constant ionic strength where possible), or by eliminating the liquid junction and using a reversible Ag–AgCl half cell where appropriate. Except in those instances specifically noted in the text, all measurements were made at room temperature (22 ± 2°C.) in solutions of 0.1N concentration or less within the pH range from 2–11.5. All solutions were prepared directly from analytical grade reagents, which were analyzed spectrographically for impurities and, when necessary, purified by several recrystallizations. Distilled water, subsequently deionized with an ion-exchange demineralizer to a conductivity equivalent to less than 0.1 p.p.m. as NaCl, was used throughout. The principal impurities of importance (Na^+ and K^+) were always maintained below $10^{-5}M$ in the final solutions as checked by both glass-electrode and flame-photometer measurements.

Solution pH was usually varied by acidifying with sufficiently small amounts of concentrated HCl so as not to alter solution volume or by alkalinizing with the hydroxide or carbonate of the cation at the same concentration as the solution. Sometimes solutions were alkalinized by using anion exchange with the OH^- form of Dowex 1, or by addition of NH_4OH or an alkaline earth hydroxide. Buffer solutions were avoided to minimize extraneous cations in the final solution. A simultaneous measurement of pH by the glass electrode was made in conjunction with most studies.

2. Time Course, Stability, and Reproducibility of Response

All electrode equations given so far describe the electrode potential in a steady state, which usually is achieved rapidly upon altering solution concentrations. The time course, stability, and reproducibility of the responses of two typical glass electrodes to various cations are illustrated in Figure 4, where the potentials observed in various solutions (labeled directly at the bottom of the figure) at 25°C. are presented as a function of time for a Na-selective electrode (NAS 11-18F) and a K-selective electrode (NAS 27-4). The time course of the response should be apparent from the data points, but occasionally has been indicated by a thin line. Before being placed in a new solution, each electrode was rinsed with three changes of deionized distilled water. For details of the early time course, see reference 51.

Figure 4 (cf. also Figs. 17, 21, 22, 27, and 31) illustrates that the K^+-selective electrode responds in a "square" manner to step changes of solution composition in mixtures of H^+ and the alkali metal cations. On the other hand, the Na^+-selective electrode exhibits a transient in some solutions before the final value is reached. Despite this transient, stable values of potential are reached within several hundred seconds; and, had the solutions been changed without interposing distilled water rinses, the transients would have been substantially reduced. From these observations it can be seen that, for practical purposes, the potential of the present glass electrodes after 500 sec. may be taken as being in a "steady state" whose value is very close to that which would be observed regardless of how much longer one

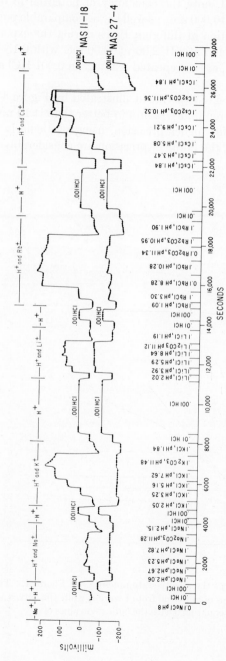

Fig. 4. Time course of the potential response of typical Na-selective (NAS 11-18F) and K-Selective (NAS 27-4B) glass electrodes. The abscissa represents time (in sec.), while the ordinate represents the potential (in mv.) of the glass electrodes referred to a saturated KCl–calomel half cell. Along the abscissa are labeled the compositions of the solutions. Data of which this figure is typical constitute the basis for most of the conclusions reached in the present paper. The temperature was 25.0 ± 0.2°C. throughout.

waited.   In this regard, note the constancy of potential in $0.001N$
HCl between 8400 and 10,000 sec., as well as the comparable potential
values for a given solution at different times during the experiment
(e.g., compare $0.1N$ NaCl at pH 2.06 at 1300 sec. with $0.1N$ NaCl
at pH 2.15 at 3800 sec., or the repeated readings in 0.001 HCl at 800,
4500, 8600 sec., etc.).

Generally, in the type of experiment illustrated by Figure 4 it has
been found possible to reproduce points to better than ±10 mv.   In
experiments designed for higher precision, using particularly stable
electrode compositions, the limits of precision are considerably better
(cf. Section II-4-C).

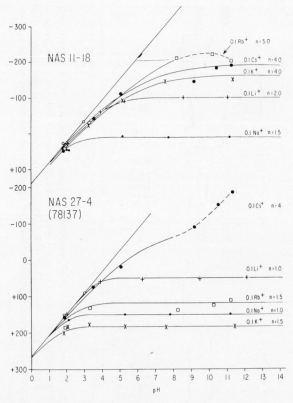

Fig. 5. Characteristics of the steady-state potentials of Figure 4.   The points
represent the "final" values of potential from Figure 4, while the curves are drawn
theoretically according to equation 9 with the indicated values of n.

The "steady-state" potential values of Figure 4 have been plotted as points in Figure 5. These "steady-state" values conform to equation 9, as can be seen by comparison with the curves drawn according to this equation.

3. Empirical Equations for the Electrode Potential

The following equations constitute empirical descriptions of the experimentally observed potentials in the "steady state" and provide a useful shorthand representation for a large amount of factual information. They enable us to describe a large amount of data in terms of a few parameters. Their theoretical meaning is discussed in Section III.

A. EQUATIONS FOR TWO-ION MIXTURES AND DEFINITION OF RELATIVE SENSITIVITY

The *relative sensitivity* of glass electrodes to various cations can be defined in terms of the parameter K^{pot} of equation 9, which describes the potential of a wide variety of glass electrodes in mixtures of any two univalent cations, as well as in certain three-ion mixtures in which one ion is held at constant activity (e.g., Na–K mixtures at constant pH). A graphical description of equation 9 will be found in Figure 1 of reference 32. A value for K^{pot} of 10 means that ion J^+ is 10 times as effective as ion I^+, on a mole-for-mole basis, in determining the electrode potential. K^{pot} and n are empirical constants characteristic of each glass for a given pair of cations I^+ and J^+. When necessary for clarity, K^{pot} and n will be written as K^{pot}_{ij} and n_{ij} to designate the pair of cations to which they refer.

Equation 9 is expressed in a form applicable to the potential of an electrode filled with a particular solution and containing any internal electrode, when an appropriate reference electrode (e.g. sat. KCl–calomel) is used. The constant in equation 9 is the sum of all constant sources of voltage in the measuring circuit.

Equation 9 can also be expressed in a form appropriate to the total potential across the glass when the solutions on both sides are varied. In this case, the potential across the glass can be written

$$V = \frac{nRT}{F} \ln \left[\frac{a_i'^{1/n} + (K^{pot}a_j')^{1/n}}{a_i''^{1/n} + (K^{pot}a_j'')^{1/n}} \right] \qquad (10)$$

where primed and double-primed quantities refer to each of the two solutions. When the potential measured between identical solutions is not zero, the value of this "asymmetry potential" must be added to the right-hand side of equation 10.

The general applicability of equation 9 is illustrated in Figure 6a for the potentials of a variety of glasses; and a more detailed test of the adequacy of this expression in a few glasses is given in Figure 6b. For all chemically stable glasses containing more than a few per cent Al_2O_3, equation 9 has been found to be valid for mixtures of H^+ with the ions Li^+, Na^+, K^+, Ag^+, and NH_4^+ at least over the pH range 2–11. Equation 9 also applies over a less extensive pH range in the case of Rb^+ and Cs^+, for which species deviations occur at high pH (cf. the dashed curves of Figures 6a and 6b).

Equation 9 is completely symmetrical between I^+ and J^+ and predicts a theoretical Nernst slope of $2.303\ RT/F$ as a function of $\log_{10} a_{i^+}$ or $\log_{10} a_{j^+}$ whenever the solution in which the electrode is dipped is effectively a "pure" solution of I^+ or J^+ (i.e., when a_{i^+} is much greater than $(K^{pot}a_{i^+})$, or when $(K^{pot}a_{j^+})$ is much greater than a_{i^+}). Of course, the value of K^{pot} and the limits of accuracy desired determine what constitutes a negligible amount of J^+ in the presence of I^+, and vice versa. Notice that in solutions of constant cation activity, such as those illustrated in Figures 5 and 6, equation 9 predicts that the observed potential should approach a constant value independent of pH in the limit toward the right as $a_{H^+} \to 0$. For a given glass, this limiting potential has a characteristic value (which is independent of the value of n) for comparable concentrations of each cation I^+, J^+, ..., N^+ and its measurement provides an easy way of assessing the value of K^{pot}. Thus, if one measures the potentials in pure $0.1N$ solutions of I^+, J^+, ..., N^+ in the limit as $H^+ \to 0$, and subtracts from these the potentials in pure $0.1N$ HCl, one finds

$$\lim_{H^+ \to 0} V_{0.1I^+} - V_{0.1H^+} = \frac{RT}{F} \ln K^{pot}_{HI}$$

$$\lim_{H^+ \to 0} V_{0.1J^+} - V_{0.1H^+} = \frac{RT}{F} \ln K^{pot}_{HJ}$$

$$\cdots$$

$$\lim_{H^+ \to 0} V_{0.1N^+} - V_{0.1H^+} = \frac{RT}{F} \ln K^{pot}_{HN} \qquad (11)$$

by taking these limits of equation 9.   One can interrelate the relative sensitivities of the cations I^+, J^+, ..., N^+ through

$$K_{IJ}^{pot} = \frac{K_{IK}^{pot}}{K_{JK}^{pot}}, \cdots, \frac{K_{IN}^{pot}}{K_{JN}^{pot}} \tag{12}$$

a result which is expected theoretically and found to be true experimentally.

The activity coefficient ratios of the ions have been taken as unity in equation 11, which is a reasonable approximation at constant $0.1N$ concentration.   More generally, one can assess K_{IJ}^{pot}, using expressions of the form

$$\frac{RT}{F} \ln K_{IJ}^{pot} = \underset{H^+ \to 0}{V_{J^+}} - \underset{H^+ \to 0}{V_{I^+}} + \frac{RT}{F} \ln \frac{C_i}{C_j} + \frac{RT}{F} \ln \frac{y_i}{y_j} \tag{13}$$

where the potentials V_{I^+} and V_{J^+} refer to the potentials observed in the limit as $H^+ \to 0$, in whatever concentrations of C_{I^+} and C_{J^+} are studied, and y_i/y_j is the ratio of the individual activity coefficients (which is identical to the ratio of the mean activity coefficients) at these concentrations.

Equations 9 and 10 indicate that the *activities* of the cations govern the electrode potential.   This has been tested and found to be true for Li^+, Na^+, K^+, Rb^+, Cs^+, Ag^+, Tl^+, and NH_4^+ over the range 10^{-5}–$10^{-1}M$ and for Li^+, Na^+, and K^+ to concentrations as high as exist in saturated solutions.   (See Sections II-4-C, 5-A–5-C, and 9, and also Figure 2 of reference 32.)   These findings may be taken as establishing that glass electrodes function as perfectly reversible electrodes for cations, neither water nor anions entering importantly into the electrode reactions.

B. EQUATIONS IN MIXTURES OF MORE THAN TWO CATIONS

In aqueous solution, H^+ is always present.   Consequently, studies of potential in "pure" solutions of the individual alkali metal cations are actually performed in mixtures of H^+ and the cation in question, and studies in mixtures in two alkali metal ions are actually carried out in a three-ion situation.   Often the concentration of H^+ is sufficiently low so that the mixture may be treated as if it were a solution containing only a single cation when one alkali ion is present, or as a two-cation mixture when two alkali ions are present.   In some cases,

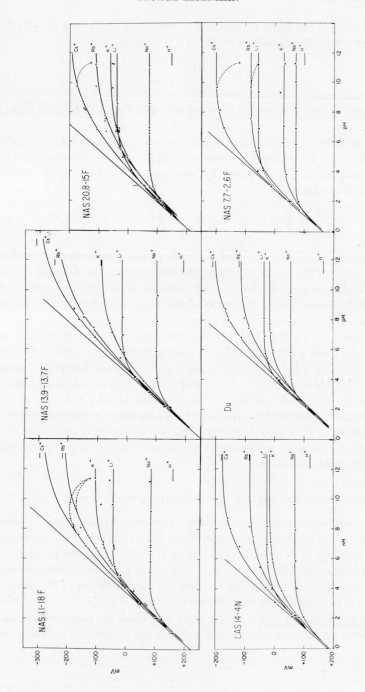

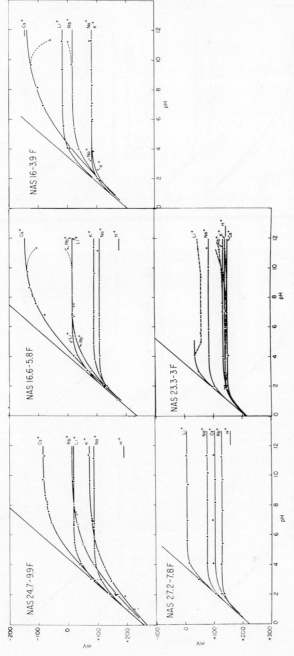

Fig. 6a. Comparison of equation 9 with experimental data. Potentials of cation sensitive glass electrodes having a wide variety of selectivities are plotted as points for comparison with curves drawn according to equation 9.

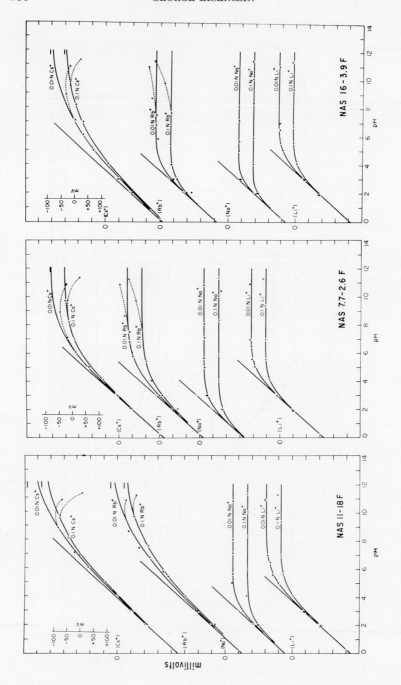

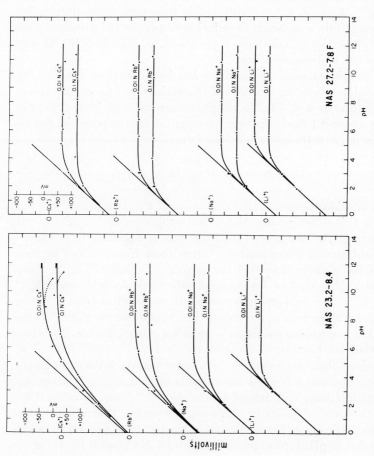

Fig. 6b. Comparison of equation 9 with experimental data. Potentials of representative glass electrodes, are plotted as solid dots (in 0.01N solutions) and open circles (in 0.1N solutions). Solid curves indicate the expected potential behavior according to equation 9, while dashed curves indicate deviations from the equation.

however, the effect of H^+ cannot be neglected. Because of this, it is necessary, for general characterization of electrode properties, to measure the response of a glass composition to the various cations as a function of pH. Figures 4–6 are typical of the measurements sufficient for assessing the parameters of equations 9 and 10. The values of K_{HNa}^{pot}, K_{HK}^{pot}, n_{HNa}, n_{HK} extractable from such a characterization then constitute a sufficient description to predict the principal electrode properties in mixtures of such ions as Na^+ and K^+ at any desired pH, as discussed below.

As mentioned above, equation 9 has been found to describe the potential, not only for mixtures of two cations, but for certain three-ion mixtures as well. In the simplest situation of an ideal system in which n equals 1 for all species, the equation for the potential can be written (cf. Ref. 16) in the multi-ion form:

$$V = \text{const.} + \frac{RT}{F} \ln \sum_{i=1}^{N} K_{1i}^{pot} a_i \qquad (3)$$

For non-ideal systems, we lack a general multi-ion equation; but even in this situation, equation 9 still applies for cation mixtures at constant pH, as can be seen from the data of Figures 7–9, which are representative of many studies. From these figures it can be seen that n has a value close to 1 for all pairs of alkali cations in those glasses having sites of low to moderate "anionic field strength,"* while in higher field-strength compositions n differs from 1, being largest for those ions whose atomic numbers differ the most. However, n never reaches values as large as are observed when H^+ is one of the ions (cf. Fig. 13).

In those three-ion mixtures to which equation 3 does not apply precisely because n is not 1 for all pairs of ionic species, certain important limits are still defined by equation 9. Thus, equation 9 defines the two-ion limits of three-ion mixtures. This is illustrated diagrammatically in Figure 10, where the left-hand portion shows as a function of pH, typical potentials in $0.1N$ Na^+ and $0.1N$ K^+ solutions, as would be observed for a Na^+-selective electrode having the typical parameters $n_{NaK} = 1$, $n_{HNa} = 1$, $n_{HK} = 4$, $-58 \log K_{NaK}^{pot} = 150$ mv. and $-58 \log K_{HNa}^{pot} = 50$ mv. The middle portion diagrams the potentials in Na^+–K^+ mixtures at pH 8, while the right-hand

---

* "Anionic field strength" is defined in Section IV.

portion diagrams the potentials for Na^+–K^+ mixtures at pH 4. Those points and limits which are common are indicated by similar letters with primes and double primes referring to the middle and right-hand diagrams, respectively. Thus, the point labeled A' in the middle figure, corresponding to the potential of a pure $0.1N$ Na^+ solution at pH 8, is the same as the limiting potential A at high pH in $0.1N$ Na^+ at the left. Similarly, B', which is the limiting potential observed in $0.1N$ K at pH 8 when Na^+ approaches zero, is the same as point B, which represents the potential of pure $0.1N$ K^+ at pH 8. C'' and D'', at the right, are related to C and D at the left in the same manner.

From Figure 10 it can be seen that the potential difference between Na^+ and K^+ solutions ($V_{01,K}$–$V_{0,1Na}$) at pH 8 defines a "practical" selectivity constant at pH 8, k_8^{pot} (for which a small letter k is used), while the potential difference between C and D defines the "practical" selectivity constant at pH 4 (k_4^{pot}). K^{pot} is defined through equations 11 or 13 by the voltage difference between A and E, while the "practical" selectivity constant k^{pot} at a particular pH can be defined in terms of the potentials observed in $0.1N$ K^+ and $0.1N$ Na^+ at the pH in question by

$$\frac{RT}{F} \ln k^{pot} = V_{0.1K}^+ - V_{0.1Na}^+ \tag{14}$$

where the potentials $V_{0.1K^+}$ and $V_{0.1\ Na^+}$ are defined, for any glass, through equation 9 by the values of K_{HK}^{pot}, n_{HK} and K_{HNa}^{pot}, n_{HNa}. Similar considerations apply for other univalent cations, in which case Na^+ and K^+ of the above example are represented more generally by I^+ and J^+.

C. EQUATIONS IN MIXTURES CONTAINING DIVALENT CATIONS

Equation 9 has been extended by Garrels et al. (54) to describe the behavior of cation-sensitive glass electrodes in mixtures of monovalent and divalent cations. In present terminology, their expressions are written as

$$V = \text{const.} + \frac{nRT}{2F} \ln \{[A^{2+}]^{1/n} + (K^{pot}[B^+]^2)^{1/n}\} \tag{15}$$

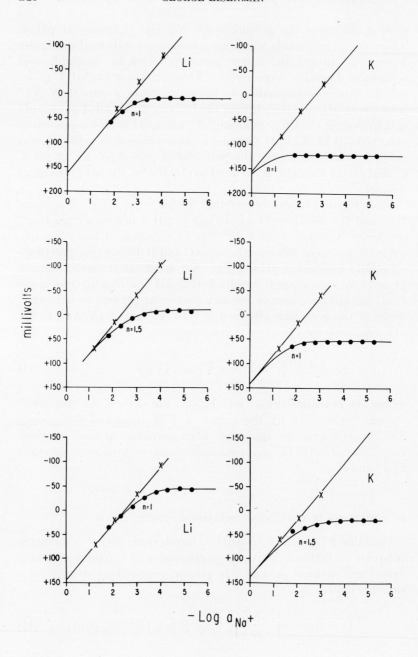

millivolts

$-$Log a_{Na^+}

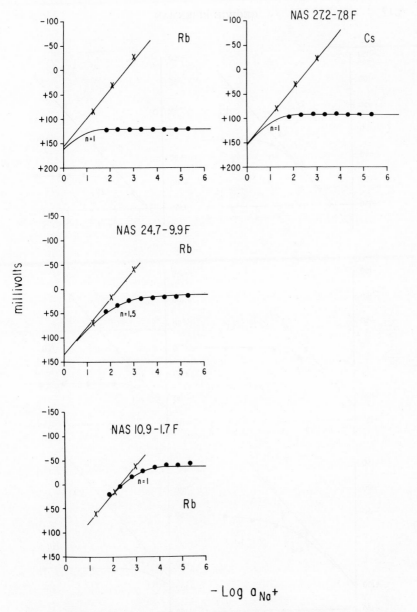

Fig. 7. Electrode potentials of representative glasses in alkali cation mixtures at pH 11.3 (low to moderate field-strength glasses). The observed potentials are plotted as a function of the negative logarithm of the Na^+ activity. The potentials in pure Na^+ solutions are denoted by x's, and the potentials observed in mixtures of Na^+ with 0.09N solutions of Li, K, Rb, or Cs are plotted as dots. The solid curves are drawn according to equation 9 with the indicated values of n. Note the Nernst slope observed in pure Na^+ solutions for each of these electrodes.

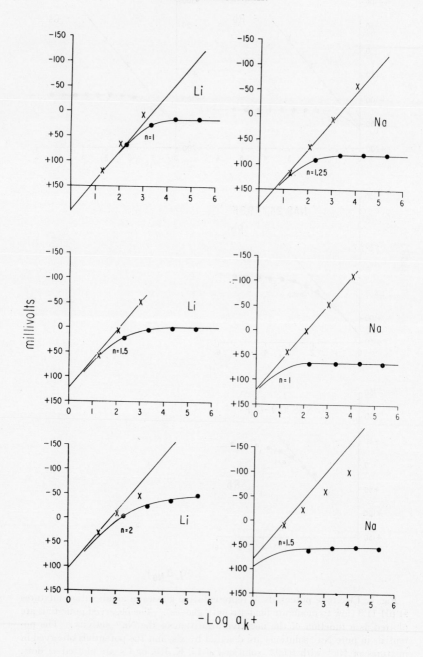

-Log $a_k{}^+$

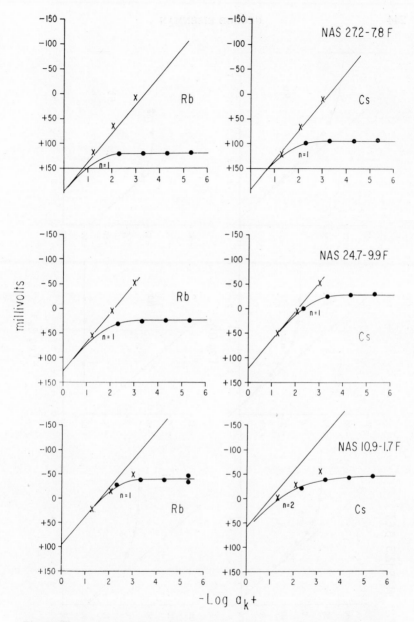

Fig. 8. Electrode potentials of representative glasses in alkali cation mixtures at pH 11.3 (low to moderate field-strength glasses). The observed potentials are plotted as a function of K^+ activity in the same manner as Figure 7, but here the x's represent the potentials observed in pure solutions of K^+, while the dots represent the potentials in mixtures of $0.09N$ solutions of indicated cations with K^+. Note the Nernst slope in pure K^+ solutions for the upper two electrodes.

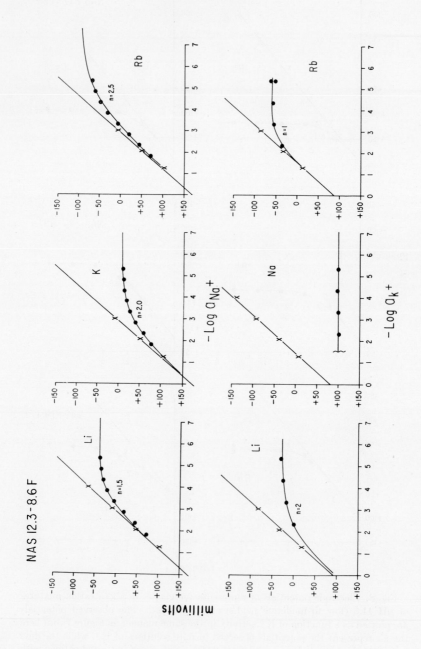

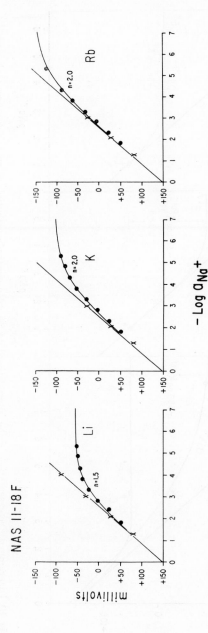

Fig. 9. Potentials in alkali cation mixtures at pH 11.3 (high field strength glasses). The observed potentials in mixtures of the indicated alkali metal cations are plotted for two glasses of higher field strength than those illustrated in Figures 7 and 8 (NAS 12.3-8.6F which has selectivity sequence IX, Na > K > Li > Rb > Cs, and NAS 11–18, which has selectivity sequence X, Na > Li > K > Rb > Cs).

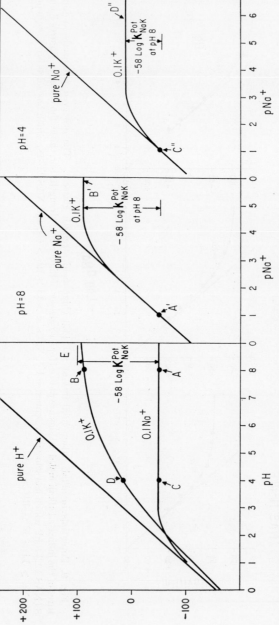

Fig. 10. Diagrammatic representation of the interrelationships between electrode potential in two-ion mixtures and three-ion mixtures. Described in the text.

for monovalent–divalent mixtures, and as

$$V = \text{const.} + \frac{nRT}{2F} \ln \left\{ [A^{2+}]^{1/n} + (K^{\text{pot}}[B^{2+}])^{1/n} \right\} \qquad (16)$$

for mixtures of two divalent cations. It should be noted that when data are plotted in the manner of Figure 36 for monovalent–divalent mixtures with constant divalent concentration and variable monovalent concentration, the curves describing the data are of the same form as given in Figure 1 of reference 32. However, the value of n in 1–2 mixtures is double the value inferred from the figure for 1–1 mixtures.

D. AN EXTENDED EQUATION FOR GLASSES WITH LOW Al_2O_3 CONTENT

Equations 9 and 10 and, in special cases, even equations 3 or 4 are valid for most, but not all, glass compositions. A complexity of potential behavior in glasses having low Al_2O_3 content has recently been recognized by Nicolskii et al. (133), which is exemplified in Figure 11. From the data of Figure 11 it can be seen that a step in the potential exists in glasses having low Al_2O_3 content. This step is less obvious in glasses having a lower alkali oxide content than those studied by Nicolskii et al. Thus, note its absence in the glass having only 1.7 mole-% Al_2O_3 illustrated in Figure 1.

The Russian workers interpret their results as indicating contributions to the electrode potential of the two different types of sites, SiO^- and $(AlOSi)^-$, which seems reasonable. They propose an equation of the form:

$$V = \text{const.} + \frac{RT}{2F} \ln ([H^+] + K[M^+]) - \frac{RT}{2F} \ln$$

$$\left[\frac{1}{[H^+] + \alpha_1[M^+]} + \frac{\beta}{[H^+] + \alpha_2[M^+]} \right] \qquad (17)$$

to describe their results, where K is an ion exchange constant, α_1 and α_2 are constants characterizing the various strengths of the H^+ bonds to the two types of sites, and β is a constant characterizing the ratio of the products of the concentration of sites of each type and their acidic dissociation constants. Equation 17 is of theoretical interest, but for most glasses in which the potential is dominated by one type of site, equation 9 is more useful.

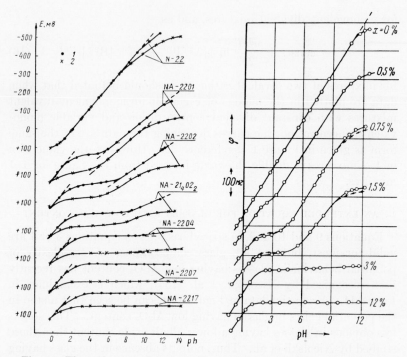

Fig. 11. Electrode potentials in sodium–silicate and lithium–silicate glasses containing small amounts of Al_2O_3. Redrawn after Nicolskii et al. (133) and Shul'ts and Belijustin (167). Electrode potentials in Na^+ and Li^+ solutions are plotted as a function of pH. *Left:* Na silicate glasses containing the indicated amounts of Al_2O_3 (N-22 refers to Na_2O 22 mole-% Al_2O_3 0 mole-%, NA-2201 refers to Na_2O 22 mole-%, Al_2O_3 1 mole-%, etc.). Dots represent data in $0.1N$ Na^+ solutions, while crosses represent data in $3.0N$ Na^+ solutions. *Right:* Li silicate glasses having a constant 27 mole-% Li_2O and the indicated mole-% of Al_2O_3. Open circles represent data in $3.0N$ Li^+ solutions.

4. The Electrode Properties of Al_2O_3-Containing Glasses for H^+ and the Alkali Metal Cations

Having characterized the general features of the electrode potential in ionic mixtures and defined the relative sensitivity, the responses of cation-sensitive glasses to particular cations will now be described. Since the most extensively studied glasses are those in which cation selectivity is produced by the addition of Al_2O_3, these will be examined first. Analogous systems, which are governed by the same rules that apply to the Al_2O_3-containing glasses, can be produced by other additions, as outlined in Section IV.

A. SPECIFICITY AS A FUNCTION OF COMPOSITION IN THE Na_2O–Al_2O_3–SiO_2 SYSTEM

Within the Na_2O–Al_2O_3–SiO_2 glass system, a wide range of particular selectivities for the various cations is found, ranging from electrodes highly specific for Na^+ to those usefully selective to K^+, as well as glasses having usefulness for Li^+, Rb^+, Cs^+, Ag^+, Tl^+, and NH_4^+ (and possibly even divalent cations in certain limited applications). In fact, all principal features of cation-sensitive glass electrodes are exemplified within the Na_2O–Al_2O_3–SiO_2 system. The steady-state electrode-potential properties for the Na_2O–Al_2O_3–SiO_2 glasses are summarized in Figures 12–14 (after Figs. 4, 5, and 7 of Ref. 32).

Figure 12 presents contours of isosensitivity (K^{pot}) at $22 \pm 2°C$. in the steady state of potential, where J^+ always represents K^+ and I^+ represents the indicated cations. Thus, those compositions lying along the isotherm labeled "10" on the Na^+–K^+ diagram are ten times as selective for K^+ as for Na^+. The coordinates are in atomic per cent (at 10% intervals) of Na, Al, and Si, each corner of the triangle representing pure Na_2O, Al_2O_3, or SiO_2. The dots on the charts represent those glass compositions for which K_{IJ}^{pot} values have been experimentally determined from data of the type presented in Figures 4–6. The solid contour lines of *iso-K_{IJ}^{pot}* values have been drawn by curvilinear interpolation between the K_{IJ}^{pot} values measured at the points. The upper left triangle labeled "H^+–K^+" illustrates the selectivity for H^+ relative to K^+. It will be noticed that toward the base of the triangle there is an abrupt change in the selectivity contours indicated by the labeling "$0.01 \rightarrow 10^{-10}$," corresponding to the abrupt development of a substantial cation sensitivity with the addition of small amounts of Al. [These densely packed contour lines correspond to the abrupt change in cation-H^+ selectivity at the left of (Fig. 2).] From this, it should be clear that H^+-specific glass-electrode compositions are characteristic of the bottom regions of the triangle, where SiO^- sites predominate; while over most of the composition field, useful cation sensitivities are present (presumably representing the properties of the $AlOSi^-$ sites). When Al content exceeds 3 at.-%, the contours become spaced more widely and resemble the

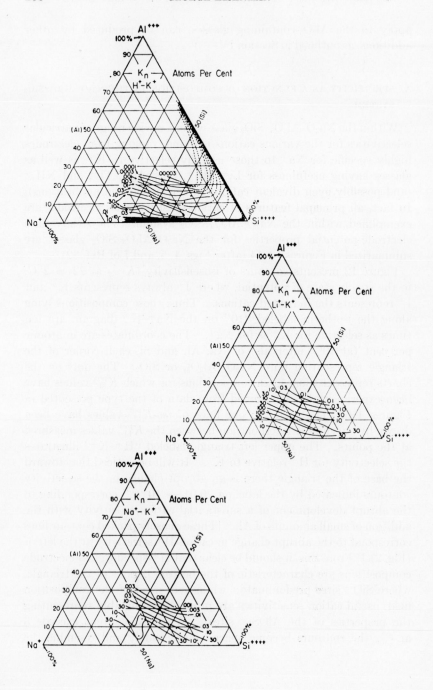

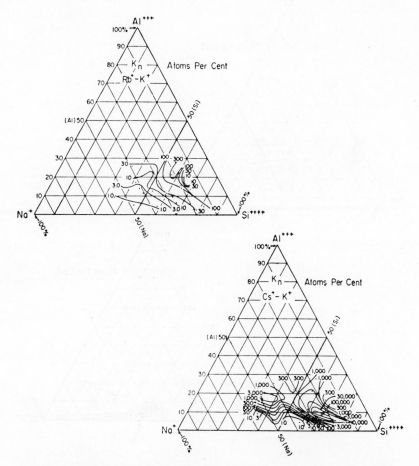

Fig. 12. K^{pot} as a function of glass-electrode composition in the Na_2O–Al_2O_3–SiO_2 system. (Reproduced with permission of the *Biophysical Journal* after Fig. 4 of Ref. 32.) The coordinates are in at.-% (at 10% intervals) of Na, Al, and Si. Data points represent all those glass compositions (chemically analyzed) for which K^{pot} values (labeled "Kn" on the figures) have been experimentally measured. The solid contour lines are curvilinear interpolations between the measurements of K^{pot} for the compositions at each of these points. The numerical values of each contour refer to the extent to which the second ion of the pair dominates the potential behavior. All data were obtained at $22 \pm 2°C$ in the steady state of potential.

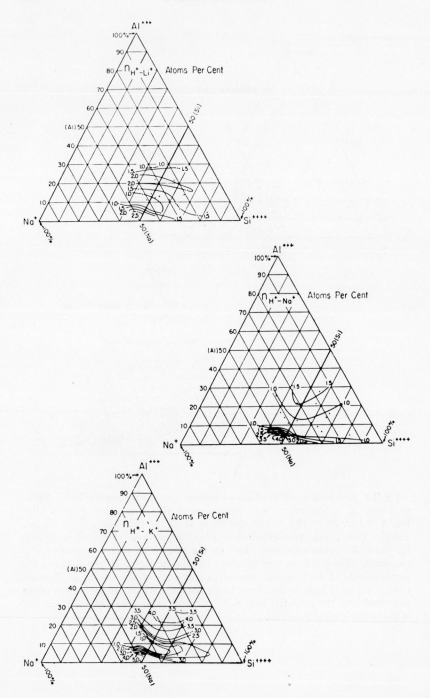

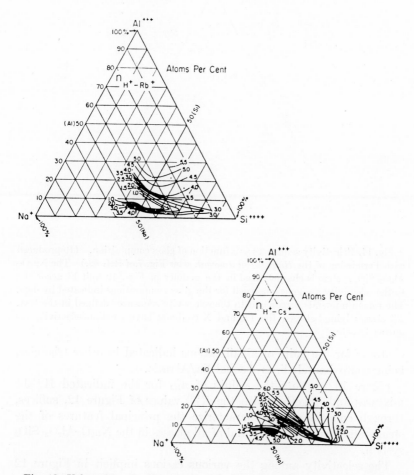

Fig. 13. Values of n for H^+-cation mixtures. (Reproduced with permission of the *Biophysical Journal*, after Fig. 5 of Ref. 32.) Data are plotted in the manner of Figure 12, but numerical designations indicate the values of n (accurate to ± 0.5 units) in the regions adjacent to a contour line rather than on it. Thus, all compositions lying between the contours labeled 1.0 and 1.5 have values of n equal to 1, etc.

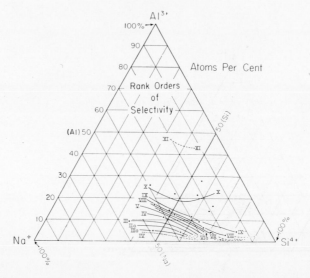

Fig. 14. Selectivity sequences as a function of glass composition. (Reproduced with Permission of the *Biophysical Journal*, after Fig. 7 of Ref. 32.) The Na_2O–Al_2O_3–SiO_2 system is characterized in the manner of Figs. 12 and 13 according to the selectivity sequence observed for the glass compositions indicated by dots. The roman numerals correspond to the selectivity sequences defined in the text. All glasses lying between the IX and X contours have a cation-selectivity sequence IX, etc.

contours for the pairs of alkali cations indicated in other triangles, being approximately lines of equal Na/Al ratio.

Figure 13 presents the values of n_{HJ} for the indicated H^+–J^+ mixtures and, together with the K_{IJ}^{pot} values of Figure 12, suffices, through equation 9, to characterize the principal features of the steady-state electrode potential of all glasses in the Na_2O–Al_2O_3–SiO_2 system.

The selectivity among the various cations implicit in Figure 12 can be most easily seen by plotting the K^{pot} values for each ion as a function of the atom percentage of Al in glasses having a constant 50 at.-% Si (i.e., the compositions lying on the lines labeled "50 (Si)" in Fig. 12.) Figure 2 presents such a plot. Upon examination of this figure, the isotherm for each cation can be seen to cross the isotherms of the others in a systematic manner, in consequence of which different sequences of responsiveness to the alkali cations occur in different composition regions. Such regions have been delimited by vertical lines and labeled by roman numerals to correspond to the particular sequences of decreasing cation selectivity defined below:

I	Cs	Rb	K	Na	Li					
II	Rb	Cs	K	Na	Li	or	IIa	Cs	K	Rb	Na	Li
III	Rb	K	Cs	Na	Li	or	IIIa	K	Cs	Rb	Na	Li
IV	K	Rb	Cs	Na	Li						
V	K	Rb	Na	Cs	Li						
VI	K	Na	Rb	Cs	Li						
VIIa	K	Na	Rb	Li	Cs						
VIII	Na	K	Rb	Li	Cs						
IX	Na	K	Li	Rb	Cs						
X	Na	Li	K	Rb	Cs						
XI	Li	Na	K	Rb	Cs						

Not only do the above sequences apply to the data of Figure 2, but they also prevail over the entire $Na_2O-Al_2O_3-SiO_2$ composition field, as can be seen in Figure 14. Figures 2 and 14 reveal the existence of a relatively simple pattern of alkali cation effects. This pattern has been found to apply not only to $Na_2O-Al_2O_3-SiO_2$ glasses, but to all glass systems characterized in this paper. Its physical basis is examined in Section IV.

Before leaving these figures, it should be noted that the selectivity rank-order isotherms of Figure 14 bear the same general relation to glass composition as those governing the magnitude of selectivity between one alkali metal cation and another. For example, compare the isotherms of Figure 14 with the Na^+-K^+ isotherms in Figure 12. In either case, the isotherms are approximately lines of constant Na/Al ratio, which indicates that one need specify only the Na/Al ratio to specify all important group Ia selectivity properties of an $Na_2O-Al_2O_3-SiO_2$ glass. Since a measurement of K_{NaK}^{pot} defines the Na/Al ratio through Figure 12, a measurement of K_{NaK}^{pot} suffices to characterize the selectivity for all other cations as well. This provides the basis for using Na–K selectivity as a general index of electrode properties as elaborated upon below. (More generally, Section IV will show that one need only specify the ratio of M^+ to Al^{3+} together with a scaling factor, x, characteristic of M^+ and Al^{3+} to specify the selectivity of other alkali aluminosilicates; and, still more generally, that it should be possible to take account of the effect of replacing Al^{3+} by another triply charged species in four-fold coordination by altering the scaling factor appropriately.)

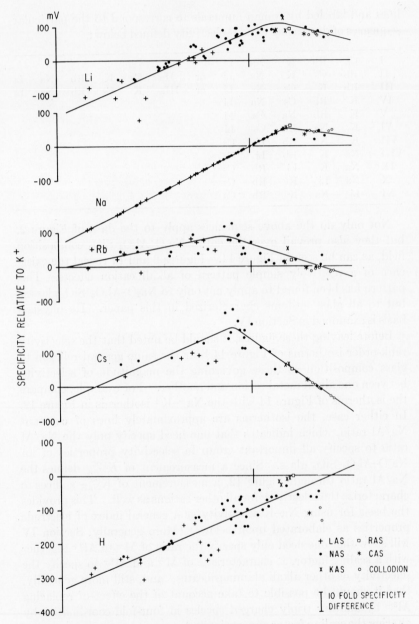

Fig. 15. Selectivities of aluminosilicate-glass electrodes and of air-dried collodion electrodes at neutral pH. Described in the text. The compositions of the electrodes are indicated by symbols beneath the figure.

B. Na–K SELECTIVITY AS A GENERAL INDEX OF ELECTRODE PROPERTIES
AND THE EXISTENCE OF A "GLASS SPECIFICITY PATTERN"

(1) **The Existence of a Pattern.** The above findings imply that all essential features of alkali cation selectivity for Na_2O–Al_2O_3–SiO_2 glasses should be representable as simple functions of the Na^+–K^+ selectivity alone. This proposition can be tested by plotting the selectivities for the other monovalent cations as a function of Na^+–K^+ selectivity, as is done in Figures 15 and 16, which present the selectivity values for H^+, Li^+, Na^+, Rb^+, and Cs^+ relative to K^+ in glasses of the systems M_2O–Al_2O_3–SiO_2 (where M_2O is Li_2O, Na_2O, K_2O, Rb_2O, or Cs_2O). The abscissa ranks the glasses in terms of their Na^+–K^+ specificity, while the values of 58 log K_{IK} at pH 7 are plotted on the ordinate. Each vertical row of points, therefore, represents the selectivities observed for the various I^+ species for a particular electrode. (The values of selectivity at pH 7 have been plotted since these are of more practical interest than the limiting K^{pot} values.) All glasses to the left of the maximum of the Na^+ isotherm have been

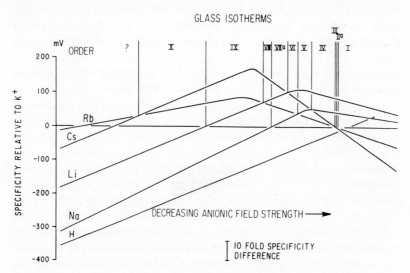

Fig. 16. The pattern of selectivity among the cations H^+, Li^+, Na^+, K^+, Rb^+, and Cs^+ in aluminosilicate-glass electrodes. This figure superposes the curves of Figure 15 in order to illustrate the pattern of selectivity for the alkali metal cations and H^+. (Figure 16 is reproduced to the identical scale as Figure 15 and is to the same scale as Figures 26, 30, 34, 35, 37–39.)

ranked directly by their Na^+–K^+ selectivity, while those to the right of this maximum have been located using the Cs^+–K^+ specificity along the extrapolated Cs^+–K^+ isotherm. (The factors necessitating this procedure are related to an increased water uptake by the glasses toward the right and are discussed briefly in Section IV. 4.)

In examining Figure 15, the reader should note that the scatter in the data does not represent experimental error in measuring the individual selectivity values (for the experimental error due to this is no more than twice the diameter of the plotted points); rather, the scatter represents the effects of pooling data from widely differing chemical compositions—a radical procedure, but one apparently justified by the pattern thereby revealed.

It should be apparent from Figures 15 and 16 that H^+, Li^+, Na^+, K^+, Rb^+, and Cs^+ differ only quantitatively in their effects, and that their selectivities can be reasonably described by the curves drawn to a visual fit in Figure 15 (and superposed in Fig. 16 to indicate the cation selectivity pattern). The pattern illustrated in Figures 15 and 16 constitutes a quantitative "glass specificity rule" for H^+, Li^+, Na^+, K^+, Rb^+, and Cs^+. Because this rule describes all glass electrode specificities (including those of many non-Al_2O_3-containing glasses) and also the specificities of dried collodion electrodes, it seems reasonable to postulate that the quantitative pattern may represent a very general aspect of the properties of a wide variety of polymerized oxyanion systems of low water content. This aspect appears to be relatively independent of the details of their chemical composition.

(2) **Practical Consequences.** From a practical point of view, the existence of the above "glass specificity rule" reduces substantially the number of experiments necessary for characterizing a glass. A measurement of Na^+–K^+ selectivity (with at most an additional measurement of Cs^+–K^+ selectivity) usually suffices to permit prediction of the sequence of the selectivities for H^+, Li^+, Rb^+, Cs^+, NH_4^+, Ag^+, Tl^+, and Mg^{2+}, Ca^{2+}, Sr^{2+}, and Ba^{2+}, as well as the order of magnitude of the individual selectivity constants. Other less tangible properties, such as electrode stability and speed of response, also correlate with Na^+–K^+ selectivity; so that all glasses having the same value of k_{NaK}^{pot} tend to have similar stabilities and response times. For these reasons, figures of the type of 15 and 16 will be used extensively throughout the remainder of this monograph to systematize electrode properties in terms of Na^+–K^+ specificity.

(3) Theoretical Considerations. The general features of the glass specificity rule are predictable from the theoretical considerations of Section IV. From these considerations, the value of the Na^+–K^+ specificity can be used as an empirical index of the "anionic field strength" (see Section IV-4) of cation exchange sites of the glass, so that glasses to the right of Figures 15 and 16 have low-field strength sites, while those to the left have sites of higher field strength. However, it must be emphasized that such an interpretation can be strictly true only for the equilibrium aspects of the electrode potentials, since diffusional processes will complicate the situation as discussed in Section III.

C. SOME PROPERTIES OF ELECTRODES FOR PARTICULAR GROUP Ia CATIONS

(1) Recommended Compositions Specific for Li^+, Na^+, K^+, Rb^+, and Cs^+. From the data of Figures 15 and 16 a number of general recommendations can now be made for electrodes specific for particular alkali metal cations. The detailed properties of such electrodes are outlined in parts (2)–(5) of this section.

For the measurement of Li^+, the compositions to the left of Figures 15 and 16 are best, provided one does not go so far to the left that H^+ dominates the potential. The best glass found so far for Li^+ in the presence of H^+ and Na^+ is LAS 15-25B, which corresponds to the lowermost data point for Li^+ in Figure 15.

For Na^+ measurement, all glasses to the left of order VIII are useful. However, for reasons discussed in part (2) below, the most highly Na^+ selective compositions may not be as desirable as the more modestly selective compositions of region X. The composition NAS 11-18F (36,37) or NAS 11-18B (as prepared by Corning) appears still to yield one of the best electrodes for Na^+, having a selectivity for Na^+ over K^+ of better than 1000:1 at high pH and a selectivity of better than 300:1 at neutral pH.

For measurement of K^+, where Na^+ is an important contaminant, any glass near the maximum in Na^+–K^+ isotherm (i.e., in order IV or V) is suitable. Such glasses have approximately 10:1 K^+ selectivity relative to Na^+. Of these glasses, the best is NAS 27-4B, although good alternatives are KAS 20-5B, RAS 20-5B, and a NAS 27-3 glass containing an additional 3 mole-% ZnO. A word about NH_4^+ effects is in order here. K^+ is preferred to NH_4^+ in all but the glasses of lowest field strength (cf. Fig. 34); and for the purposes of K^+ measurement, the minimum NH_4^+ response is exhibited by glasses of intermediate field strength, where NH_4^+ is one hundred times less effective than K^+. Thus, if one wishes to measure K^+ in an NH_4^+ rich solution, it may be preferable to use a composition from region VI or VIIa.

For the measurement of Rb^+, any K^+ selective glass can be used if K^+ is not an important contaminant. The best Rb^+ electrodes, where K^+ is an important contaminant, are those lying to the right of Figures 15 and 16. If Cs^+ is the sole contaminant of importance, then a glass from regions V–IX would be best.

For the measurement of Cs^+, glasses lying to the extreme right of Figures 15 and 16 are best.

(2) **Particular Properties of Na^+-Selective Electrodes.** The time course of response to Na^+ of a typical Na^+ selective glass (NAS 11-18F) is rapid and reproducible (see Refs. 36,37,47,51, and also Section V for other references), and the stability has already been illustrated in Figure 4. (Fig. 17, to be discussed below, gives additional details on the response time of this composition.) Since the selectivity for Na^+ of this glass composition is sufficiently high that one can usually neglect all other species, the details of the measurement of Na^+ in ionic mixtures will not be discussed here. Instead, the emphasis will be upon certain aspects of the electrode response which have not been heretofore discussed in detail.

(a) *Time Dependence of Na^+–K^+ Selectivity in Extremely Na^+ Specific Compositions.* With NAS 11-18 glass, the Na^+–K^+ selectivity is a relatively time-independent property of the electrode, but with compositions whose selectivity for Na^+ is higher than NAS 11-18, the Na^+–K^+ selectivity can be dependent on time. This complication is present because the response of a highly Na^+-selective electrode on being placed in a pure solution of Na^+ or K^+ generally consists of a rapid step followed by a slower creep as illustrated in Figure 17.

Figure 17 compares the time course of potential of the moderately Na^+ selective NAS 11-18F glass with those of two extremely Na^+ selective Li_2O–Al_2O_3–SiO_2 glasses. The potential observed on changing from $0.1N$ Na_2CO_3 to $0.1N$ K_2CO_3 solutions is plotted as a function of time. (The ordinate corresponds to $-58 \log k_{NaK}^{pot}$ at pH 11.3, which is almost identical to $-58 \log K_{NaK}^{pot}$.) Let us first examine the

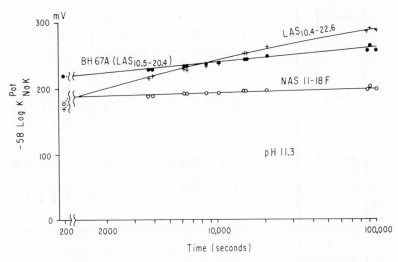

Fig. 17. Dependence of Na–K selectivity upon time in highly Na$^+$-selective glasses. Described in the text.

data for NAS 11-18F glass (open circles).   200 sec. after Na$^+$ was replaced by K$^+$ the potential had changed by 179 mv., a value which subsequently increased slightly over 28 hr. (corresponding to an increase in the apparent Na$^+$–K$^+$ selectivity from a value of 1200 at 200 sec. to a value of 2800 at 100,000 sec.).   In this glass, the "creep" after 200 sec. is negligible relative to the initial "step," for practical purposes.   On the other hand, with more highly Na$^+$-selective electrodes, the "creep" is more pronounced.   Thus, the LAS 10.4-22.6F glass shows an initial "step" of 169 mv. by 200 sec., which increases by 121 mv. over 100,000 sec., corresponding to an increase in the Na$^+$–K$^+$ selectivity from 820 to 100,000.   A similar, although less pronounced, "creep" is also seen with the Na$^+$ electrode of LAS 10.5-20.4 composition (Electronic Instruments Ltd. BH67 glass).

Similar phenomena are seen in the reverse experiment on changing from K$^+$ to Na$^+$ solutions, but all the above changes are negligible for Na$^+$-selective electrodes when Na$^+$ is the predominant cation in the solution.

(b) *Precise Measurement of Na$^+$ Activity.*   The use of an Na$^+$ electrode to measure the activity coefficient of Na$^+$ over a wide concentration range taxes the electrode's stability and reproducibility.

TABLE I

Mean-Activity Coefficients of NaCl Solutions Measured by NAS 11-18 Glass Electrode at 0, 25, and 50°C.

Temperature	Molality of solution	Experiment number	Time (seconds)	Experimental sequence	Observed potential (mv.)	$\gamma \pm$ Measured	$\gamma \pm$ Tabulated
1	2	3	4	5	6	7	8
25.0 ± 0.1°C.	0.1265	1	300–800	1	−100.0	0.766	0.763
	0.1265	2	4,800–5,000	7	−99.1	0.766	0.763
	0.1265	3	14,500–14,900	17	−99.3	0.763	0.763
	1.0	1	900–1,140	2	−1.69	0.657	0.657
	1.0	2	5,200–5,400	8	−0.79	0.657	0.657
	1.0	3	13,800–14,200	16	−0.68	0.657	0.657
	2.0	1	1,400–1,600	3	+34.81	0.669	0.668
	2.0	2	5,600–5,800	9	+35.49	0.666	0.668
	2.0	3	13,000–13,400	15	+36.05	0.671	0.668
	4.0	1	1,800–2,000	4	+78.75	0.786	0.783
	4.0	2	6,100–6,300	10	+79.43	0.783	0.783
	4.0	3	12,300–12,700	14	+80.33	0.795	0.783
	5.0	1	2,100–2,300	5	+95.99	0.879	0.874
	5.0	2	6,500–6,700	11	+96.67	0.876	0.874
	5.0	3	9,700–11,800	13	+97.45	0.887	0.874
	6.145	1	2,500–2,700	6	+115.1	1.039	—
	6.145	2	6,800–7,000	12	+114.8	1.014	—
	6.145	3	9,200–9,400	12	+114.8	1.012	—
50.0 ± 0.2°C.	0.1265	1	500–700	1	−100.7	0.745	0.7545
	0.1265	2	2,500–2,700	6	−100.3	0.753	0.7545
	0.1265	3	6,100–6,600	15	−99.93	0.751	0.7545
	1.0	1	900–1,100	2	+7.32	0.656	0.656

0.0 ± 0.2°C.

1.0	2	3,000–3,200	7	+7.21	0.656	0.656
1.0	3	5,600–5,800	14	+7.66	0.656	0.656
2.0	1	1,300–1,500	3	+47.54	0.675	0.678
2.0	2	3,400–3,600	8	+47.54	0.674	0.678
2.0	3	5,100–5,300	13	+47.54	0.671	0.678
4.0	1	1,700–1,900	4	+95.76	0.803	0.802
4.0	2	3,700–3,900	9	+95.54	0.801	0.802
4.0	3	4,800–5,000	12	+95.65	0.796	0.802
5.0	1	2,000–2,200	5	+114.5	0.898	—
5.0	2	4,000–4,200	10	+115.0	0.909	—
5.0	3	4,300–4,500	11	+114.5	0.893	—
0.1265	1		1	−100.9	0.828	0.764
0.1265	2		7	−100.8	0.781	0.764
0.1265	3		18	−99.48	0.774	0.764
1.0	1		2	−13.97	0.6375	0.6375
1.0	2		8	−13.07	0.6375	0.6375
1.0	3		17	−11.27	0.6375	0.6375
2.0	1		3	+20.28	0.660	0.630
2.0	2		9	+19.72	0.640	0.630
2.0	3		16	+19.49	0.613	0.630
4.0	1		4	+58.70	0.746	0.717
4.0	2		10	+58.36	0.727	0.717
4.0	3		15	+59.94	0.723	0.717
5.0	1		5	+74.81	0.841	—
5.0	2		11	+74.92	0.827	—
5.0	3		14	+75.60	0.807	—
6.14	1		6	+91.03	0.965	—
6.14	2		12	+91.37	0.954	—
6.14	3		13	+91.03	0.912	—

The presentation of the results of a typical experiment will help the reader assess the possible usefulness of the Na^+ electrode for his application. The results of a typical measurement of Na^+ activity coefficients are presented in Table I.

Flow-through electrodes (made of NAS 11-18B glass by W. Angst and H. D. Portnoy, and kindly supplied to the present author) were used to measure the potentials of NaCl solutions (saturated with AgCl) over the concentration range from $0.1m$ to greater than $5m$. Temperature was maintained by an oil thermostat at 0, 25, and 50°C. All potentials were referred to an Ag–AgCl reference electrode. Three separate experimental runs were carried out at each temperature as indicated in the third column of Table I, with measurements obtained in the sequence indicated in the fifth column. (It will be noticed that the first two experiments were done in a sequence of increasing concentrations, for which the electrode was but merely flushed with fresh solution, while in the third experiment the concentrations were decreased, which required interposing a distilled water rinse between successive solutions.) For convenience, a digital voltmeter was used to record the voltage output of the vibrating reed electrometer to four significant figures. The system was calibrated at the input with a Weston Standard Cell and a precision voltage divider. The observed potentials are given in the sixth column, while the seventh column gives the values of mean-activity coefficients calculated from these potentials (all standardized for each run relative to the potential in $1.0m$ NaCl). The eighth column presents the mean-activity coefficient values of Robinson and Stokes (156) for comparison with those measured by the glass electrode.

Consider the results at 25°C. first. The mean-activity coefficients measured by the glass: Ag–AgCl pair can be seen to agree excellently with those tabulated by Robinson and Stokes, which establishes that the glass electrode is responding perfectly to Na^+ activity. The internal agreement between the activity coefficients calculated from run to run indicates the reproducibility of the measurements when referred to standard solution to $1.0m$ NaCl. Usually, the agreement is better than 1% in terms of concentration, although, with extreme care, it is possible to obtain agreement in activity coefficient meaurements to within 0.1%. On the other hand, direct comparison of the potentials observed in a given solution between the first, second, and third experiments indicates the long-term stability and reproducibility of the electrode. The reproducibility of such measurements can be seen to be better than 0.5 mv. over the course of several hours. The electrode potentials reached stable values within 300 sec. after changing solutions in all cases; and each voltage tabulated is the last reading of at least four individual readings recorded over a 200 sec. period. The last reading was usually the same as the first reading to the third significant figure. It will also be seen that approximately 100 to 200 sec. were used in flushing through the fresh solutions in experiments 1 and 2, while about double that time was required in experiment 3. Thus, it can be seen that making the measurements with increasing concentration, a single solution could be measured in less than 10 min., including solution changes; and a total run was complete in approximately 40 min.

Similar data are presented in the second portion of Table I for 50°C., where it will be noticed that the reproducibility of the potentials from run to run is somewhat better than at 25°C., although the values of the mean-activity coefficients calculated from these data have about the same accuracy. The third portion of Table I presents data at 0°C., which can be seen to be somewhat less precise than the data at the higher temperatures, probably as a result of the higher resistance of the glass electrode at this temperature. Comparison of the measured activity coefficients at 0 and 50°C. with those from the compilation of Harned and Owen (66) indicates excellent agreement at both temperatures, signifying that the Na^+ glass electrode also measures Na^+ activity perfectly at 0 and 50°C.

(3) **Particular Properties of K^+ Electrodes.** (a) *Typical Data.* Representative data for the behavior of three typical K^+ selective electrode compositions in $0.1N$ K^+ and $0.1N$ Na^+ solutions as a function of pH, as well as in mixtures of Na^+ and K^+ at alkaline and neutral pH, are illustrated in Figure 18. All three glasses have comparable K^+–Na^+ selectivities of about 10 to 1 and n_{NaK} values of 1. However, the NAS 27-4B and KAS 20-5B glasses retain the response to K^+ to the greatest dilutions of "pure" K^+ solutions. In these glasses, a theoretical Nernst response is found even in solutions more dilute than $10^{-4}M;$ and a useful response is still present at $10^{-4}M$.

(b) *Aging Effects.* From the diffusion studies described in Section III it appears that K^+ selective glasses of the NAS 27-4 type become extensively hydrated when exposed to aqueous solutions. Despite this, they are durable (some NAS 27-4 electrodes have been in continuous use for more than four years); and their K^+ selectivity, as well as the stability and rapidity of response, invariably improve with aging.

The properties of most K^+-selective compositions change during the first two weeks of exposure to aqueous solutions. This is illustrated in Figure 19 which examines the K^+–Na^+ selectivity as a function of time for five electrodes made from a glass of composition Na_2O 27, Al_2O_3 3, ZnO 3, and SiO_2 67 mole-%. The abscissa plots the time in days for which the electrodes were exposed to $0.1N$ solutions of Na^+ or K^+ at neutral pH, as labeled, while the ordinate plots the K^+–Na^+ selectivity in mv (i.e., 58 log K_{NaK}^{pot}) measured by testing the potential difference between $0.1N$ Na^+ and $0.1N$ K^+ solutions interposed during the exposure to the solution indicated on the abscissa. The K^+–Na^+ selectivity can be seen to increase with time from an initial value of 58 log K_{NaK} = 30 to 35 mv. observed 2 hr.

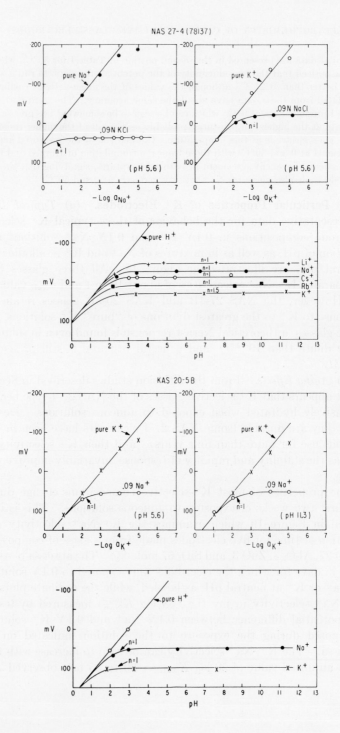

NAS 27-4 (78137)

KAS 20-5B

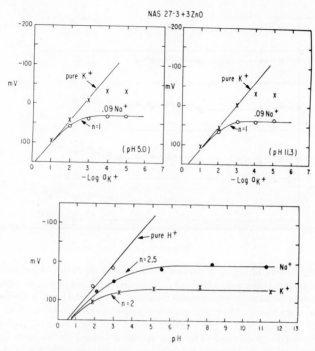

Fig. 18. Electrode potentials of three typical K⁺-selective electrodes plotted in the manner of Figures 5 and 8. Described in the text.

after first exposing the electrodes to the solution to a value of 55 mv. in one month corresponding to an increase of K⁺–Na⁺ selectivity from about 3 to 1 initially, to about 9 to 1 by the end of a month. With longer aging, the electrodes ultimately achieve a selectivity in excess of 10 to 1, which then remains stable for years. From Figure 19 it should also be noted that no major difference exists whether electrodes are aged in Na⁺ or K⁺ solutions; although careful examination of the data at the right indicates that the K⁺–Na⁺ selectivity is temporarily slightly higher when electrodes have had a history of previous exposure to K⁺ solutions. The results also indicate that no important differences can be seen after two weeks of aging between electrodes blown at high or low temperatures.

Entirely similar changes are observed with NAS 27-4B glass; and this observation accounts for the apparent discrepancy between Beckman's published data (5) for their 78137 electrode (which is of

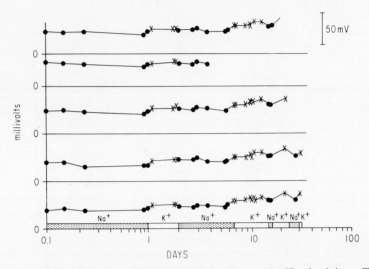

Fig. 19. Effects of aging K$^+$-selective electrodes on Na–K selectivity. The upper three electrodes were blown at deliberately high temperatures (white heat in gas-oxygen flame with considerable "boiling" of the glass), while the lower two electrodes were blown at low temperatures (almost no oxygen in the flame and no "boiling" of the glass), to see whether or not the conditions of glass-working altered electrode properties. The data points indicated by x's were measured when the electrodes had been in K$^+$ solutions, while those indicated by dots were measured when electrodes had been in Na$^+$ solutions. Described in text.

NAS 27-4 composition according to J. Leonard) and the properties of NAS 27-4 glass as described here. Beckman 78137 electrodes invariably achieve K$^+$–Na$^+$ selectivities approaching 10 to 1 after prolonged aging, although the Beckman specifications (5) state that this glass has only a slight K$^+$ over Na$^+$ preference.

Other beneficial effects of aging have also been regularly noted in K$^+$ selective glasses. Thus, the selectivity of cations relative to H$^+$ improves; and deviations from equation 1 at extremes of pH, which are seen in fresh electrodes, also disappear with age. The simplest interpretation of these observations is that hydration of the glass is the principal factor in aging, and it would seem desirable, therefore, to hydrate K$^+$-selective glasses immediately after preparation and thereafter to store them continuously in aqueous media.

(4) **Particular Properties of Li$^+$ Electrodes.** (a) *General Properties.* Some properties of LAS 15–25B glass mentioned in section (1) are

given in Figure 20 where this glass can be seen to have a slight preference for Li^+ relative to Na^+, and excellent Li^+ selectivity relative to
the other alkali cations.   Its response to $0.1N$ Li^+ is independent of
pH above 5, and n_{HLi} is 1.   Thus, Na^+ is the only important contaminant for this electrode.

The time course of response to Li^+ is illustrated in Figure 21 for
NAS 11-18F composition, useful in some applications, and also for
the more highly Li^+ selective BH68 Electronics Instruments Ltd.

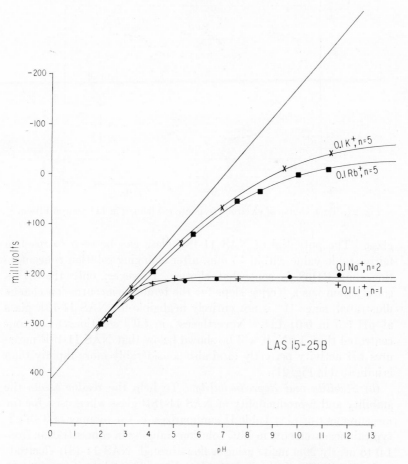

Fig. 20. Characteristic potentials of an Li^+-selective glass electrode.   The data
are plotted in the manner of Figure 5 for a glass of composition LAS 15–25B.

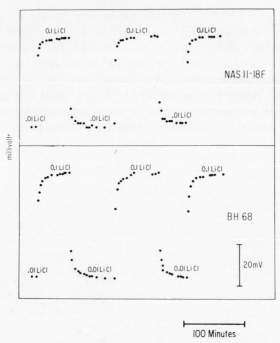

Fig. 21. Time course of electrode response to changes in Li$^+$ concentration.

glass. The potential of NAS 11-18F glass can be seen to reach a fairly stable value within 15 min. after changing solution concentration, but BH68 is somewhat slower. However, only the BH68 composition has a Nernst slope for the tenfold concentration change illustrated, since H$^+$ is not entirely negligible for NAS 11-18F glass at pH 5.5 in 0.01 Li$^+$. Nevertheless, in LiCl solutions more concentrated than 1.0N, it will be shown below that NAS 11-18F measures Li$^+$ activity perfectly (and also considerably more rapidly than is indicated in Fig. 21).

(b) *Stability and Reproducibility.* To help the reader assess the stability and reproducibility of NAS 11-18B glass when used for the measurement of Li$^+$, Table II summarizes, in the manner of Table I, typical measurements in LiCl solutions ranging in concentration from 1.0 to nearly 20m made using a flow-through NAS 11-18B electrode and an AgAgCl reference electrode. From these data it can be seen that the potentials are quite reproducible and, moreover, that the

TABLE II

Mean Activity Coefficients of LiCl Solutions Measured by NAS 11-18B Glass Electrode at 25 ± 0.1°C.

Molality of solution	Experimental sequence	Observed potential (mv.)	γ ± Measured	γ ± Tabulated
1.0	1	−148.7		
1.0	5	−149.8	0.774 stand.	0.774
1.0	10	−149.8		
4.0	2	−47.66		
4.0	6	−47.43	1.41 av.	1.510
4.0	11	−47.77		
7.0	3	26.36		
7.0	7	26.81		
7.0	12	26.36	3.38 av.	3.71
7.0	14	25.58		
14.0	4	156.6		
14.0	8	156.6		
14.0	13	156.6	21.6 av.	26.2
14.0	15	158.9		
14.0	17	156.6		
20.1	9	224.2		
20.1	16	222.1	58.4 av.	—
20.1	18	224.2		

activity coefficients measured by the glass are in agreement with published values. This means that, in this concentration range, NAS 11-18 glass behaves as a perfect Li^+ electrode. Despite the fact that the potential may differ by as much as 2 mv. from one reading to another (cf. readings 15 and 17), the readings sometimes agree to better than 0.1 mv. (cf. readings 5 and 10 or 4, 8, 13, and 17), suggesting that an NAS 11-18 electrode should be usable for Li^+ measurement with good reproducibility.

(5) **Electrodes for Rb^+ and Cs^+.** The composition optimal for Rb^+ and Cs^+ selectivity have already been noted in relation to Figures 15 and 16. The behavior of the potentials in mixtures of Rb^+ or Cs^+ with Na^+ or K^+ can be seen in Figures 8 and 9 for the reasonably Rb^+ or Cs^+ selective NAS 27.2-7.8F glass. In general, the

behavior of glass electrodes in response to Rb^+ and Cs^+ is similar to that in response to K^+, so that the conditions applying to K^+ measurement should provide a general guide for the measurement of Rb^+ and Cs^+. It should also be apparent that the K^+ selective compositions recommended in part (1) will be useful for some applications. It may, however, be necessary to use a pair of electrodes, one from the VIIa region and one from the I–IV region to separate Rb^+ and Cs^+ activities in mixtures of these ions.

5. The Responses of Al_2O_3-Containing Glasses to Ag^+, Tl^+, and NH_4^+

All cation-sensitive glass electrode compositions have been found to be responsive, with varying degrees of specificity, to many cations other than H^+, Li^+, Na^+, K^+, Rb^+, and Cs^+. The characteristics of the response of Al_2O_3-containing glasses to Ag^+, Tl^+, and NH_4^+ are described in this section.

A. SILVER ION

(1) Special Experimental Methods. The methods used in characterizing the response of glass electrodes to Ag^+ are similar to those described above for the alkali metal cations and hydrogen. However, because of the insolubility of AgCl, it is necessary to use chloride-free solutions (usually nitrates) and to interpose an additional saturated KNO_3-salt bridge between the usual saturated KCl–calomel reference half cell and the solutions to be studied. The potentials of a bright silver wire were also measured as a control for the complete dissociation of Ag^+ above neutral pH (pH 7.2 was the highest studied). Since it was observed in preliminary studies that slow changes in the electrode potential occurred when some glass compositions were first introduced into Ag^+ solutions, the properties reported here were characterized after the electrodes had been preequilibrated with Ag^+ solutions for at least 1 day. With such preequilibration, the drift of potential during the experiment was negligible.

(2) Results. (a) Time Course. Figure 22 illustrates the time course of response of typical high field strength (NAS 11-18B) and low field strength (NAS 27-4B) glasses to various concentrations of Ag^+ in the pH range 5.5–6.5. The results illustrate not only the general features of the response to varying Ag^+ concentration, but also

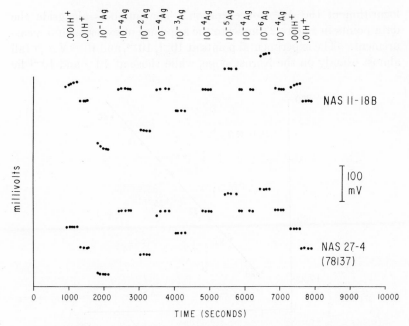

Fig. 22. The time course of electrode response to Ag^+. The electrode potential was measured in reference to a saturated KNO_3-saturated KCl-double salt bridge. The compositions of the test solutions are indicated above the figure. No distilled water rinses were used when going from a lower silver concentration to a higher silver concentration, instead one rise with the new solution was used. Conversely, when going from concentrated to more dilute solutions, the electrodes were rinsed with six changes of distilled water followed by one rinse in the new Ag^+ solution. Note the reproducibility of the potential in $10^{-4}N$ Ag^+ solutions throughout the experiment, as well as the agreement between the potential in the H^+ solutions at the beginning and end of the experiments.

the time course, stability, and reproducibility of Ag^+ measurements by glass electrodes (cf. the reproducibility of the potentials in $10^{-4}N$ Ag^+ throughout the experiment, as well as in the $10^{-2}N$ H^+ solutions at 1300 sec. and 7600 sec.). Data of which these are typical are the basis for the construction of all subsequent figures.

(b) *Nernst Slope.* A Nernst slope for Ag^+ is indicated by the data of Figure 22 over at least the range 10^{-5} to $10^{-1}M$ at neutral pH, as can be seen more clearly in Figure 23, where the steady potential values from Figure 22 are plotted as a function of the negative logarithm of the Ag^+ concentration. The numbers alongside the data points in Figure 23 indicate the sequence of experimental measurement. The experimental points at 10^{-3}, 10^{-4}, and 10^{-5} N Ag^+ fall almost exactly on the Nernst slope, while those at 10^{-2} and 10^{-1} lie

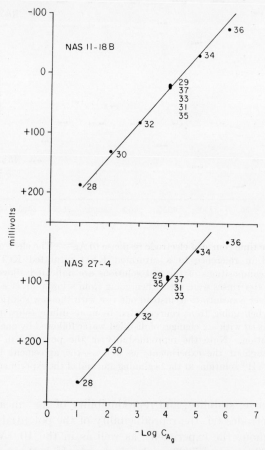

Fig. 23. Electrode potentials in response to varying concentrations of Ag^+. The steady-state potentials observed at neutral pH in Figure 22 are plotted as a function of negative logarithm of silver ion concentration here to illustrate the stability and reproducibility of the electrode response. The numbers next to each dot correspond to the sequence of experimental measurement. Notice the excellent agreement between the five check responses on Figures 22 and 23. The diagonal straight lines represent the Nernst slope. $T = 22°C$.

slightly above the line, as expected from the small decrease of activity coefficient at these concentrations. The deviation of the potential in $10^{-6}\,N$ Ag$^+$ from the Nernst slope is due to the effect of H$^+$ at the pH (5.57) of this solution. Similar data over a wider range of Ag$^+$ concentrations are presented in Figure 24 for glasses having a variety of field strengths, as well as for a bright silver wire. The results demonstrate that certain electrode compositions still respond to Ag$^+$ (at pH 5.6) in dilutions as low as $10^{-9}\,M$.

(c) pH *Independence.* The pH independence of the Ag$^+$ response is indicated in Figure 25 for representative compositions of various "anionic field strengths." Differences in the selectivity for Ag$^+$ relative to H$^+$ are also apparent from these data but are more conveniently analyzed from the data of Figure 26.

(d) Ag$^+$ *Selectivity Isotherm.* From data of which Figure 25 is typical, the Ag$^+$ selectivity was measured in representative glasses and plotted relative to K$^+$ in Figure 26 as a function of the Na$^+$–K$^+$ selectivity measured for the same electrodes, exactly as was done in constructing Figure 15. This procedure permits direct quantitative comparison of the Ag$^+$ selectivity with the selectivities to the other cations since the glasses are ranked along the abscissa exactly as in Figures 15 and 16. (The same method and scale will be used in plotting all subsequent figures for other ions, so that all cation selectivity isotherms presented in this paper will be comparable to each other.) Glass compositions are indicated by the same symbols as in Figure 15.

From Figure 26, it is apparent that a single selectivity isotherm characterizes the response of aluminosilicate glass electrodes to Ag$^+$, which can be expressed as a function of the Na$^+$–K$^+$ selectivity. From this result, it should be clear that a measurement of Na$^+$–K$^+$ selectivity in a given glass suffices to predict the Ag$^+$ selectivity. Moreover, all cation-responsive glasses have been found to show marked sensitivity to Ag$^+$, which is usually the most preferred of all cations (including H$^+$) (cf. Fig. 26 with Figs. 16, 30, 34, 35, 37, and 38). It should also be noted that including Ag$^+$ in the glass melt leads to no important changes in the Ag$^+$ response; for the compositions symbolized by the glasses labeled "NAS 22-3 + Ag 5" contain 5 mole-% of Ag$_2$O, replacing an equivalent amount of Na$_2$O in a composition originally NAS 27-3, and the observed properties of these glasses are very close to those of the original glass.

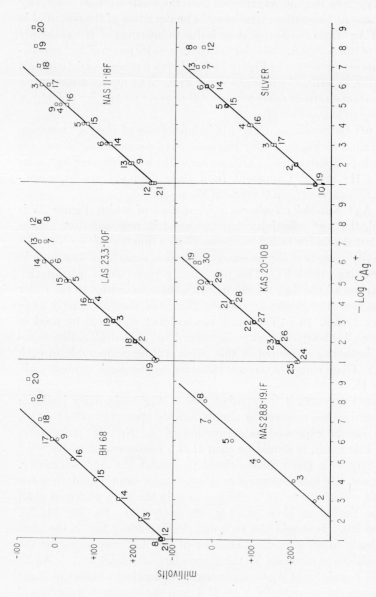

Fig. 24. Electrode potentials in response to a wide range of Ag^+ concentration. The numbers next to the data points indicate the sequence in which the observations were obtained. The diagonal straight lines plot the Nernst slope. $T = 22°C$.

(3) **Recommended Compositions.** The above data permit the following conclusions: Glass electrodes should be useful for Ag^+ measurement, perhaps even in concentrations as low as $10^{-9}M$. Comparison of Figures 26 and 16 indicates that the composition having the highest selectivity for Ag^+ relative to H^+ is NAS 28.8-19.1F, which is nearly 100,000 times more selective for Ag^+ than H^+. However, glasses of more modest Ag^+ selectivity may be preferable for Ag^+ measurement since the reproducibility of measurements with the above glass is poor, as can be seen from Figure 25. For many applications, NAS 11-18 glass should be appropriate.

B. THALLIUM ION

(1) **Special Experimental Methods.** Solutions of the nitrates were used, as in the case of Ag^+, because of the low solubility of TlCl. Electrodes were also preequilibrated with Tl^+ solutions for at least 12 hr. prior to study, although preliminary experiments indicated that the slow potential changes of the type observed with Ag^+ were relatively minor.

(2) **Results.** The time course of response to Tl^+ is much the same as that to the group 1a cations, a stable potential usually being established within 2 min. after changing solutions, as is illustrated in Figure 27, which also indicates the reproducibility of the response to Tl^+ for a typical Tl^+ sensitive composition (KAS 20-5B).

Figures 28 and 29 illustrate, respectively, the potentials observed in solutions of varying Tl^+ concentration at constant (neutral) pH, and in solutions of constant Tl^+ concentration of variable pH, while Figure 30 summarizes the behavior of Tl^+ selectivity as a function of glass composition (as systematized by the measured Na^+-K^+ selectivity in the manner of Figs. 15, 16, and 26).

From the above data, it is clear that most alkali cation-responsive glass electrodes respond rapidly and reproducibly to Tl^+, obeying equation 1 and yielding a Nernst slope for Tl^+ in pure solutions. The Tl^+ selectivity of glass electrodes is, moreover, a systematic function of glass composition, which can be expressed in terms of Na^+-K^+ selectivity, and a knowledge of the Na^+-K^+ selectivity of a given glass suffices to define the approximate selectivity for Tl^+.

(3) **Recommended Compositions.** A glass electrode for the general measurement of Tl^+ would normally be chosen from those

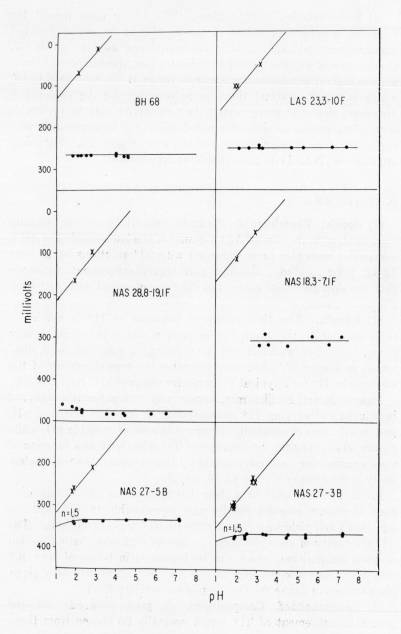

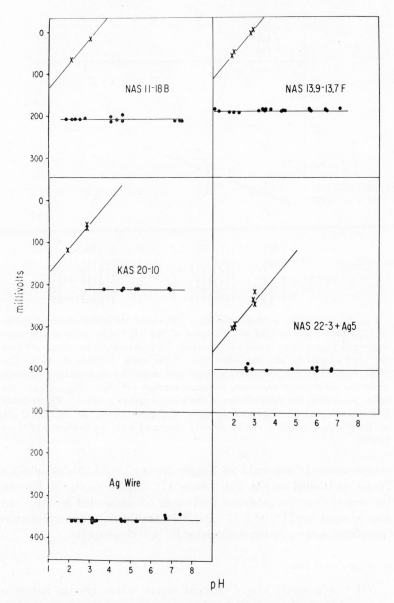

Fig. 25. pH independence of Ag$^+$ response of glass electrodes.   Dots refer to potentials in 0.1N AgNO$_3$, crosses to potentials in HNO$_3$.

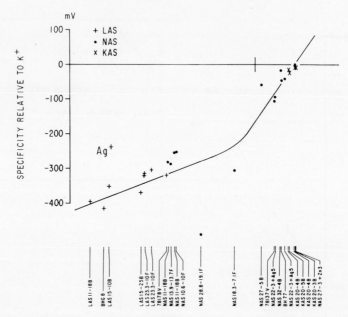

Fig. 26. Selectivity isotherm for Ag^+. The experimentally observed values of K^{pot}_{Ag-K} have been plotted as a function of Na^+-K^+ selectivity in the same manner as Figure 15 to reveal the existence of a systematic relationship between Na^+-K^+ selectivity and the selectivity of the glass electrode to Ag^+. The points represent the experimental measurement in various aluminosilicate glasses, while the solid curve represents a visual average for these data. Below the figure are labeled the compositions of the various glasses studied. The ordinate and abscissa scales are identical to those of Figures 15, 16, 30, 34, 35, 37–39, so that the Ag^+ isotherm can be directly compared with the isotherms of those figures.

compositions at the right of Figure 30 (e.g., KAS 20-5B or KAS 20-4B, as labeled on Fig. 26). Since Tl^+ is quite similar to Rb^+ in its effects, those compositions previously recommended for Rb^+ can also be used for Tl^+, or if H^+ and Na^+ are the only important contaminants, a composition suitable for K^+ will be adequate.

C. AMMONIUM ION

NH_4^+ is a small, singly charged cation whose crystal radius is comparable to that of Rb^+. Not surprisingly, the present glass electrodes respond rapidly and reproducibly to NH_4^+. The charac-

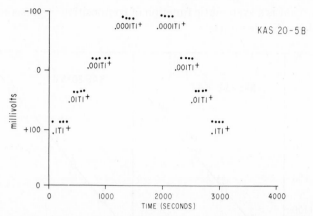

Fig. 27. Time course of electrode response to Tl^+. Three distilled water rinses were interposed between each successive dilution, as well as between the two 0.0001 Tl^+ solutions; while no distilled water rinses were interposed when increasing the Tl^+ concentration. $T = 22°C$.

teristics of the glass electrode response to NH_4^+ are illustrated in Figures 31–34.

(1) **Special Experimental Methods.** The characterization of the glass-electrode potential in solutions containing NH_4^+ has been carried out in a manner similar to that used for the alkali metal cations, but with the precaution to correct for any association of NH_4^+ with OH^- at high pH. From the value of the dissociation constant of NH_4OH (1.774 $\times$ 10^{-5}), such association should not decrease the amount of ionized NH_4^+ by more than 1% in chloride solutions more dilute than 0.1 at pH 7 or lower, which encompasses a sufficient range for characterization of NH_4^+ selectivity. Consequently, all observations reported here were carried out in solutions more dilute than $0.1N$ and at pH below 7.6. (A series of experiments in $0.1N$ NH_4OH solutions at high pH, when corrected for association, yielded results in agreement with those at neutral pH presented here.)

(2) **Results.** Figure 31 illustrates the time course of response to NH_4^+ of a typical NH_4^+-selective glass (NAS 27-3 $+$ 3 mole-% ZnO), while Figure 32 plots the steady response to varying NH_4^+ as a function of pH. From data, of which Figure 33 is representative, an NH_4^+-selectivity isotherm has been plotted in Figure 34 as a function of Na^+–K^+ selectivity.

As with the other cations considered above, the selectivity of glass for NH_4^+ ion is a systematic function of composition, representable in terms of Na–K selectivity.

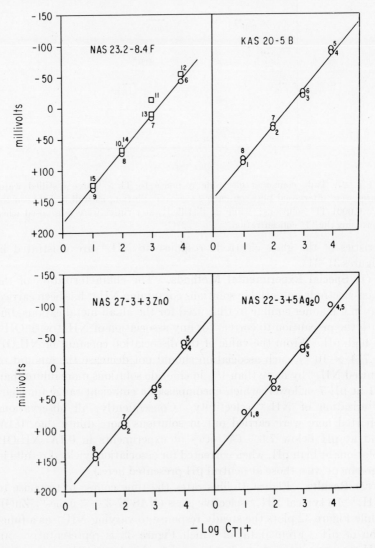

Fig. 28. Representative Tl^+ responses of glass electrodes. The diagonal straight lines represent the Nernst slope. $T = 22°C$. The numbers refer to the sequence of experimental measurement.

(3) Recommended Compositions. If Na^+ and H^+ are the principal contaminants and K^+ concentration is sufficiently low, any

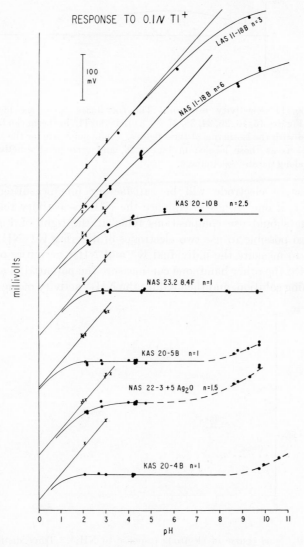

Fig. 29. Potentials of Tl^+-sensitive glass electrodes in mixtures of Tl^+ and H^+. $T = 22°C$. Dots represent potential in $0.1N$ Tl^+ solutions, while x's represent potential in pure H^+ solutions.

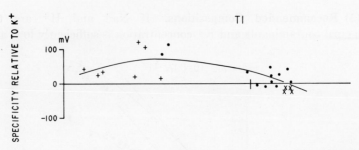

Fig. 30. Tl$^+$-selectivity isotherm. The coordinate scales are identical to those of Figures 15, 16, 26, 34, 35, 37–39, so that the Tl$^+$ isotherm can be directly compared with the isotherms of these figures. Data points are for the same glass compositions as those labeled in Figure 26, and correspond exactly in their position along the abscissa to these.

K$^+$-selective electrode will be satisfactory for measuring NH$_4^+$. However, if one wishes to enhance the NH$_4^+$ selectivity relative to K$^+$, one should use compositions lying at the right of Figure 34. It is also possible to use two electrodes of differing K$^+$–NH$_4^+$ selectivities to measure the individual K$^+$ and NH$_4^+$ activities of a mixture. On the other hand, one can measure the potential in an NH$_4^+$ containing solution, and then reduce the NH$_4^+$ activity of the solution

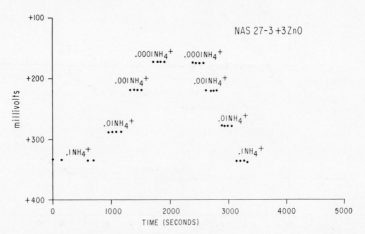

Fig. 31. Time course of electrode response to NH$_4^+$. Three distilled water rinses were interposed between each successive dilution as well as between the two 0.0001 NH$_4^+$ solutions, while no distilled water rinses were used when concentration was increased. $T = 22°C$.

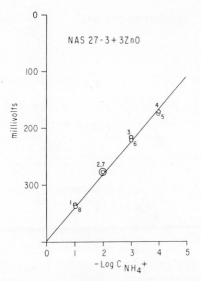

Fig. 32. Electrode response to varying concentration of NH_4^+. Data from the steady state of potential are plotted. The numerals next to the data points correspond to the sequence of observation, and the diagonal line represents the Nernst slope. $T = 22°C$.

by alkalinizing (e.g., with a few anion-exchange beads in the OH^- form). In this way, by using one electrode, it should be possible to evaluate both K^+ and NH_4^+ in a mixture by first measuring the sum of K^+ and NH_4^+ at neutral pH, and then measuring the K^+ alone after removing NH_4^+ by alkalinizing.

D. SUMMARY OF Ag^+, Tl^+, NH_4^+ RELATIVE SENSITIVITIES

Figure 35 summarizes, in the manner of Figure 16, the relative sensitivities to Ag^+, Tl^+, and NH_4^+ by superposing the isotherms of Figures 26, 30, and 34. Figure 35 should be compared directly with Figure 16 to relate these specificities to those for H, Li, Na, K, Rb, and Cs, and to Figure 38 to relate them to those of the divalent cations.

6. The Responses of Al_2O_3-Containing Glasses to the Alkaline Earth Cations

Much interest exists in electrodes for measuring Ca^{2+} activity, and some fundamental work has been published on the Ca^{2+} response of

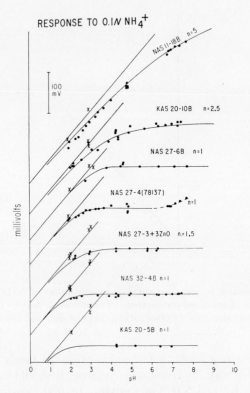

Fig. 33. Electrode potentials in $NH_4^+ - H^+$ mixtures. $T = 22°C$. Dots represent potential in $0.1N$ NH_4^+ solutions, x's in pure H^+ solutions.

blown glass by Tendeloo et al. (182–187), of sintered mineral membranes by Marshall (108), and of thinly ground or blown membranes of natural and synthetic glasses cemented onto insulating stems by Garrels et al. (54) and by Truesdell and Pommer (196) (cf. Section V). To avoid confusion between the results of the present section and those of Garrels and Truesdell and Pommer, it should be emphasized that the present section is confined to the properties of blown bulb electrodes.

Bulb electrodes blown from most of the present glasses are primarily responsive to singly charged cations, and much less so to divalent cations. Nevertheless, it is useful to describe here the salient features of the response to Mg^{2+}, Ca^{2+}, Sr^{2+}, and Ba^{2+}, for such a

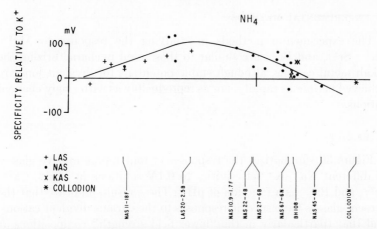

Fig. 34. NH₄⁺-selectivity isotherm. Most of the compositions studied are the same as those labeled in Figure 26, and correspond in their position along the abscissa to them. Additional compositions are labeled directly on the figure. The coordinate scales are identical to those of Figures 15, 16, 26, 30, 35, 37–39.

description provides some clues for development of divalent selective electrodes.

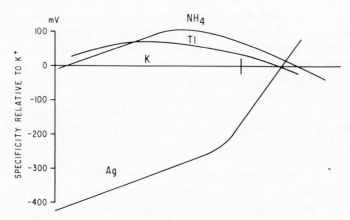

Fig. 35. Combined selectivity isotherms for Ag⁺, Tl⁺, and NH₄⁺. The coordinate scales are identical to those of Figures 15, 16, 26, 30, 34, 37–39.

A. EXPERIMENTAL METHODS

The experimental methods in studying the response to Mg^{2+}, Ca^{2+}, Sr^{2+}, and Ba^{2+} are similar to those used in characterizing the alkali metal cations, although stable potentials for divalent ions are achieved neither as rapidly, nor as reproducibly as with singly charged cations.

B. RESULTS

Figure 36 summarizes the responses of four representative glasses of different Na^+–K^+ selectivities to $0.1N$ solutions of Mg^{2+}, Ca^{2+}, Sr^{2+}, and Ba^{2+} as a function of pH. These results indicate that the present glasses have specific responses to the various divalent cations, and that (particularly in the "lower field strength" compositions at the bottom of the figure) this response may be sufficiently great to be of some practical use.

From data, of which those of Figure 36 are typical, it is possible to plot isotherms for the apparent selectivity for each of the divalent cations at neutral pH (in the manner of Figs. 15, 16, 26, 30, 34, and 35). Such selectivity isotherms are presented in Figure 37. The data of Figure 37 represent the differences of the potential observed at pH 7.6 in $0.1N$ solutions of the indicated divalent cations relative to that in $0.1N$ K^+ at pH 7.6. Because of the relatively poor divalent selectivity relative to H^+, the effect to be expected from the $10^{-7.6}$ H^+ present at pH 7.6 has been indicated by the dashed line. Since equations 15 and 16 must be used in defining the potential selectivity constant, it should be apparent that 29 mv. rather than 58 mv. corresponds to a factor of ten difference in selectivity between divalent ions. Moreover, the selectivity constant between monovalent and divalent ions depends upon the total concentration of the ions in solution. Thus, for each factor of ten dilution, the apparent divalent selectivity relative to the monovalent will improve by a factor of ten over the values given in Figure 37.

The separate isotherms of Figure 37 have been superposed in Figure 38 to show the pattern of selectivity among divalent cations. From the existence of a pattern among divalent cations as a function of Na^+–K^+ selectivity it would seem that the selectivities among divalent cations are at least partially under control of the factors determining selectivity among monovalent cations.

C. SUGGESTIONS FOR PRACTICAL ELECTRODES

While none of the present glasses are usefully selective for Ca^{2+} in the presence of Na^+ at high concentrations, some of the compositions at the extreme right of Figures 37 and 38 may be useful in dilute solutions by taking advantage of the increase in divalent to monovalent selectivity with dilution. The most intriguing feature of Figures 37 and 38 is the indication that if one could make electrodes of still lower field strength (i.e., further to the right) than those explored so far, one might be able to produce electrodes of greater sensitivity to divalent ions than to monovalent ions. This suggestion notwithstanding, the scatter of the data at the right of Figure 37, together with the finding that the best Ca^{2+} electrode observed to date is a composition, NAS 32.8-3.5F, which does not have the lowest anionic field strength, suggest that other factors in addition to anionic field strength may be involved. One such factor could well be the ionic mobility, since it is shown in Section III that the mobility of ions in the glass contributes importantly to the electrode selectivity; and one might well expect the mobilities of divalent cations in glass to be substantially lower than those of monovalent cations.

7. The Responses of Al_2O_3-Containing Glasses to Substituted Ammonium Ions, Amines, and Amino-Acids

Since the present glass electrodes are generally responsive to cations, they may be usable for measuring the activities of substituted ammonium ions, amines, and the cationic form of amino acids. The electrode responses to a number of substituted amines and quaternary ammonium compounds are presented as a function of Na^+–K^+ selectivity in the upper portion of Figure 39 (using potentials measured in $0.1N$ solutions at the indicated pH), while the lower portion presents comparable data for four amino acids. From this figure, the existence of a systematic relationship between glass composition and the relative sensitivities to these ions is apparent.

8. Effects of Temperature

Relatively small changes from room temperature (i.e., $\pm 10°C$.) produce no important alterations in the selectivity characteristics of glass electrodes other than the expected change in the factor RT/F; and the numerical values of K^{pot} and n at $22°C$. can still be used to

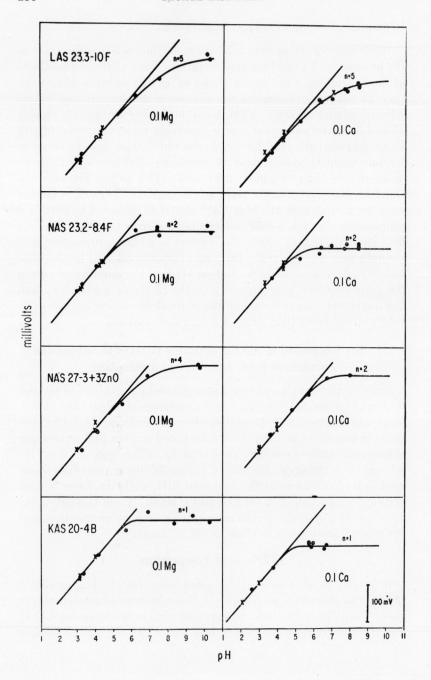

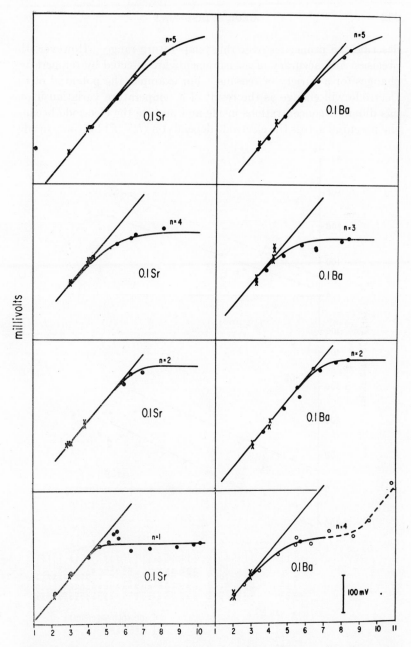

Fig. 36. Electrode responses to divalent cations. Glasses of various compositions are arranged with low field-strength glasses toward the bottom and high field-strength glasses toward the top. From data such as these, the individual selectivity isotherms of Figure 37 have been constructed. $T = 22°C$. Dots represent potentials in 0.1N solutions of the indicated cations.

describe the properties over this temperature range. However, the precision and accuracy of measurements are affected by temperature changes for a variety of reasons. For example, the potential of the electrode will change as the result of a temperature variation if one has different concentrations inside and outside the electrode because the potential across the electrode depends on (RT/F) ln (conc. inside/

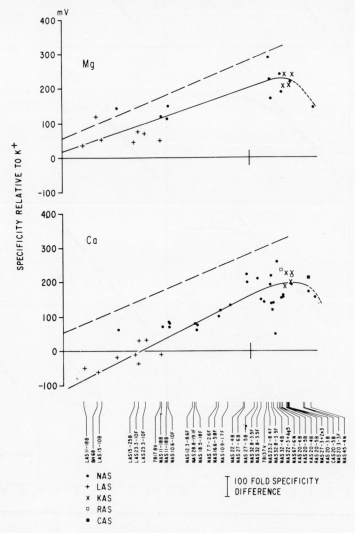

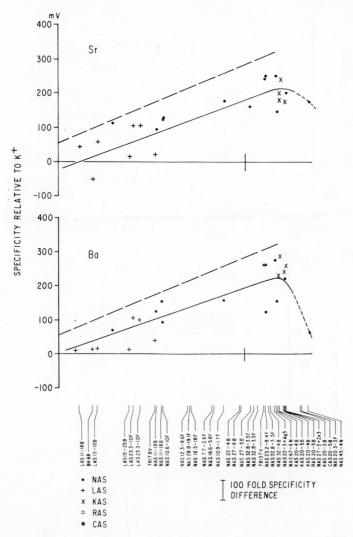

Fig. 37. Selectivity isotherms for divalent cations. In addition to the isotherms for the indicated divalent cations, an isotherm for the effect of the $10^{-7.6}$ H^+ ion present in these solutions has also been indicated by the dashed line, so that the reader can ascertain which effects are predominantly due to the divalent cations and which to the pH of the solutions. The coordinate scales are identical to those of Figures 15, 16, 26, 30, 34, 35, 38, and 39.

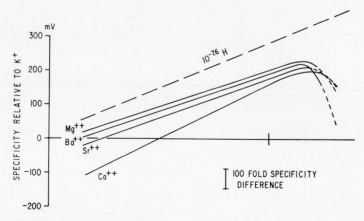

Fig. 38. The selectivity pattern of divalent cations. The coordinate scales are
identical to those of Figures 15, 16, 26, 30, 34, 35, 37, and 39.

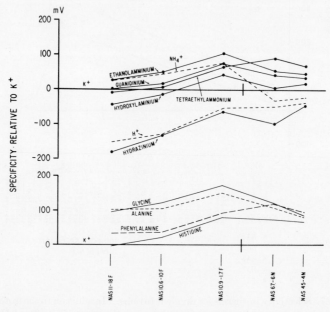

Fig. 39. Electrode responses to substituted ammonium ions. Electrode potentials in $0.1N$ solutions of substituted ammonium ions (upper) and of amino
acids (lower) are plotted as a function of the Na^+–K^+ selectivity of a variety of
glass electrodes in the same manner as Figure 15. $T = 22°C$. The coordinate
scales are identical to those of Figures 15, 16, 30, 34, 35, 37, and 38.

conc. outside). Also, if one has solutions of different ionic composition inside and outside, the temperature coefficient of K^{pot} will lead to a temperature dependence of the electrode potential. Careful temperature control will solve both of these problems, but they can also be minimized by filling the electrode with an internal solution as similar to the external solution as possible.

Representative effects of temperature variation on electrode selectivity are illustrated in Figures 40 and 41. The former figure compares the potentials of a variety of glasses at 2.8 and 46.2°C., while the latter compares the selectivities among the alkali cations for each glass at the two temperatures. From these figures, the electrode responses can be seen to be generally similar at the two temperatures, but complex changes occur with temperature in the values of the potential selectivity constants. The largest change with temperature consistently occurs in the selectivity of cations relative to H^+, the preference for cations usually increasing relative to H^+ with increasing temperature (although the Rb^+ and Cs^+ data for NAS 11-18 glass in Figures 40 and 41 indicate that this is not always true). With the exception of high field-strength glasses (such as NAS 11-18), the K^+ selectivity relative to Na^+ generally increases with increasing temperature. Also, the values of n decrease substantially as temperature increases, the change being more marked the larger the value of n. Finally, the high pH deviations from equation 8 becomes less marked at lower temperatures, suggesting that such deviations may represent chemical attack on the glass.

9. Electrode Response in Non-Aqueous Media

A. GENERAL PROPERTIES

Cation-sensitive glass electrodes function adequately not only in aqueous solutions, but also in non-aqueous media such as alcohol (cf. 166) and in aqueous solutions containing as much as 90% Dioxane. Typical electrode potentials for $0.01N$ solutions of Li^+, Na^+, Rb^+, and Cs^+ in water, 50% water–50% methanol (by volume), and 100% methanol are compared in Figures 42 and 43, the former figure comparing the responses for each cation in varying methanol concentrations and the latter comparing the responses among the cations for a given methanol concentration (pH was measured by a pH glass electrode in all solutions, and an aqueous saturated KCl–calomel

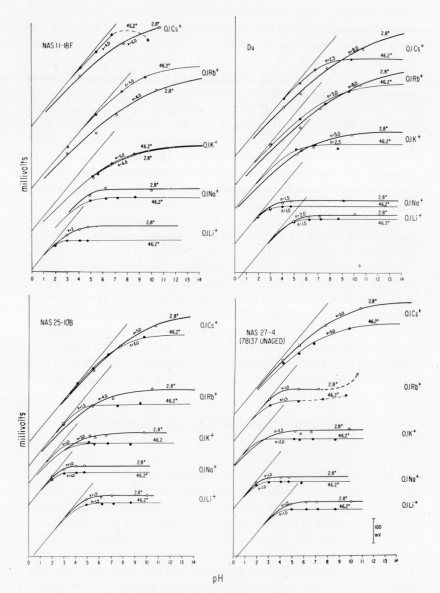

Fig. 40. The effects of temperature on electrode potentials. Upper 2.8°C, lower 46.2°C. Cation concentration 0.1N.

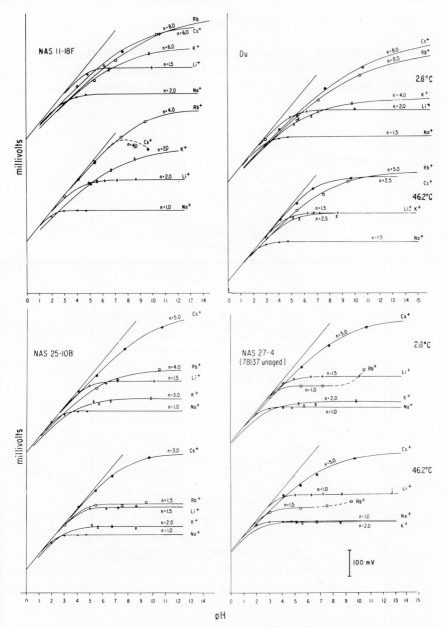

Fig. 41. Effects of temperature on selectivity among cations. Note that the data for NAS 27-4 glass (Beckman 78137) is on an unaged electrode and indicates that high K$^+$ selectivity has not yet developed. Cation concentration 0.1N.

reference electrode was used as a reference). Although changes in apparent selectivity occur with changing methanol concentration, the general behavior of the electrodes is similar in methanol to that in water.

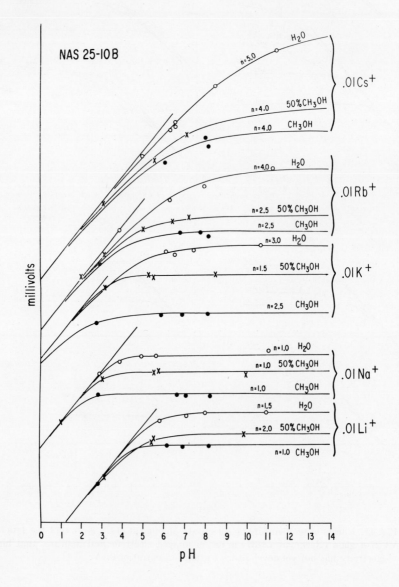

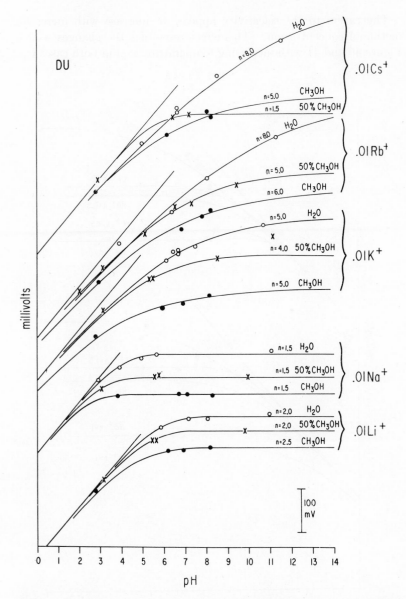

Fig. 42. Electrode potentials in H⁺-cation mixtures as a function of CH_3OH content. Electrode potentials in H_2O, 50% H_2O–50% CH_3OH (by volume), and CH_3OH (absolute) at 2.7°C are plotted for two typical cation-sensitive glasses of moderate field strength. Cation concentration was 0.01N throughout.

The cation to H^+ selectivity appears to increase with increasing methanol concentration. This effect resembles the changes seen in Figure 40 and 41 with increasing temperature, and in both cases may

NAS 25-108

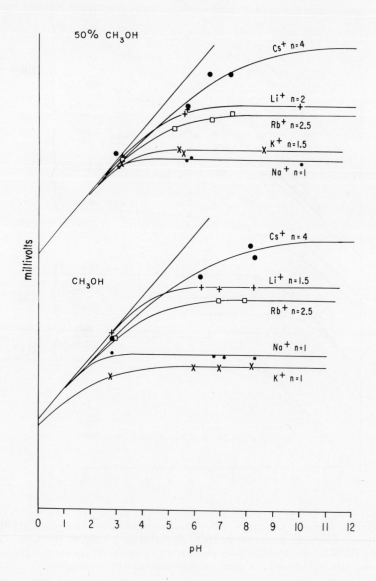

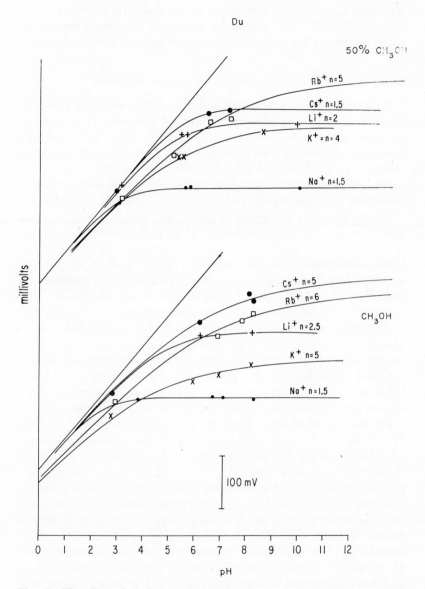

Fig. 43. The effect of alcohol on electrode response to alkali cations at 2.7°C. Described in text.

represent the effect of a decrease in the dielectric constant of the solvent. The K^+–Na^+ selectivity also often increases substantially with increasing CH_3OH content, but this is not an invariant finding.

B. COMPARISONS OF ACTIVITIES IN DIFFERENT SOLVENTS

It is possible to measure the activity of Na^+ in water–methanol mixtures as can be seen from the results of Figure 44 which presents the mean activity coefficients of NaCl in 20%, 40%, 60%, and 80% Methanol (by weight) as measured with NAS 11-18 flow-through electrode referred to an Ag-AgCl reference electrode. The activity coefficients measured by the glass electrode compare well with those previously measured by Akerlöf (2) using an Na amalgam electrode.

While the results of Figures 42–44 indicate that it is possible to use glass electrodes for the measurement of the cation activities in a given solvent or solvent mixture, they are not sufficient by themselves to indicate whether or not the electrodes can be used to compare ion activities from one solvent to another. To answer this question, the potentials of various types of glass electrodes were compared (using Ag–AgCl reference electrodes) in saturated solutions of NaCl or KCl in pure H_2O, pure CH_3OH, and mixtures of H_2O and CH_3OH. If the glass electrode itself were unaffected by the solvent and responded to the activities of Na^+ or K^+ alone, the potentials should be identical in H_2O and CH_3OH solutions. (Recall that the chemical potentials of the ions in all saturated solutions must be the same regardless of the solvent since the solutions are in equilibrium with the same salt.)

(1) **NAS 11-18 Glass.** Table III plots the potentials of the NAS 11-18B-Ag–AgCl electrode pair in CH_3OH–H_2O mixtures saturated with NaCl and AgCl. The first column plots the sequence in which the measurements were obtained, the second column plots the weight per cent of CH_3OH in the mixtures, while the third column plots the observed potential in mv. The absolute value of the observed potential is not given since the total voltage was offset by a bucking voltage in order that the readings could be measured with a high sensitivity. The experiment was carried out at a temperature of $24 \pm 0.5°C$. Examination of Table III indicates that there is no systematic difference between pure methanol or pure aqueous solutions, which exceeds a fraction of a millivolt. It should be noted that between the 17th and 18th reading, the silver wire was rechlorided

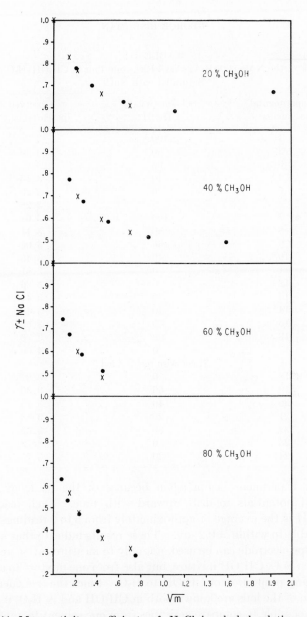

Fig. 44. Mean-activity coefficients of NaCl in alcohol solutions at 25°C. Filled circles represent mean-activity coefficients of NaCl in various weight per cent CH_3OH mixtures measured by an NAS 11-18-glass electrode referred to a Ag–AgCl half cell. For comparison, x's plot the values measured by Akerlöf (2) using an Na amalgam electrode. The agreement of results between glass electrode and amalgam electrode can be seen to be excellent.

TABLE III
Potentials of the NAS 11-18B-Ag–AgCl Electrode Pair in CH_3OH–H_2O Mixtures
Saturated with NaCl

Experimental sequence	Solvent (wt.-% CH_3OH)	Observed potential (mv.)
1	100	3.28
2	80	3.26
3	60	3.27
4	40	3.15
5	20	3.20
6	0	3.28
7	100	3.61
8	80	3.11
9	60	3.06
10	40	3.45
11	20	3.81
12	0	3.36
13	20	3.44
14	40	3.48
15	60	3.59
16	80	3.76
17	0	4.00
	Silver wire rechlorided	
18	0	3.02
19	60	3.30
20	40	3.15
21	20	3.13
22	80	3.62
23	0	3.72
24	20	3.75

and the experiment begun again because of the tendency of the observed potentials to drift upward with time. Each reading in Table III is the average of approximately from 6 to 9 readings, which were stable to within ±0.2 mv. These results indicate that an NAS 11-18 type electrode can be used, not only to measure cation activities in a given H_2O–CH_3OH mixture, but also from one mixture to another having any proportion of CH_3OH to H_2O. Since the free energies of solvation of the ions are known both in CH_3OH and in H_2O, it should even be possible to compare activities from one solvent to another on an absolute scale.

(2) **NAS 27-3 (+3 ZnO) Glass.** The independence of electrode potential of the solvent described above is *not* a general property of

cation-sensitive glass electrodes. Those compositions which tend to hydrate more extensively than NAS 11-18 exhibit a difference of potential between saturated solutions of NaCl or KCl in pure water vs. pure methanol. This is illustrated in Table IV, which compares the potential differences observed in saturated NaCl solutions in water vs. methanol for a typical K$^+$-selective electrode (NAS 27-3 + 3 ZnO). The potential in water vs. methanol differs by 15–20 mv. whether the measurements are compared at 15 min. or 1 hr. after exposure to each solution. A comparison of the potentials in saturated KCl solutions in CH$_3$OH and H$_2$O gives similar results. From the above results, one can conclude that the properties of certain electrodes are affected by the solvent, and even though an electrode may yield a correct response to cation activity in a given solvent mixture, one cannot measure ionic activities in different solvents without first evaluating the effect of a change of solvent *per se* on the electrode potential.

TABLE IV

Potentials of the NAS (27-3 + 3ZnO)—Ag–AgCl Electrode Pair in CH$_3$OH- H$_2$O Mixtures Saturated with NaCl

Potentials (mv.) observed after 15 min. in the indicated solution		Potentials (mv.) observed after 1 hr. in the indicated solution	
H$_2$O	CH$_3$OH	H$_2$O	CH$_3$OH
96.4	78.4	93.6	77.7
94.5	78.3	92.2	71.1
93.9	78.8	89.6	62.9
94.0	79.3	83.5	

III. THE ORIGIN OF THE GLASS-ELECTRODE POTENTIAL

In this section, the origin of the glass-electrode potential is analyzed, and it is shown to depend both on the ion-exchange equilibrium constant at the glass-solution interfaces and on the mobility ratio of the ions within the glass. The following Section IV is concerned with the origin of specificity in equilibrium systems and gives a physical basis for the contribution glass-electrode specificity due to the ion-exchange equilibrium constant. A theoretical analysis of the origin of the ionic mobility ratio, comparable to Section IV, which would be desirable for completeness, is yet to be accomplished.

The origin of the glass electrode potential has been a question of enduring interest (24–26, 32, 103, 106, 112, and 205). The question was originally formulated for the pH electrode but, with the present evidence that the usual pH responsive glass electrodes are merely extreme members of the family of cation responsive glasses, a more general formulation has become necessary. Since an answer to this question for glass requires a resolution of some, although not all, of the problems to be encountered in attempting the corresponding analysis of bioelectric potentials, it is hoped that the present section will have relevance to the understanding of bioelectric potentials as well as to the understanding of the mechanism of the glass electrode potential.

Theories to date have considered the glass-electrode potential to arise either as an equilibrium-surface ("phase-boundary") potential or as a diffusion potential within the interior of the membrane. They have failed to recognize that the physical requirements for ionic specificity of either the surface potential or of the interior potential necessitate the simultaneous existence of both diffusion and equilibrium processes; for it is difficult to conceive of a situation in which one can have greatly different equilibrium ion-exchange selectivities for various cations without their mobilities also being different, and vice versa. Thus, the classical "phase-boundary" and "diffusion" hypotheses should be thought of not as alternatives, but rather as necessarily coexisting consequences of the restrictions set by the membrane on the equilibrium interactions *and* motions of ions. The question of the origin of glass electrode potential, therefore, becomes a quantitative problem of deciding how much of each process is involved, rather than being a qualitative question of excluding one or the other.

The above point of view follows directly from the crucial insight of Teorell (188–192) who recognized that a membrane potential must be the sum of equilibrium processes at the membrane-solution boundaries together with diffusion processes in the membrane interior. Helfferich (67,68) and Mackay and Meares (105) extended Teorell's theory to the steady-state potentials for zero-membrane current of ion-exchange membranes having specificity differences among cations, and Karreman and Eisenman (82) developed this further to obtain analytical solutions for the potentials of cation specific ion-exchange membranes having the n-type, non-ideal behavior of the present glass electrodes.   Recently, Conti and Eisenman have extended the analysis to ion-exchange membranes, whose sites need not be uniformly distributed, and have obtained explicit analytical solutions valid for the nonsteady state (16) and for nonzero electric current (17).   The analyses of Karreman and Eisenman and Conti and Eisenman lead to the conclusion that the potential selectivity constant (or permeability ratio), which determines glass-electrode potential through equations 3, 4, 9, and 10 is analyzable into separate contributions due to the mobility ratio and the ion-exchange equilibrium constant by

$$\frac{P_j}{P_i} = K_{ij}^{\text{pot}} = K_{ij}\left[\frac{u_j}{u_i}\right]^n \tag{18}$$

where K_{ij} represents the ion-exchange equilibrium constant, u_j/u_i represents the ratio of the individual ionic mobilities in the glass, and n is a parameter describing non-ideal behavior (Eq. 9).   From equation 18 it should be apparent that in order to analyze the origin of the glass-electrode potential, it is necessary to carry out either an independent, experimental measurement of the mobility ratio, or of the ion-exchange equilibrium constant.   Such measurements, based upon tracer diffusion studies, are reported below in Section III-1-B, and methods for carrying out such an analysis from current-voltage data are suggested in Section III-2.

1. The Electrode Potential Under Conditions of Zero Current

A. THEORETICAL

The conclusions presented in this section are based upon Karreman's and Eisenman's theoretical analysis of electrode potentials in the steady state under zero-current conditions (82).   The applicability of this analysis to the glass electrode requires the assumption that glass is an ion exchanger solely permeable to cations.

Evidence for the cation-exchange properties of glass is ample, as can be seen in the papers by Douglas and Isard (29) and by Doremus (27,28).   The interested reader is referred to the following further references: 3,14,78,79,80,91,104,109,110,137,153,160–62,184, and 194. In further support of the assumption that glass is a cation exchanger, it should be noted that the properties of diffusion and potential in hydrated glass cited in the next section are in detail those of a perfect cation exchanger, and also that Doremus' elegant studies on diffusion in dry glass (28) provide definitive proof of the ion-exchange properties of glass. Evidence for anion impermeability of glass electrodes is implicit in the observation reported here that the glass electrode responds ideally to cations even in highly concentrated solutions (cf. Ref. 32, Fig. 2), an observation which can also be taken as evidence against any significant bulk solution flow (which was also assumed to be zero by Karreman and Eisenman).

(1) **Total Potential.** When a glass electrode separates two aqueous solutions, the glass-electrode potential can be written, following Teorell (192), as the sum of a diffusion potential in the interior of the glass and boundary potentials at the two interfaces between the glass and solution:

$$V \quad = \quad V_B' \quad + \quad V_D \quad + \quad V_B'' \quad (19)$$

| Total potential | Boundary potential with solution (') | Diffusion potential | Boundary potential with solution (") |

(2) **Boundary Potentials.** The values of the boundary potentials are given by equations 20 and 21, which have been derived from a thermodynamic argument by Eisenman (32, appendix), assuming glass to be a perfect cation exchanger obeying n-type, non-ideal behavior. The expressions are, therefore, not restricted to ideal ($n = 1$) behavior of the glass. (Non-ideal behavior of the n type occurs whenever the activities of ions in an exchanger phase are proportional to the nth power of their concentrations, cf. Ref. 32,82, and 202 for experimental evidence for such non-ideal behavior.)

$$V_B' = \text{const.} + \frac{nRT}{F} \ln [a_i'^{1/n} + (Ka_j')^{1/n}] \qquad (20)$$

and

$$V_B'' = -\text{const.} - \frac{nRT}{F} \ln [a_i''^{1/n} + (Ka_j'')^{1/n}] \qquad (21)$$

where K refers to the equilibrium constant for the ion exchange between the I^+ and J^+ species (Eqs. 43–45), and a_i', a_j' and a_i'', a_j'' are the activities of ions I^+ and J^+ in solutions (') and ("), respectively. The constant term in equations 20 and 21 is not thermodynamically defined and is probably not measurable. However, it cancels when equations 20 and 21 are added; so that the *sum* of the two boundary potentials is a meaningful quantity.

(3) **Diffusion Potential.** The diffusion potential is given by

$$V_D = \frac{-nRT}{F} \ln \left[\frac{a_i'^{1/n} + (Ka_j')^{1/n}}{a_i''^{1/n} + (Ka_j'')^{1/n}} \cdot \frac{a_i''^{1/n} + \dfrac{u_j}{u_i} (Ka_j'')^{1/n}}{a_i'^{1/n} + \dfrac{u_j}{u_i} (Ka_j')^{1/n}} \right] \tag{22}$$

which has been derived by Karreman and Eisenman (82) using a general flux equation valid for n-type, non-iderl behavior.

(4) **Explicit Equation for the Total Potential.** We obtain the expression for the total potential V by adding equations 20–22 in accordance with equation 19 to yield

$$V = \frac{nRT}{F} \ln \frac{a_i^{1/n} + \dfrac{u_j}{u_i} [Ka_j']^{1/n}}{a_i''^{1/n} + \dfrac{u_j}{u_i} [Ka_j'']^{1/n}} \tag{23}$$

which, when compared directly with the empirical equation 9, results in the relationship expressed by equation 18, which defines the potential selectivity constant (or permeability ratio) as the product of the ion-exchange equilibrium constant and the nth power of the mobility ratio. This result provides a basis for analyzing the origin of the glass electrode potential in terms of the relative contributions of phase-boundary and diffusion processes since K reflects the equilibrium (phase-boundary) processes alone, while u_j/u_i reflects solely the diffusional processes. From this, it should be clear that the relative importance of each process to the total origin of potential can be resolved only on the basis of quantitative measurements of either K or u_j/u_i, and preferably of both. From equations 18 and 23 it should also be clear that while K^{pot} and n can be assessed by potential measurements (under zero-current conditions) alone, other methods must be used to measure K and u_j/u_i. Such measurements are presented below.

B. EXPERIMENTAL

The experimental techniques and mathematical analyses necessary to characterize the origin of potential in two types of K^+-selective, sodium aluminosilicate glasses are outlined in this section.* Bulb electrodes of about 1 cm.² surface area and 0.1 mm. thickness were studied both for electrical potential properties and radioactive tracer uptake. All glass electrodes hydrate when exposed to aqueous solutions, and such hydration can produce an heterogeneity in glass properties incompatible with the restriction of the theoretical analysis to chemically homogeneous systems. The two glasses considered here hydrate to a sufficient depth so that the properties of the hydrated "surface" (probably thicker than 10,000 A.) can be characterized independently from the properties of the "dry" interior. Moreover, the measured diffusion and ion-exchange properties of these glasses indicate that the chemical properties are sufficiently uniform over the entire hydrated thickness for the theory to be directly applicable. Other glasses (notably those having high Na selectivity) show a more complex behavior indicating that only a thin surface layer is hydrated, so that the electrode properties are a mixture of hydrated surface and "dry"-bulk glass properties. For this reason, this discussion is restricted to K^+-selective electrodes.

(1) **Potential Studies.** The electrode potentials in Na^+–K^+ mixtures at pH 5.6 and 11.3 at 25 ± 0.2°C. were very carefully measured in order to characterize the potential selectivity properties of five electrodes from two differing batches of K^+-selective glass (designated "I" and "II," but both of approximate composition NAS 27-4). The electrodes had been aged in aqueous solutions for at least 1 yr. prior to study, and had constant properties throughout the studies, which took several years to complete.

In all electrodes, the electrode potential showed a "step" response to changes in concentrations of Na^+ or K^+ in solution, and the K_{NaK}^{pot} values were time independent over a period from 5 min. to more than 12 hr. The values of K^{pot} have, therefore, been assumed to represent the steady-state values for the purpose of applying Karreman's and Eisenman's steady-state analysis. This behavior is indeed to be expected and the above assumption is supported by the recent analysis of Conti and Eisenman (16), which has proven that the steady-state electrode potential should be observed (in a uniformly hydrated glass electrode) as soon as boundary equilibria have been established at

---

* The results of preliminary experiments were reported in reference 39, and a detailed description of the present experiments is being prepared for publication (35).

the glass-solution interfaces, despite the fact that the counterion-concentration profiles and electric-potential profile within the membrane continue to change with time.

In both types of glasses equation 9 was obeyed and K_{NaK}^{pot} had the same values over the pH range 6–11 and the cation concentration range 0.01–0.10 normal. Moreover, n was found to be 1 for Na^+–K^+, Na^+–H^+, and K^+–H^+ mixtures for both compositions. The potential selectivity constants (K_{NaK}^{pot}) for type I glass in 3 separate electrodes were measured to be 10.3, 10.2, 10.3, while two electrodes made from type II composition had values of 8.7 and 8.2, all measurements on a given electrode being within ±0.1 of these values.

(2) **Diffusion Studies.** To assess the individual ionic mobility ratios of Na^+ and K^+ needed to solve equation 18, repeated studies of Na^{24} and K^{42} uptake as a function of time, after previous conditioning with nonradioactive Na^+ and K^+, were carried out on the above electrodes at $25 \pm 0.5°C$. These studies yielded the ratio of the self-diffusion coefficients which, by the Nernst–Einstein relationship (whose validity in glass has been verified by Doremus in ref. 28), equals the desired mobility ratio. Both pH and solution concentration were varied in order to measure the true self-diffusion coefficients, which are observed only when H^+ no longer displaces Na^+ and K^+ from the ion-exchange sites of the glass. The following results were obtained.

The uptake of Na^{24} and K^{42} were each found to be linear functions of the square root of time, over times as short as 30 sec. and as long as 60 hr., in both type I and type II glasses (cf. Fig. 45 for representative data on one electrode). This result is expected for diffusion from an aqueous solution of constant concentration and specific radioactivity into a semi-infinite ion exchanger, which initially contains no radioactive species.

From the slopes of Figure 45, apparent diffusion coefficients D' can be calculated through the use of equation 24 (after Crank, Ref. 17a, Eq. 3.15):

$$M_t = 2C_0 \left[\frac{D't}{\pi} \right]^{1/2} \tag{24}$$

where M_t is the total uptake of ions by the glass after a time t and C_0 is the concentration of counterions just inside the glass at solution interface.

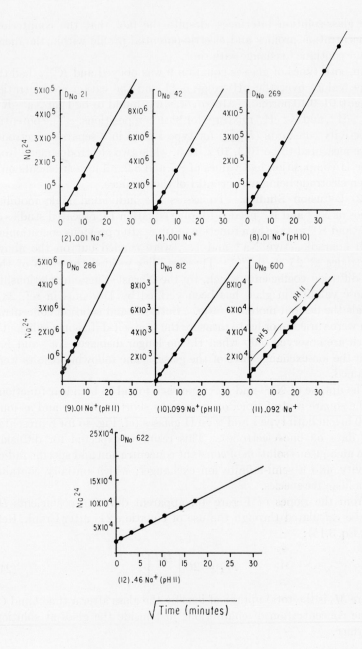

$\sqrt{\text{Time (minutes)}}$

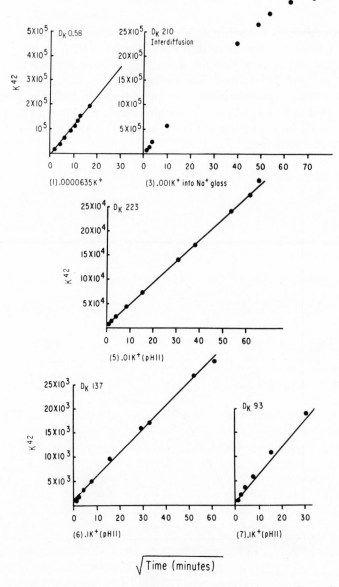

$$\sqrt{\text{Time (minutes)}}$$

Fig. 45. Na^{24} and K^{42} uptake curves by K$^+$ selective glasses. Typical curves for Na^{24} and K^{42} uptake by electrode #3 of type I glass (area 0.916 cm.^{2}). The uptake in counts per half minute (corrected for decay and background) is plotted as a function of the square root of time. The experimental sequence and solution concentrations are given below each curve (i.e., 1 means the first experiment, 2 the second, etc.). pH is 5–6 unless otherwise noted. Experiment 11 shows the lack of effect of a large pH change on the rate of uptake, while experiment 3 gives the results of an interdiffusion study in which an Na$^+$ preequilibrated glass was exposed to 0.001 K^{42} solution. 10^{18} times the values of the apparent diffusion coefficients, calculated using equation 24 in cm.^{2}/sec./C^2, are given above each curve.

If the glass is behaving as a cation exchanger as postulated, D' should become independent of the solution concentrations of Na^+ or K^+ when the ratio of Na^+ (or K^+) to H^+ becomes sufficiently high, in which limit H^+ competition for ion-exchange sites becomes negligible. This expectation was confirmed for both types of glass, as illustrated in Figure 46, for the combined data of type I glass. This result stands in strong support of the assumption that glass electrodes are cation exchangers.

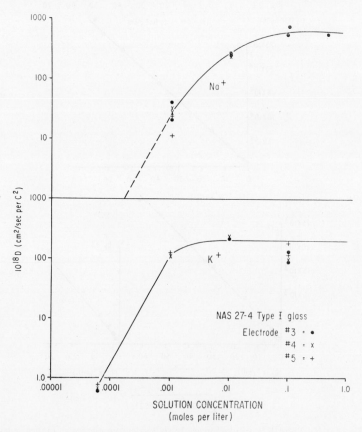

Fig. 46. Apparent diffusion coefficients for Na^+ and K^+ as a function of solution concentration. The apparent diffusion coefficients of Na^+ and K^+ for Type I glass are plotted as a function of the solution concentration of Na^+ and K^+. Experimental conditions are given in Figure 45.

The limiting values of D_{Na}' and D_K' should equal the self-diffusion coefficients D_{Na} and D_K of Na^+ and K^+ in the glass, and are taken as such for the purposes of this analysis.

From the limiting values of Figure 46, the ratio $D_K/D_{Na} = u_K/u_{Na}$ for types I and II glasses was found to be importantly different from unity, being $0.12 \pm 30\%$ and $0.23 \pm 30\%$, respectively. (Note that it is not necessary to know the value of C_0 to measure the mobility ratio.)

Combining the mobility ratios with the average potential selectivity-constant values of 10.3 ± 0.1 and 8.5 ± 0.3 for types I and II compositions, we find, through equation 18, that the ion-exchange equilibrium constants for the surface of these glasses must be $49 \pm 30\%$ and $83 \pm 30\%$, respectively, which indicates an even stronger K^+ preference by both glasses as ion exchangers than is indicated by the electrode potential selectivity.*

These results may be summarized as follows:

	K_{NaK}^{pot}. or P_K/P_{Na}	D_K/D_{Na} or u_K/u_{Na}	K_{NaK} (calculated)
Type I glass	10.3 ± 0.1	$0.23 \pm 30\%$	$49 \pm 30\%$
Type II glass	8.5 ± 0.3	$0.12 \pm 30\%$	$83 \pm 30\%$

(3) Ion-Exchange Studies. The linearity of the Na^{24} and K^{42} uptake as a function of the square root of time (up to 60 hr.) in the present K^+-selective glasses indicates that we are dealing with a reasonably uniform set of chemical properties, and that the theory developed for homogeneous chemical systems ought to be appropriate to the analysis of such glasses. Fortunately, we can carry out an independent test of the applicability of the theory to the present glasses. This consists of measuring directly the ion-exchange equilibrium constant K at the surface of the glass, and comparing the results of this measurement with the value of K, which was calculated above.

* Interestingly, careful examination of the Na^+–K^+ selectivity data at the right of Figure 8b (32) indicates that in aluminosilicate systems a higher K^+–Na^+ selectivity is achieved for ion exchange than for electric potential. This is evidenced by the continued increase in K^+–Na^+ selectivity seen in the ion-exchange data points for Na^+ to the right of the maximum in the glass Na^+ isotherm. This finding is in accord with the present results and is perhaps now more easily understandable.

Because of the inordinately long times which would be required for equilibration in electrodes of the thickness studied here, an equilibrium ion-exchange procedure was not used. Instead, the uptake of K^{42} from solutions containing mixtures of Na^+ and K^+ by electrodes preequilibrated with Na^+ was measured. The rate of K^{42} uptake, from solutions containing a constant $0.1N$ Na_2CO_3 concentration and variable K^+ concentration (of constant specific radioactivity), was examined in the limit as K^+ concentration in solution approached zero. One can express the rate of uptake of the tracer K^+ species by including in equation 24 the effect of Na^+–K^+ competition on the concentration C_0 of K^+ through the use of the ion-exchange equilibrium constant K and the ratio of Na^+–K^+ in solution (recall that $n = 1$) to yield

$$M_t = 2CK \frac{(K^+)}{(Na^+)} \left[\frac{D_K' t}{\pi} \right]^{1/2} \tag{25}$$

where C is the ion-exchange capacity of the glass, K is the ion-exchange equilibrium constant, $(K^+)/(Na^+)$ is the ratio of K^+ to Na^+ activities in solution, and D_K' is the *apparent* diffusion coefficient of K^+ in the glass.

In the limit as $K^+ \to 0$ (for a constant Na^+ concentration), it can be shown that the apparent diffusion coefficient D_K' should become equal to the self-diffusion coefficient of the tracer species, K^+. Rearranging equation 25 in the form of equation 26:

$$K^2 D_K' = \frac{(Na^+)^2}{(K^+)^2} \frac{(M_t)^2}{(2C)^2} \frac{\pi}{t} \tag{26}$$

we, therefore, have an expression in which $K^2 D_K'$ is defined completely by the known or measurable quantities on the R.H.S. of equation 26. Thus, if we measure $K^2 D_K'$ by the experiment outlined above, this value should become constant in the limit as $K^+ \to 0$, and in this limit should, moreover, be equal to the value of $K^2 D_K$ calculated from the self-diffusion and potential measurements of the preceding section. Such a comparison is presented in Figure 47 and shows satisfactory agreement, which supports both the general theory and the particular assumptions made about the glass.

(4) **Additional Properties of the Hydrated Glass Surface Revealed by Diffusion Studies.** From the above studies one can also calculate an approximate value for the self-diffusion coefficients of Na^+ and K^+

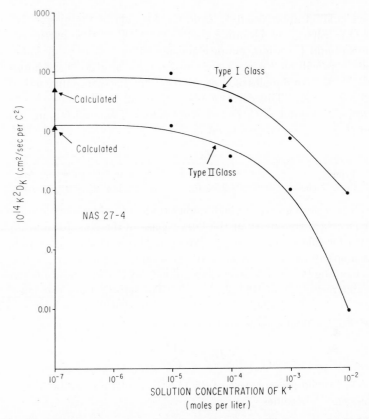

Fig. 47. Direct measurement of the ion-exchange equilibrium constant of the glass. $K^2 D_K' C^2$ calculated from uptake measurements by equation 26, is plotted as a function of K^+ concentration in solutions containing a constant $0.1N$ Na_2CO_3. In the limit to the left as the concentration of K^+ approaches zero, $K^2 D_K' C^2$ should approach a constant value, which should agree with the value of $K^2 D_K C^2$ calculated from the previous self-diffusion and potential studies as labeled at the left. The agreement can be seen to be reasonably good in both Type I and Type II glasses, and the solid curves represent a visually drawn average to the data. Individual data for Electrode #3 of Type I glass and Electrode #1 of Type II glass were used for the comparison. For these particular electrodes K and D_K were 64.4 and 112×10^{-18} cm.^{2}/sec. per C^2 and 98.4 and 11.5×10^{-18} cm.^{2}/sec. per C^2, respectively.

in the hydrated glass surface. To do this it is necessary to know the value of C_0 of equation 24, which equals the value for the ion-exchange capacity C when the glass is in the purely Na^+ or K^+ form. C can be calculated approximately from the formula of the glass $(Na_2O)_{27}$ $(Al_2O_3)_4$ $(SiO_2)_{69}$ by assuming that only $(AlOSi)^-$ sites participate in the Na^+ and K^+ migration mechanism. Thus, the formula indicates that there will be 8 g. moles of sites/g. mole of glass (i.e. 8 moles of sites/6226 g., or 8 moles of sites/2490 cm.^{3} of glass, assuming a density of 2.5 g./cm.^{3}). This corresponds to $C = 3.2 \times 10^{-3}$ moles/cm^3.

Using this value of C the following values of D_K and D_{Na} in types I and II glasses can be calculated.

	D_K	D_{Na}
Type I glass	0.2×10^{-10}	0.7×10^{-10} cm.^{2}/sec.
Type II glass	0.2×10^{-11}	1.3×10^{-11} cm.^{2}/sec.

These values are very much higher than the values calculated from the electrical resistivity of the "dry" glass in the Na^+ form at 25°C, which for this composition according to Morey (124a, Fig. XVII.10) has a specific resistivity, ρ, of 10^{10} ohm cm. (unpublished data from the Corning Glass Works on the similar NAS 27-3 composition gives a specific resistivity of $10^{9.2}$ ohm cm.). The self-diffusion coefficient of Na^+ in the glass should be related to the specific resistivity of the glass by Doremus' (27), equation 25:

$$D_{Na} = \frac{RT}{CF^2} \frac{1}{\rho} \qquad (27)$$

which, for the present case at 25°C with C assumed to be 3×10^{-3} moles cm.$^{-3}$, becomes

$$D_{Na} = 0.88 \times 10^{-4} \frac{1}{\rho} \qquad (28)$$

By inserting the value of ρ for "dry" glass in equation 28, we calculate the self-diffusion coefficient expected for Na^+ in dry glass to be between 10^{-13} and 10^{-14} cm.^{2}sec.$^{-1}$. The values measured in the hydrated glass can be seen to be at least 1000 times higher in type I glass, and at least 100 times higher in type II glass. The diffusion coefficients in hydrated glass are, therefore, intermediate between those in free solutions ($D = 10^{-5}$ cm.^{2}/sec.) and those in dry glass.

The simplest interpretation of the above observations is that hydration of glass increases the ionic mobility. Consistent with this interpretation is the finding that in certain compositions (e.g., highly Na^+-selective glasses such as NAS 11-18), which never develop a deep hydration of the surface, typical uptake curves consist of an initial rapid "step" followed by a later "creep," which is proportional to the square root of time. The Na^+ self-diffusion coefficient calculated for the "creep" agrees with the Na^+ self-diffusion coefficient measured from the electrical resistance of the dry glass, suggesting that the earlier rapid "step" corresponds to diffusion in the hydrated glass surface, while the "creep" corresponds to the diffusion in the dry glass. It therefore seems reasonable to suggest that, at least in Na_2O–Al_2O_3–SiO_2 glasses, highly Na^+-selective compositions hydrate to only a limited depth, whereas K^+-selective compositions hydrate much more deeply. Both of these observations are consistent with the view that hydration of the glasses increases with decreasing field strength. It is of interest to note that the larger diffusion constants in type I than in type II glass correlate with a lower field strength of type I glass (as judged by their selectivity-rank orders of IV and V in type I and type II glasses, respectively). Notice also that in the type I glass, now thought to be more hydrated than type II, the Na–K mobility ratio is much closer to 1, while the ion-exchange equilibrium constant is also smaller, both of which observations would be expected intuitively in a more hydrated system.

C. CONCLUSIONS

These results demonstrate that the glass-electrode potential has a mixed origin, both K and u_K/u_{Na} contributing substantially to K^{pot} (or P_K/P_{Na}), at least in two typical K^+-selective glass electrodes. The particular values measured signify that the electrode potential is made up of a phase-boundary contribution in the same direction as the total potential and a diffusion-potential contribution in the opposite direction.* The surface of both glasses shows a strong ion-exchange preference for K^+ over Na^+. K^+ is thus at the same time more permeant, less mobile, and more strongly bound than Na^+, so that the most permeant species in these glasses is not the most mobile one.

The relative contributions of the diffusion and phase-boundary potentials to the total potential in K^+-selective electrodes are illus-

---

* This conclusion is at variance with, and supersedes, the conclusion reached from preliminary experiments (39) that in K^+ selective glasses the diffusion potential accounts almost perfectly for the total potential.

trated diagrammatically in Figure 48 using the parameters from typical glass. From this it is clear that the *form* of the boundary potential is the same as the form of the total potential, whereas that of the diffusion potential is quite different. This accounts for the success of purely ion-exchange theories in accounting for the form of the glass-electrode potential. Moreover, whenever an electrode is responding with a Nernst slope to a given ion (e.g., in pure solutions), the change in potential is occurring by virtue of changes in the phase-boundary potential alone. The diffusion potential is constant in this situation and has its maximum value, $RT \log u_K/u_{Na}$, when the glass separates pure solutions of K^+ and Na^+, regardless of their concentrations.

2. The Electrode Potential Under Conditions of Nonzero Current

The conclusions presented here are based upon the analysis by Conti and Eisenman (17) of the steady-state electrical properties of a very general type of ion-exchange membrane. This analysis yields a description of the steady-state properties to be expected of glass electrodes under conditions in which current is permitted to flow across the glass membrane; and, although experiments are usually not carried out under such conditions, some of the theoretical conclusions are of sufficient importance to warrant their being given here.

A. THE EFFECT OF APPLIED CURRENT ON ELECTRODE SPECIFICITY

When an electrical current is allowed to flow through an ion-exchange membrane such as a glass electrode (or is applied to it), equation 23 must be replaced by the more general equation:

$$V = \frac{nRT}{F} \ln \frac{a_i'^{1/n} - \frac{1}{f}\frac{u_j}{u_i}[Ka_j']^{1/n}}{a_i''^{1/n} - \frac{1}{f}\frac{u_j}{u_i}[Ka_j'']^{1/n}} \tag{29}$$

which differs from equation 23 only by the presence of $-\frac{1}{f}$ multiplying u_j/u_i, where f is the ratio of the flux of J^+ to the flux of I^+. Equation 29 follows directly from equation 46 of reference 17. For zero-electric current, f, equals -1, so that for this case equation 29 reduces to 23. For nonzero membrane current, f depends upon the current as discussed below.

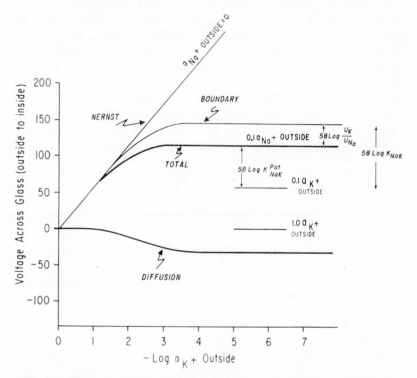

Fig. 48. Diagram of the relative contributions of diffusion potential and phase-boundary potentials to the total potential of a K⁺-selective glass electrode. This figure summarizes the various contributions to the total potential in a typical Type I glass electrode filled with a solution whose K⁺ activity is 1.0 when it is dipped in solutions having a constant 0.1N Na⁺ activity and variable K⁺ activity. The voltage measured across the glass is given on the ordinate (positive values indicating outside positive to inside) as a function of the negative logarithm of the outside K⁺ activity. The observed potential in this situation follows the heavy curve labeled "total" and is directly comparable to the data of Figure 8. The curves labeled "diffusion" and "boundary" give the diffusion potential and the sum of the boundary potentials, respectively, under these conditions. When the outside solution contains no Na⁺, the Nernst potential is observed. Notice that the boundary potential differs from the total potential by the value of the diffusion potential. The two horizontal lines labelled "0.1 aK⁺ outside" and "1.0 aK⁺ outside" represent the values of potential which would be observed in pure K⁺ solutions of these activities. Interrelationships among the values of potential are given by the arrows.

Equation 29, which is valid only in the steady state, indicates that the selectivity of an electrode can, in principle, be made infinite for either ion I^+ or J^+ by an appropriate applied current, even with an electrode having no selectivity under the usual (zero current) conditions of measurement. This can be visualized most clearly with the aid of Figure 49 (after Fig. 3 of Ref. 17), which plots the effect on the flux ratio, f, of an applied current, I. (The results of Fig. 49 are expressed in general coordinates, so that they are valid under any solution conditions for a membrane in which ions I and J can have any mobility ratio, $r = u_j/u_i$, n-type, non-ideal behavior, and any valence

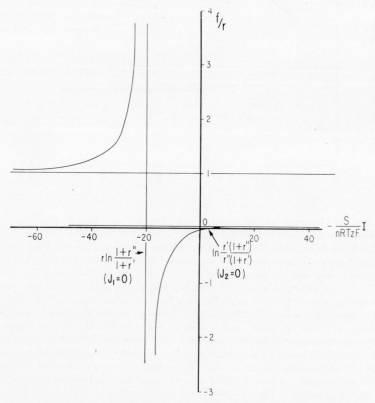

Fig. 49. Flux ratio—current relationship. (Reproduced after Fig. 3 of Ref. 17.) Species I^+ is referred to here as 1, while species J^+ is referred to as 2. $J_1 = 0$ and $J_2 = 0$ represent the currents for which the flux of I^+ and J^+, respectively, are zero. For further details in relation to the symbols, reference 17 should be consulted.

Z. The membrane need not have a uniform distribution of sites but may have any distribution, which determines the value of S.) From Figure 49 it can be seen that for the particular current for which the flux, J_1 of one species (e.g. I^+) is zero, f is infinite, while for the particular current for which the flux J_2 of the other species (e.g., J^+) is zero, f is zero. In these cases, equation 29 reduces to the respective Nernst potential for I^+ and J^+:

$$V = \frac{RT}{F} \ln \frac{a_i{}'}{a_i{}''} \tag{30}$$

and

$$V = \frac{RT}{F} \ln \frac{a_j{}'}{a_j{}''} \tag{31}$$

so that the electrode behaves as if it were infinitely selective for I^+ or J^+, respectively. This has obvious practical implications as have been noted in reference 17.

B. METHOD OF ANALYZING ALL MEMBRANE PARAMETERS FROM THE CURRENT–VOLTAGE RELATIONSHIP IN THE STEADY STATE

The results of Conti's and Eisenman's analysis also provide a method for measuring the values of u_j/u_i, K, and n (and also S) for any membrane without the need for tracer uptake studies of the type described above in Section III-1-B. This method is based on equation 84 of reference 17, which gives the current voltage relationship as

$$-I = \frac{nRTzF}{S} \left[\frac{1 - \exp\left\{\dfrac{zFV^*}{nRT}\right\}}{\alpha_1 - \alpha_2 \exp\left\{\dfrac{zFV^*}{nRT}\right\}} \right] \left(\frac{zFV^*}{nRT} + \ln \frac{\alpha_2}{\alpha_1} \right) \tag{32}$$

where I is the electric current per cm.^{2}, n is a parameter characteristic of the non-ideal behavior of the membrane (n is 1 for ideal behavior), R is the gas constant, T is the absolute temperature, z is the valence of the permeant ion, F is the Faraday constant, S is a constant for a given membrane defined by its structure (cf. Ref. 17, for details), V^* is the observed voltage for current I minus the voltage observed at zero current under the same solution conditions, and α_1 and α_2 are defined below in terms of the membrane properties and solution conditions (when water is the only solvent) as:

$$\alpha_1 = \frac{1 + \left[K\, \dfrac{a_j'}{a_i'} \right]^{1/n}}{1 + \dfrac{u_j}{u_i}\left[K\, \dfrac{a_j'}{a_i'} \right]^{1/n}} \tag{33}$$

and

$$\alpha_2 = \frac{1 + \left[K\, \dfrac{a_j''}{a_i''} \right]^{1/n}}{1 + \dfrac{u_j}{u_i}\left[K\, \dfrac{a_j''}{a_i''} \right]^{1/n}} \tag{34}$$

In equations 33 and 34, K is the ion-exchange equilibrium constant of the membrane surface, u_j/u_i is the mobility ratio of ions J^+ and I^+ within the membrane, and a_i', a_j' and a_i'', a_j'' are the activities of ions I^+ and J^+ in solutions $(')$ and $('')$, respectively.

In the limit for $V^* \to \infty$, equation 32 becomes

$$-I = \frac{nRTzF}{S\alpha_2}\left(\frac{zFV^*}{nRT} + \ln \frac{\alpha_2}{\alpha_1} \right) \tag{35}$$

While in the limit for $V^* \to -\infty$, equation 32 becomes

$$-I = \frac{nRTzF}{S\alpha_1}\left(\frac{zFV^*}{nRT} + \ln \frac{\alpha_2}{\alpha_1} \right) \tag{36}$$

Therefore, the current–voltage relationship approaches a straight line in each of these limits. These limiting straight lines intersect the V^* axis at one point

$$V^* = -\frac{nRT}{zF} \ln \frac{\alpha_2}{\alpha_1} \tag{37}$$

and the ratio of their slopes (which represent the limiting values of the dynamic conductance, Gd) is

$$\frac{\lim\limits_{V' \to -\infty} G_d(V')}{\lim\limits_{V' \to +\infty} G_d(V')} = \frac{\alpha_2}{\alpha_1} \tag{38}$$

The properties of the membrane appear in the above equations through u_j/u_i, n, K, and S. An example of a series of measurements to evaluate these quantities follows.

(1) **Measurement of Mobility Ratio,** u_j/u_i. From the definitions of α_1 and α_2 we see that for $a_j' \to 0$ and $a_i'' \to 0$:

$$\alpha_1 = 1; \quad \alpha_2 = \frac{u_i}{u_j}$$

Therefore, when of the two permeant species only the I^+ species is present in solution (') and only the species J^+ is present in solution (''), equation 38 gives

$$\frac{\lim_{V' \to -\infty} G_d(V')}{\lim_{V' \to +\infty} G_d(V')} = \frac{u_i}{u_j} \tag{39}$$

and the measurement of the ratio of the limiting slopes of the current–voltage relationship provides a direct measurement of the mobility ratio, u_i/u_j.

(2) **Measurement of Non-Ideal Behavior,** n. The intersection of the limiting straight lines with the V^* axis gives the value of n through equation 37, since α_2/α_1 is known from the above measurements.

(3) **Measurement of Equilibrium Constant,** K. Once we know n and u_i/u_j, a measurement of α_2/α_1 through equation 38 for any particular set of solution conditions can be used to obtain the value of K. One convenient set of solutions could be: $a_j' = 0$; $a_i'' = a_j''$. In this case

$$\frac{\alpha_2}{\alpha_1} = \frac{1 + K^{1/n}}{1 + \dfrac{u_j}{u_i} K^{1/n}} \tag{40}$$

so that

$$K = \left[\frac{\dfrac{\alpha_2}{\alpha_1} - 1}{1 - \dfrac{u_j}{u_i}\dfrac{\alpha_2}{\alpha_1}} \right]^n \tag{41}$$

(4) **Measurement of Structural Integral,** S. For the usual ion-exchange membrane or glass with uniformly spaced sites, $S = d/u_iC$, where d is the thickness of the membrane, u_i is the mobility of the ion I^+ in the membrane, and C is the ion-exchange capacity of the membrane (in moles/cm.³). However, in a membrane with non-uniformly distributed sites, a measurement of I for a particular value of V^* gives the value of S, once we know the value for n and u_i/u_j, through equation 32, which becomes for the case $a_j' = 0$, $a_i'' = 0$:

$$-\mathrm{I} = \frac{nRTzF}{S}\left[\frac{1 - \exp\left\{\dfrac{zFV^*}{nRT}\right\}}{1 - \dfrac{u_i}{u_j}\exp\left\{\dfrac{zFV^*}{nRT}\right\}}\right]\left(\frac{zFV^*}{nRT} + \ln\frac{u_i}{u_j}\right) \quad (42)$$

IV. THE ORIGIN OF EQUILIBRIUM SPECIFICITY

Since the specificity of glass electrodes is determined jointly by the mobility ratio, u_j/u_i, of ions within the glass and by the ion-exchange equilibrium constant, K, at the glass-solution boundaries, it is meaningful to examine their physical bases separately even though they doubtless depend on the same atomic forces characteristic of the structure of glass. This section summarizes the principal atomic factors which result in equilibrium ion-exchange specificity previously described in more detail elsewhere (31,32,35).

1. The General Equations Defining Equilibrium Specificity

A. THE ROLE OF FREE ENERGY IN ION EXCHANGE AND ELECTRIC POTENTIAL

The equilibrium specificity of a given phenomenon, such as an ion-exchange reaction, is a direct consequence of the value of the Gibbs' free-energy change of the reaction. The ion exchange of glass can be represented by

I^+ (glass) $+$ J^+ (aqueous) $\rightleftharpoons$ J^+ (glass) $+$ I^+ (aqueous) $+$ $\Delta F_{ij}{}^\circ$

where I^+ (glass) and J^+ (glass) represent the cationic species I^+ and J^+ in the glass, I^+ (aqueous) and J^+ (aqueous) represent the ions in dilute aqueous solution, and $\Delta F_{ij}{}^\circ$ is the standard free-energy change of the reaction. $\Delta F_{ij}{}^\circ$ determines directly the ion-exchange equilibrium constant K through

$$\Delta F_{ij}{}^\circ = -RT \ln K \tag{44}$$

where

$$K = \frac{a_i{}^{sol} a_j{}^{glass}}{a_j{}^{sol} a_i{}^{glass}} \tag{45}$$

in which $a_i{}^{sol}\, a_j{}^{sol}$, $a_i{}^{glass}$, $a_j{}^{glass}$ are the activities of the ions I^+ and J^+ and the solution and glass, respectively.

K also determines the specificity of the phase-boundary potentials through equations 20 and 21 and contributes to the specificity of the diffusion potential through equation 22. K appears in the total potential through equations 23 and 29.

B. THE MANNER IN WHICH FREE ENERGY DEPENDS ON CHEMICAL NATURE OF THE GLASS

The problem of understanding equilibrium specificity thus becomes one of characterizing the free-energy change of reaction 43 as a function of the chemical composition of the glass. This free-energy change can be written in terms of the interactions of the ions with water vs. their interactions with glass as

$$\Delta F_{ij}{}^\circ = (\bar{F}_{i^+}{}^{Hyd} - \bar{F}_{j^+}{}^{Hyd}) + (\bar{F}_{j^+}{}^{glass} - \bar{F}_i{}^{glass}) \tag{46}$$

where $(\bar{F}_{i^+}{}^{Hyd} - \bar{F}_{j^+}{}^{Hyd})$ represents the difference in partial molal free energies of hydration of the ions I^+ and J^+, while $(\bar{F}_{j^+}{}^{glass} - \bar{F}_{i^+}{}^{glass})$ represents the difference of their free energies of interaction with the glass.

What do we know of these energies? Those representing the interactions of the cations with water are constants characteristic of each cation and are known experimentally with great accuracy. The differences of their values referred to Cs^+ in Kcal./mole, as extracted from reference 157, are: $H^+, -192.7$; $Li^+, -54.3$; $Na^+, -30.4$; $K^+, -12.7$; $Rb^+, -7.7$; $Cs^+, 0$. On the other hand, the free energies of interaction of these ions with the glass depend upon the chemical composition of the glass. The problem of analyzing the origin of equilibrium specificity thus simplifies to the problem of characterizing the affinities of the various cations for glass as a function of its chemical composition.

2. Methods of Solution

A. SIMPLIFYING ASSUMPTIONS—THE "HALIDE MODEL"

The rigorous calculation of the energies of cation interactions with molecular anionic groups in a polymerized structure has not yet been accomplished. Nevertheless, an approximation is feasible. The most obvious simplification is to represent the principal features of the interaction between cations and the oxyanion structures of the glass by a monopolar (e.g., halide) model for the oxyanions. Under this approximation, there are two, mutually complimentary, methods of evaluating the free energy. In one, entirely empirical methods are used to evaluate the free energy of equation 46. This method, since it relies on essentially thermochemical data, will be referred to as the "thermochemical" method. It provides precise values for the free energy independent of a knowledge of the nature of forces involved or of the details of molecular structure. The other approach involves attempts to calculate the free energy of equation 46 from theoretical considerations of the elementary forces involved. This approach, which will be called the "theoretical" method, suffers from the restrictive assumptions which must be made as to the principal forces involved, but provides deeper insight into the physical basis of specificity.

B. THERMOCHEMICAL METHODS

(1) The Sixfold Coordinated Anhydrous State. Let us represent the cation-exchange sites of glass by halide prototypes. The first prototype to be considered corresponds to the situation in most of the alkali halide crystals, in which six anionic sites surround each cation and six cations surround each site, while no water molecules are present in the vicinity of sites or counterions; these restrictions will be relaxed subsequently. In such a system one can solve equation 46 directly by utilizing tables of standard free energies of formation of the alkali halide crystals, for in this case equation 46 becomes

$$\Delta F_{ij}{}^\circ = (\bar{F}_{i^+}{}^{\text{Hyd}} - \bar{F}_j{}'^{\text{Hyd}}) + (\bar{F}_{j^+}{}^{\text{Cryst}} - \bar{F}_{i^+}{}^{\text{Cryst}}) \qquad (47)$$

where $(\bar{F}_{j^+}{}^{\text{Cryst}} - \bar{F}_{i^+}{}^{\text{Cryst}})$ is the difference of crystal-lattice free energies.

In evaluating the free-energy change of equation 47 it is not necessary to solve explicitly for the partial molal free energies of hydration and of the crystal lattice, since $\Delta F_{ij}°$ can be calculated directly from standard free energies of formation by expressing the free-energy change of equation 43 as the free energies of formation ($\Delta F_f°$) of the products less those of the reactants, so that

$$\Delta F_{ij}° = \Delta F_f°I^+(aq., \text{ Hyp. } 1.0M) - \Delta F_f°J^+(aq., \text{ Hyp. } 1.0M)$$
$$+ \Delta F_f°JX(crystal) - \Delta F_f°IX(crystal) \quad (48)$$

where X represents F, Cl, Br, or I. All of the terms which we seek in equation 48 are available in standard tabulations of thermochemical data (89,157). The calculated free energies are plotted in Figure 50 as a function of the anion X^-, which is the only variable. This has been done by locating the particular anions along the abscissa in terms of their crystal radii, r^-. The particular values chosen for the radii do not alter any of the subsequent conclusions, since straight lines have been used in connecting the data points.

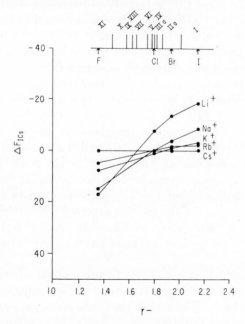

Fig. 50. Equilibrium-cation selectivity as a function of anionic crystal radius. (Reproduced with permission of the *Biophysical Journal*, after Fig. 20 of Ref. 32.)

The data points at the extreme right of Figure 50 correspond to the cation selectivity manifested by an "iodide type" site; and we note that Cs^+ is preferred to all other cations, while the sequence of decreasing cation preference is that of the lyotropic series: Cs^+, Rb^+, K^+, Na^+, Li^+. On the other hand, the data points at the extreme left correspond to a "fluoride type" site. Here, the situation is reversed, with Li^+ being preferred to all the other cations; and the sequence of decreasing preference is that of increasing naked ionic size: Li^+, Na^+, K^+, Rb^+, Cs^+. Between these two extremes, the selectivities can be seen in Figure 50 to change systematically as a function of r^-; so that the isotherms for each cation are monotonic functions of the anionic radius. The manner in which the isotherms cross each other results in a particular pattern of selectivity sequences among the cations, and the regions over which given selectivity sequences apply have been delimited by the vertical lines, each region being designated by a roman numeral to correspond to a particular rank order of cation effects (e.g. IV corresponds to the decreasing sequence: K, Rb, Cs, Na, Li). It can be seen that in this pattern, as in any other pattern of crossovers of five monotonic isotherms, there are 11 particular sequences of selectivity encountered (instead of 120 sequences expected for random behavior).

If the reader now compares these predicted sequences with those observed experimentally in Section II-4, he will find that the sequences predicted from the above simple model come very close to accounting for the sequences observed in the glass electrodes. The principal difference between the observed data and the predicted sequences is the VII a sequence ($K^+ > Na^+ > Rb^+ > Li^+ > Cs^+$) observed in the glass. This situation can be described by saying that the experimental data indicate that the Li^+ isotherm in glass appears to be displaced to the right of the position expected theoretically, so that in proceeding from right to left on Figure 16, the Li^+ isotherm crosses that of Cs^+ before the Na^+ isotherm has completed crossing those of Rb^+ and K^+.

The agreement between simple theory and experiment is initially surprising, but probably signifies that the consequences of cation–anion interaction in glass are similar to the consequences of the interaction of cations with the simplest types of anions, the halides. On the other hand, recalling that the mobility ratio has not been considered in the above calculations, the agreement with experimental results may also imply that the mobility ratio is either roughly constant (or not very different from 1) over the entire range of field strengths in the glass or that it has a very simple dependence on field strength. In this regard, note that the theoretical expectations agree with equilibrium ion-exchange data in aluminosilicates (cf. Fig. 8b of Ref. 32) in which mobility is not involved.

(2) **The Onefold Coordinated, Ion Pair, State.** It is also possible to apply the thermochemical approach to a hypothetical state with widely separated sites by considering the diatomic molecular gases of the alkali halides as an alternative state. The results of such an analysis have been presented elsewhere (cf. Figs. 4C and 4D of Ref. 31), with the conclusion that the principal features of selectivity in this state were similar to those deduced for the crystal state. Presumably, the real situation must lie somewhere between these two extremes.

C. THEORETICAL METHODS

Since it is somewhat easier to assess the effect of site spacing in terms of a purely theoretical approach, we will now use this complementary method to examine ionic specificity at equilibrium still further. The simplest theoretical case to consider retains the assumption that a halide anion is an adequate prototype for a molecular anionic site, but now we restrict the forces considered by assuming the site to be a rigid sphere and take into account only direct electrostatic interactions with the cation. Here, we shall consider first the case of widely separated sites and follow this by the case of closely spaced sites, since the theory of the latter case follows directly from that of the former.

(1) **Widely Separated Sites.** If we first assume the sites in glass to be in a state of wide separation, with water molecules excluded from their vicinity, then the free energies of interaction between cation and site needed to solve equation 46 are approximately given by the work of separating the charges as expressed by Coulomb's Law:

$$\bar{F}_{i^+}{}^{\text{glass}} \cong \frac{-332}{r_{i^+} + r^-} \tag{49}$$

and

$$\bar{F}_{j^+}^{\text{glass}} \cong \frac{-332}{r_{j^+} + r^-} \tag{50}$$

where r_i^+ and r_j^+ symbolize the naked radii of the ions I^+ and J^+. The free energies of equations 49 and 50 are in kcal./mole when the distances are in angstrom units.

Then to account for repulsion forces, equations 49 and 50 are modified using Born's approximation (cf. Ref. 8) to yield

$$\bar{F}_{i^+} \cong \frac{8}{9}\left(\frac{-332}{r_{i^+} + r^-}\right) \tag{51}$$

and

$$\bar{F}_{j^+} \cong \frac{8}{9}\left(\frac{-332}{r_{j^+} + r^-}\right) \tag{52}$$

Equations 51 and 52 differ from equations 49 and 50 only by the factor $^8/_9$, which appears because the Born exponent is approximately 9 for all alkali cations.

(2) **Closely Spaced Sites.** If, on the other hand, the sites in the glass are assumed to be very closely spaced (e.g. with six sites coordinated around each cation and six cations around each site), then the free energies of interaction of the cation in this situation will be given through the Born-Landé (8) equation for the energy of the alkali halide crystal lattice by

$$\bar{F}_{i^+} \cong 1.56\left(\frac{-332}{r_{i^+} + r^-}\right) \tag{53}$$

and

$$\bar{F}_{j^+} \cong 1.56\left(\frac{-332}{r_{j^+} + r^-}\right) \tag{54}$$

Equations 53 and 54 differ from equations 51 and 52 only by the inclusion of the geometrical Madelung constant (1.75 for sixfold coordination and the negligibly different value, 1.76, for eightfold coordination).

(3) **Conclusions.** It can be seen from equations 49–54 that the only variable determining $\Delta F_{ij}°$ for a given pair of cations is the radius of the anion, r^-. Therefore, we can represent the free-energy changes

calculated from these theoretical models as a function of r^- alone, in a manner identical to that used in drawing Figure 50.   When this was done, a nearly identical selectivity pattern to that of Figure 50 was obtained, not only for the case of closely spaced sites, but also for the case of widely spaced sites (32).

(4) **H^+ Specificity.**   If an approximate isotherm for H^+ selectivity is calculated by taking as a prototype for H^+ a point charge capable of penetrating about 0.4 A. into an ion (31,32,35) the position of this isotherm indicates that the "high field strength" anionic sites to the left of Figure 50 prefer H^+ over the group Ia cations, while low field strength sites to the right prefer the group Ia cations over H^+.

3. The Effect of Hydration of the Glass

The surfaces of all glass electrodes become hydrated to a varying extent when exposed to aqueous solutions, and the above models are only approximate since they have been restricted to situations in which water molecules are excluded from the vicinity of the counterions or the sites.   However, the specificity of systems containing water molecules should be susceptible to both thermochemical and theoretical analysis.   Since we know nothing of the intimate details regarding the numbers, positions, orientations, or freedom of motion of the water molecules in a glass surface, we will restrict our considerations here to the thermochemical approach and will base our conclusions upon the *assumption* that the state of water molecules, counterions, and sites in the hydrated glass is the same as that in an aqueous solution of comparable molality.   Under this assumption, the factors governing ionic specificity in water-swollen systems can be studied by taking an aqueous solution of a particular molal concentration in place of the crystal state considered previously so that equation 47 becomes

$$\Delta F_{ij}^{\circ} = (\bar{F}_{i^+}^{\text{Hyd}} - \bar{F}_{j^+}^{\text{Hyd}}) + (\bar{F}_{j^+}^{\text{aq., m}} - \bar{F}_{i^+}^{\text{aq., m}'}) \qquad (55)$$

where $(\bar{F}_{j^+}^{\text{aq., m}} - \bar{F}_{i^+}^{\text{aq., m}'})$ represents the difference in partial molal free energies of solutions of the halides of species J^+ and I^+ having molalities m and m'.

A. SATURATED SOLUTION MODEL

The most similar state to those considered previously is that in which m and m' are the molal concentrations in saturated aqueous solutions.   The selectivity to be expected of such a "water-swollen" system has been examined in Figure 20 of reference 32 with the finding that essentially the same selectivity pattern of the present Figure 50 continues to describe the hydrated system.

B. THE FREE SOLUTION MODEL FOR VARYING DEGREES OF WATER
  SWELLING

One can examine equation 55 further to assess the role of variable hydration on cation specificity by considering m and m' to be equal and examining the free energy of equation 55 as a function of m. $\Delta F_{ij}{}^\circ$ can be readily calculated from the values of osmotic and activity coefficients (cf. Ref. 19) by

$$\Delta F_{ij}{}^\circ = 2RT(\theta_{IX} - \theta_{JX} + \ln \frac{\gamma JX}{\gamma IX}) \qquad (56)$$

where θ and γ are the osmotic and mean-activity coefficients at molality m. When $\Delta F_{ij}{}^\circ$ is plotted as a function of r^- for a given molality, the selectivity pattern of Figure 50 is still obeyed (cf. Fig. 18 of Ref. 32), although in dilute solutions some of the sequences become obscured. Thus, regardless of the extent of "water swelling," a "fluoride type" site always selects the cations in the sequence XI (Li > Na > K > Rb > Cs), while an "iodide-type" site invariably selects the cations in the reverse sequence I (Cs > Rb > K > Na > Li). On the other hand, when $\Delta F_{ij}{}^\circ$ is plotted as a function of molality for various anion types, the effect of an increasing degree of "water swelling" is principally to decrease the magnitude of selectivity without altering the sequence of selection for a given "field strength" of anion (cf. Fig. 19 of Ref. 32).

4. General Conclusions.

The sequence (and also the magnitude) of cation effects in all of the above models, whether hydrated or not, depends only on those properties of the anion which can be represented in terms of a variable anionic radius, r^-; r^- can be regarded as controlling the "equivalent anionic field strength" of the site. Thus, we may conclude that the primary physical variable controlling equilibrium-cation specificity is the "anionic field strength" of the site. On the other hand, the amount of water admitted into the system affects the magnitude of specificity but not the sequence of relative ionic effects for a site of a given field strength.

From the above considerations it can now be seen that the data of

Figures 15, 16, 26, 30, 34, 35, and 37–39 have been plotted in such a way that the abscissa represents a continuously decreasing "anionic field strength" of the glasses.   It will now be useful to compare the theoretical conclusions with the data of Figures 15 and 16.   If "anionic field strength" were the sole factor determining not only the sequence of cationic specificity in glass electrodes but the magnitudes as well (as would be anticipated if all glass electrodes were comparably hydrated), the cation selectivity isotherms would be monotonic functions of the anionic field strength.   On the other hand, if glass electrodes tend to become increasingly hydrated as "anionic field strength" decreases toward the right of Figures 15 and 16 monotonic isotherms would no longer be expected, and the observed maximum in the Na^+–K^+ specificity isotherm would be anticipated.

One implication of the finding of a single quantitative pattern for all glass electrodes should also be commented upon here.   Considerations of anionic field strength alone can explain the qualitative aspects of the pattern, but the quantitative aspects require that hydration of the glass cannot be a variable independent of field strength.   For, as mentioned above, while anionic field strength alone governs the sequence of ion specificity, the degree of hydration can affect the magnitude of specificity.   Thus, the sequence of ion effects is characteristic of a particular field strength regardless of the extent of hydration of the system, but the magnitude of the selectivity manifested by a site of a particular field strength depends both upon the field strength and the extent of hydration of the system.   Thus, the existence of a *quantitative* pattern for glass electrodes implies not only that anionic field strength is involved in determining the electrode specificity properties, but also that all compositions of comparable field strength have comparable degrees of hydration.   It seems reasonable to postulate, therefore, that the field strength of the sites in glass must, of itself, determine the extent of hydration of the glass in a manner analogous to the way in which the number of water molecules present in a stable hydrate of an alkali halide crystal is determined by the "field strengths" of the anions and cations of the crystal lattice.

5. Theoretical Considerations of the Specificity of Ag^+, Tl^+, and NH_4^+

Ag^+, Tl^+, and possibly NH_4^+ would be expected to have substantial noncoulomb interactions with glass.   Nevertheless, the experimental isotherms of Figures 26, 30, 34, and 35 indicate that the electrode response to these ions is related in a simple way to the alkali cation specificity and, therefore, presumably also depends on the anionic field strength of the glass. The observed behavior of these ions will be compared here with the expectations of thermochemical and theoretical models to obtain further insight into the factors involved in their specificity.

If the anionic sites of glass were negligibly deformable and if the deformation of Ag^+, Tl^+, and NH_4^+ were also negligible, a purely coulombic model should predict the observed selectivities. On the other hand, if the anionic sites of the glass have a polarizability (42, 43,203,204), which varies inversely with their field strength as does that of the halide anions, and if the cations are also deformed in the same manner in glass as on the halide crystal, then a thermochemical model of the halides should predict more closely the properties of the glass. The selectivities expected for Ag^+ and Tl^+ on the basis of a thermochemical model have been calculated using the free energies of formation of the appropriate halide crystals from the tabulations of references 157 and 89 (calculations are not presented for NH_4^+ because of the absence of data for the free energies of formation and the necessity to calculate an entropy term if one wishes to use the heats of formation). The results of these calculations are given in Figure 51. For comparison with these, the selectivities were calculated by

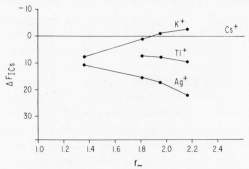

Fig. 51. Equilibrium selectivities for Ag^+ and Tl^+, calculated from the thermochemical model.

equations 53 and 54 for purely electrostatic interactions, using the crystal radii of the ions (Ag^+ 1.26 A, Tl^+ 1.44 A., NH_4^+ 1.48 A.) and assuming sixfold coordination, with the results of Figure 52.

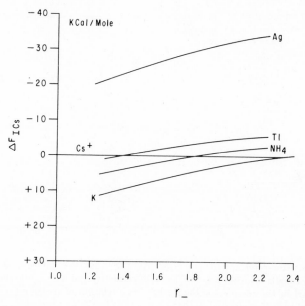

Fig. 52. Equilibrium selectivities for Ag^+, Tl^+, and NH_4^+ calculated from the theoretical model. Lattice free energies were calculated using equations 49 and 50 and the Pauling crystal radii. Heats of hydration were used to approximate the free energies of hydration and had the following values relative to Cs^+: $Ag^+ -50.68$, $Tl^+ -14.98$, $NH_4^+ -12.46$ kcal./mole (157).

For Ag^+, comparison of Figures 51 and 52 with the experimental data indicates that the situation in the glass is intermediate between that of Figure 51 (where large noncoulomb interactions of both cation and anion accompany changes of r^-) and Figure 52 (where noncoulomb interactions are disregarded). The experimental data are intermediate between the coulombic and thermochemical models at low field strengths, where the effects of polarization of Ag^+ should be most negligible but polarization of the anion is at its maximum. On the other hand, at high field strengths (where polarization of Ag^+ should be at a maximum and polarization of the anionic sites should be at a minimum), the thermochemical model is more appropriate. Therefore, it seems that the polarizability of Ag^+ plays an important role in its preference by high-field strength glasses, but that the polarizability of the anionic sites of glass is of lesser importance. For Tl^+, agreement is better with the electrostatic model than with the thermochemical model. This finding is reasonable since Tl^+ is much

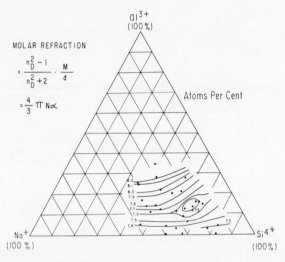

Fig. 53. Molar refractivity of $Na_2O-Al_2O_3-SiO_2$ glasses. The molar refractivity, R, calculated from measurements of refractive index (n_D) and density (d) are plotted in the manner of Figure 12. The relation of molar refractivity to polarizability (α) is indicated on the figure.

less polarizable than Ag^+. For NH_4^+, a predominantly electrostatic interpretation also seems possible for the origin of specificity.

In this regard, Figure 53 plots the molar refractivity (which is proportional to the polarizability) of $Na_2O-Al_2O_3-SiO_2$ glasses as a function of glass composition. Comparison of Figure 53 with Figure 14 indicates that the average polarizability of glass decreases with decreasing field strength, which is opposite to the situation in the "halide" model. The polarizability of oxyanion sites of the glass is, moreover, expected to be much less than that of the more polarizable halides.

6. Theoretical Considerations of the Specificity of Alkaline Earth Cations

The factors which affect the equilibrium specificity of divalent cations relative to monovalent ions depend not only on the anionic field strength of individual sites, but also very strongly upon site spacing. A brief analysis of the principal factors involved has been presented elsewhere (35), while a more detailed theoretical study of divalent ion selectivity has been carried out by A. H. Truesdell (197).*

7. Specificity Considerations Applied to the Molecular Anions of Glass

The site of cation exchange in the usual H^+ responsive glasses, which are generally alkali silicates, is diagrammed at the left of Figure 54 and will be referred to as an SiO^- type site. (Such a site occurs wherever a lattice-breaking alkali cation exists in an alkali-silicate glass or crystal. It would also occur as a result of hydrolysis at the surface of pure SiO_2.) The large circles represent oxygens (the upper one projects toward the reader). The small dark circle represents silicon, which lies at the center of the four oxygens, while the shaded cation represents Na^+. The partial circles represent adjacent oxygens of the glass. All species are drawn to a scale corresponding to their ionic crystal radii.

On the other hand, the atomic structure of the site in aluminosilicate cation-sensitive glasses or ion exchangers, is illustrated at the right of Figure 54 and will be referred to as an $(AlOSi)^-$ site. As long as the ratio of M^+/Al^{3+} in the glass exceeds 1, each Al^{3+} enters into tetrahedral coordination forcing one alkali cation from its "lattice breaking" position in the alkali silicate glass into the "interstitial" position diagrammed here. The negative charge is distributed over the entire AlO_4 configuration in this case, as symbolized by the notation "$(AlOSi)^-$".

The selectivity properties of these two types of sites have been

*Truesdell ("Theory of Divalent-Cation Exchange Selectivity," Geological Society of America, Special paper No. 76, p. 170, 1964) has recently calculated theoretically the effects of site charge, as well as of site spacing on divalent-cation selectivity, and it is appropriate to quote his conclusions here. Truesdell states: "The present investigation extends Eisenman's theory to include the selectivity of anionic substrates toward divalent cations. The assumptions made are similar to Eisenman's, with two important additions, namely, that the substrate contains $(2-)$ sites or pairs of $(1-)$ sites. The calculations showed that preference for $(2+)$ cations relative to $(1+)$ cations increased by a factor of 10^{10} when the separation of the $(1-)$ sites decreased from 20 to 5 A. Divalent ions were only preferred at $(1-)$ sites separated by less than 5 A., and were not preferred on $(2-)$ sites. The selectivity predictions from model theory agree well with experimental results on natural glasses, clays, synthetic aluminosilicate glasses and gels, and resins."

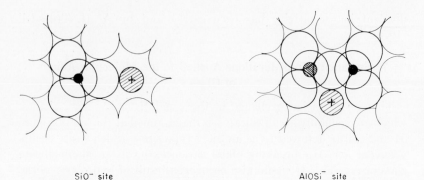

SiO⁻ site   AlOSi⁻ site

Fig. 54. Diagram of SiO⁻ and (AlOSi)⁻ sites in silicate glasses. (Reproduced with permission of the *Biophysical Journal*, after Figs. 12 and 13 of Ref. 32.) *Left*, a typical SiO⁻ site and its counterion is drawn surrounded by adjacent oxygens of the glass (partial circles). The large circles represent oxygens, the small dark circle represents silicon, while the shaded cation represents Na⁺. All species are drawn to a scale corresponding to their ionic crystal radii. *Right*, a typical (AlOSi)⁻ site is drawn to the same scale as the SiO⁻ site.

calculated elsewhere (32) by applying the considerations of the previous section to multipolar models for the SiO⁻ and (AlOSi)⁻ sites. The silicate anion, $H_3SiO^-_4$ was taken as a prototype for the SiO⁻ site, and the hypothetical "aluminate" ion, $[H_4AlO_4]^-$, was used as a prototype for the (AlOSi)⁻ site. It was concluded that the difference in the selectivity properties of these two types of sites was a consequence of the difference of their anionic field strengths, SiO⁻ having a much higher field strength than (AlOSi)⁻.

We can, therefore, conclude that particular glass electrodes (e.g., the pH electrode) are representatives of a continuous family of generally cation-sensitive compositions, which differ only as a consequence of the differing field strengths of their sites. Glasses having high field strength sites are H⁺ selective, while glasses, whose sites are of an appropriately lower field strength, are selective for other cations. From this we can understand why an alkali silicate glass is pH selective and why the introduction of Al into such a glass results in cation-responsive electrodes. Moreover, we can also understand why a glass need not contain in its original composition the cation to which it is primarily responsive. All of the present experimental observations for Ag⁺, Tl⁺, NH_4^+, Mg^{2+}, Ca^{2+}, Sr^{2+}, and Ba^{2+}, as well as the previous results for Li⁺, Na⁺, K⁺, Rb⁺, Cs⁺, and H⁺ are consistent with the view that the "anionic field strength" of the glass is a principal parameter in determining selectivity. The following section will, therefore, develop explicit methods for assessing the "anionic field strength" as a function of glass composition.

8. Methods for Assessing the Anionic Field Strength of Glass

A. QUALITATIVE EFFECTS: ANIONIC FIELD STRENGTH ASSESSED BY USING PAULING'S ELECTROSTATIC VALENCE RULE

The "anionic field strength" of the sites in glasses of diverse composition can be estimated qualitatively using Pauling's "Electrostatic Valence Rule" (140). To do this we assume, following Pauling, that the residual bonding strength of oxygen will be given by the difference between its charge $(2-)$ and the strength of the bonds (usually 2 in number) from the adjacent (lattice forming or modifying) cations. Pauling's "Electrostatic Valence Rule" defines the strength of the electrostatic bond from each such cation as the ratio of its charge (or oxidation state), Z, to its coordination number, V.

Consider the residual bonding strength of an oxygen in configuration **1**, which represents the (predominantly H^+ preferring) cation-

$$—Si^{IV}—O^-$$

$$(1)$$

exchange site of a silicate glass in which the alkali ions have interrupted some of the bridging oxygen bonds between adjacent silica tetrahedra. The oxygen is reached by only one bond from silicon of strength $(Z/V = {}^4/_4)$ and, therefore, bears a residual bond of strength 1 (i.e., $2 - 1$). Such a site is expected on the basis of theory (cf. Sec. IV-7) to be highly H^+ specific, and this expectation is amply confirmed by experiment. On the other hand, the bridging oxygen between the two silica tetrahedra in configuration **2** has a residual

$$—Si^{IV}—O—Si^{IV}—$$

$$(2)$$

bonding strength of 0 (i.e., $2 - \frac{4}{4} - \frac{4}{4}$) and does not function as a site for cation exchange since it bears no net charge.

When an element R in oxidation state III is introduced into glass in place of Si^{IV}, we have configuration 3, in which the replacement has

$$\left[-R^{III}-O-Si^{IV}- \right]^{-}$$

$$(3)$$

produced a site for cation exchange, the local structure bearing a net negative charge as indicated on the diagram. The oxygen common to the R and Si tetrahedra is reached by bonds of total strength $(\frac{3}{4} + \frac{4}{4})$ and, therefore, has a residual strength of only $\frac{1}{4}$. Such a site from previous theory (cf. Sec. IV-7) has a low field strength and should be cation selective, as is born out by experiment.

The configuration illustrated in diagram 2 also occurs when any element in oxidation-state IV occurs in four fold coordination, as is diagrammed for the case of Zr^{IV} below.

$$-Zr^{IV}-O-Si^{IV}-$$

$$(4)$$

Here, as in configuration 2, there is no net charge and the residual bonding strength is zero. However, since Zr^{IV} is capable of existing in sixfold coordination, the possibility also exists for configuration 5,

$$\left[-Zr^{IV}-O-Si^{IV}- \right]^{2-}$$

$$(5)$$

which leads to a group bearing a double negative charge (and hence becoming an ion-exchange site for two singly charged counter-cations or one doubly charged counterion). Despite the double charge, the residual bond strength of the oxygen is only $\frac{1}{3}$ (i.e., $2 - \frac{4}{4} - \frac{4}{6}$); and such a bond strength has been found experimentally (32,93) to exhibit cation sensitivity relative to H^{+}.

For silicate-type glasses to which various lattice forming or modifying elements are added to produce the desired cation sensitivity, one of the bonds to the oxygen comes from silicon and the other from the added element. Since Si(IV) exists in four fold coordination in these situations, it may be thought of by Pauling's "Electrostatic Valence Rule" as neutralizing one of the charges of the oxygen completely. The residual bonding strength of the oxygen (RBS) will, therefore, depend solely upon the ratio of the oxidation state (Z) and coordination number (V) of the added element by

$$RBS = 1 - Z/V \qquad (57)$$

the residual bonding strength being given by subtracting, from the oxygen's single remaining charge, the value of the strength of the bond (Z/V) from the introduced cation. It has been found experimentally that when residual bonding strength $\leq$ $^1/_2$, the resulting "anionic field strength" is appropriate for substantial cation sensitivity relative to H$^+$. This requirement is satisfied when $1 > Z/V \geq {}^1/_2$ (if $Z/V >$ 1, anion exchange* sites are produced); and permits the formulation of the following hypothesis:

The essential requirement for producing cation selectivity is the introduction of a structural element into the lattice in a coordination state higher than its oxidation state. Such an introduction produces a fixed anionic site of a field strength appropriate to cation selectivity whenever the disproportion between oxidation state and coordination leads to a residual bonding strength of the oxygen of $^1/_2$ or less.

The above hypothesis can be used to explain the effects of introducing such species as Al^{III}, B^{III}, Sc^{III}, and Zr^{IV} all of which lead to cation selectivity (32) when added to glass. It also can explain why replacing Si^{IV} by Ge^{IV} in fourfold coordination leads to no important change in selectivity properties (32), although when Ge^{IV} is introduced in sixfold coordination, cation specificity is to be expected and has been found (6).

To simplify terminology, configurations 1–3 and 5 can be abbreviated as Si^{IV}O$^-_4$, Si^{IV}O$_4$Si, [R^{III}O$_4$Si]$^-$, and [Zr^{IV}O$_6$Si]$^{2-}$, respectively, where the roman superscripts correspond to Z and the Arabic subscripts correspond to V. The number of exchangeable counterions resulting for each atomic substitution is indicated by the net charge of the group. Thus, an element R entering into a glass in oxidation

---

* For considerations of anion selectivity see reference 35.

state V and coordination number 6 would produce a cation-sensitive site having one countercation attracted by a residual bonding strength of $1/6$ and would be symbolized as $(R^V O_6 Si)^-$.

B. QUANTITATIVE EFFECTS—THE EFFECT OF THE M/R RATIO ON ANIONIC FIELD STRENGTH

The preceding section has indicated a method for calculating those replacements which will lead to systems having useful cation sensitivity relative to H^+. The present section will set forth a working hypothesis for the quantitative effects of varying glass composition in such systems.

(1) **Implications of the Existence of a Single Specificity Pattern.** In Section II-4-B it was established that a single specificity pattern describes the effects of the various alkali metal cations in Al_2O_3-containing glasses, regardless of whether these contain Li_2O, Na_2O, K_2O, Rb_2O, or Cs_2O. A similar finding has been illustrated in Sections II-5 and II-6 for Ag^+, Tl^+, NH_4^+, Mg^{2+}, Ca^{2+}, Sr^{2+}, and Ba^{2+}. A number of simplifications result directly from these findings. The most important result is that the selectivity for all ions was shown to be expressible in terms of the Na^+–K^+ selectivity alone. The dependence of Na^+–K^+ selectivity on glass composition will be examined below, and the relationships presented will, therefore, describe the effects of composition not only on Na^+–K^+ selectivity, but on the selectivities for all of the above mentioned cations.

It should also be noted that the existence of a single specificity pattern for the present glasses is to be expected from theory if the principal interactions between the cations and the glass are between the cations and their first nearest neighbors (oxygen atoms), while the effects of more distant atoms appear only by altering the effective field strength of the oxygen. This correspondence between theory and experimental observation implies a similar theoretical basis for the quantitative pattern of biological cation effects, which is similar to that of glass electrodes (33).

(2) **Na-K Selectivity as a Function of the Na/Al Ratio.** The Na^+–K^+ selectivity in sodium aluminosilicate glasses has been shown in Section II-4 A to depend only on the ratio Na^+/Al^{3+} (or the equivalent ratio, Na_2O/Al_2O_3). This relationship is conveniently expressed by plotting the Na^+–K^+ selectivity of Figure 12 as a func-

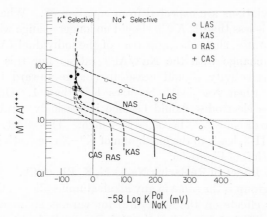

$$-58 \ \text{Log} \ K^{\text{Pot}}_{\text{NaK}} \ (\text{mV})$$

Fig. 55. Dependence of Na$^+$–K$^+$ selectivity on the alkali cation to aluminum ratio in glass. The curve labeled NAS plots the empirical relationship between $K^{\text{pot}}_{\text{NaK}}$ and Na$^+$/Al^{3+} (at constant 50 atom%) extracted from the data of Figure 12. The curves labeled LAS, KAS, RAS, CAS correspond to the relationships expected for Li, K, Rb, and Cs aluminosilicate glasses, respectively. Experimental data are plotted as open circles for LAS, as solid circles for KAS, as open squares for RAS, and as crosses for CAS. The vertical line separates K$^+$-selective from Na$^+$-selective compositions. From the values of $K^{\text{pot}}_{\text{NaK}}$ one can predict the approximate selectivities for the other alkali cations through Figures 15 and 16 and for other cations through Figures 26, 30, 34, 35, 37, and 38.

tion of Na$^+$/Al^{3+} ratio, as has been done in the solid curve of Figure 55. Notice that over a significant range there is a linear relationship between Na$^+$/Al^{3+} ratio and log $K^{\text{pot}}_{\text{NaK}}$, expressible by equation:

$$\log K^{\text{pot}}_{\text{NaK}} = 7.42 \log \frac{\text{Na}^+}{\text{Al}^{3+}} - 3.2 \qquad (58)$$

(The fine straight lines in Figure 55 correspond to the linear region described by Eq. 58.) The above dependence of $K^{\text{pot}}_{\text{NaK}}$ upon Na$^+$/Al^{3+} ratio is to be expected under the postulate that the electrostatic field strength of the (AlOSi)$^-$ site governs selectivity, since every Na$^+$ in excess of Al^{3+} will "screen" the (AlOSi)$^-$ site so as to lower the effective field strength. Therefore, for all glasses in which Na$^+$/Al^{3+} exceeds 1, the larger the Na$^+$/Al^{3+} ratio, the lower will be the field strength. Consequently, the larger the Na$^+$/Al^{3+} ratio, the less preferred should Na$^+$ be relative to K$^+$. This leads to the linear portion of the NAS curve.

Two deviations are expected from equation 58. When the $Na^+/$ Al^{3+} ratio is less than 1, K_{NaK}^{pot} should no longer change with changing Na^+/Al^{3+} ratio, since the properties of the individual $(AlOSi)^-$ sites no longer change with the Na^+/Al^{3+} ratio. For this reason, the Na^+-K^+ selectivity should cease to change toward the right of Figure 55 when Na^+/Al^{3+} becomes less than 1. On the other hand, glass electrodes should become increasingly "water swollen" as the ratio of Na^+/Al^{3+} becomes very high. This effect, as discussed in Section II-3, leads to the maximum of K^+-Na^+ selectivity observed toward the left of Figure 55.

(3) **The Effect of Replacing Na by Li, K, Rb, or Cs.** Although the $(AlOSi)^-$ group is the same in any alkali aluminosilicate, the screening effects (or effects on the structure) for various alkali cations, M^+, should be different for each cation (cf. Fajans, Refs. 42, 43 and Weyl, Refs. 203, 204). Let us, therefore, postulate that the only difference from one alkali aluminosilicate to another will be that a different ratio of M^+/Al^{3+} will be needed to produce a given field strength (and hence a given selectivity). This leads to the prediction that not only does the ratio Na^+/Al^{3+} determine the selectivity of sodium aluminosilicates, but more generally, that the ratio M^+/xAl^{3+} determines the selectivity of alkali aluminosilicates, where x is a proportionality constant characteristic for each alkali cation. Thus, all Al^{3+}-containing glasses having the same ratio M/xAl would be expected to have the same electrode selectivity properties.

This line of reasoning can be used to predict the dashed curves labeled LAS, KAS, RAS, CAS of Figure 55 for the Li_2O, K_2O, Rb_2O, and Cs_2O homologues of the $Na_2O-Al_2O_3-SiO_2$ glasses. The extent to which these predictions are satisfactory is indicated by the plotted data points for these glasses. Since the data agree with the expectations, we can write equation 58 more generally as

$$Log\ K_{NaK}^{pot} = 7.42 \log \frac{M}{Al} - 7.42 \log x - 3.2 \qquad (59)$$

where x has the following values for Li, Na, K, Rb, and Cs, respectively: 2.5, 1.0, 0.6, 0.5, 0.37. This means that when one replaces Na_2O by Li_2O one needs to use only $1/2.5$ as many moles of Al_2O_3 to obtain a given set of electrode selectivity properties. On the other hand, if one replaces Na_2O by K_2O, one needs nearly twice as much Al_2O_3 to obtain a given selectivity, and so forth.

(4) **The Effect of Replacing Al by Other Elements.** It seems reasonable to propose that a similar relationship should also be true when Al is replaced by any other elements which give sites of an appropriate "anionic field strength" by the considerations of Section IV-8-A. For the particular case in which Al^{III} is replaced by another element, R^{III}, in fourfold coordination, all that should be needed to characterize such a system would be a new set of scaling factors, x', for the various alkali cations in place of the ones appropriate in the Al^{III} system.

C. SUMMARY

The above results suggest a general method for designing new cation-selective glass compositions. First, calculate the residual bonding strength of the proposed composition to decide whether a contemplated substitution will yield a system of appropriate field strength. Next, prepare glasses in such a system and characterize the Na^+–K^+ selectivity as a function of the M/R ratio, particularly in those regions to which equation 59 should apply. This provides a description of the dependence of Na^+–K^+ selectivity upon composition, which should define approximate selectivities for all other cations according to the cation-specificity isotherms of Figures 15, 16, 26, 30, 34, 35, and 37–39.

V. REVIEW OF THE LITERATURE

This section includes a survey of uses to which cation-sensitive electrodes are being applied, and provides a comprehensive bibliography. Some earlier uses have been surveyed elsewhere (32,49,77, 112,126,127) and a contributed volume is in preparation detailing the principles and practice of glass electrodes sensitive to H^+ and other cations (35a).

1. Studies of Fundamental Properties

The applied studies in the following part 2, have contributed much to our knowledge of the fundamental properties of cation-sensitive glasses. However, the recent work of a number of authors, which has been directed toward characterizing the fundamental properties of glass electrodes, will first be summarized here.

A. EFFECTS OF GLASS COMPOSITION

Outstanding among the recent studies of the effect of composition on glass-electrode properties is a series of papers from the U.S.S.R. by Nicolskii et al. (6,133–137,167–176). (I am indebted to J. O. Isard and A. Lev for calling these papers to my attention and to the Corning Glass Works and to M. Cable for translations.) Nicolskii et al. (134) have shown that alkali silicate glasses (from the class of Li_2O or Na_2O silicates) develop selectivity for the alkali metal cations when Al_2O_3, Ga_2O_3, B_2O_3, Fe_2O_3, or SnO_2 are added to the glass, and Shul'ts et al. (172,174) have extended these observations to TiO_2 and ZrO_2. In a further paper, Belijustin and Shul'ts (6) find significant cation selectivity to be produced in sodium silicate glasses by addition of oxides of Ge^{IV}, Sn^{IV}, P^V, Sb^{III}, and Bi^{III}. Shul'ts and Belijustin (167) and Shul'ts et al. (171) have also examined the cation selectivity, which results from adding Ga_2O_3 and In_2O_3 to $Na_2O–SiO_2$ glasses, and of adding B_2O_3 or Ga_2O_3 to $Li_2O–SiO_2$ glasses. Shul'ts proposes "that the oxides B_2O_3, Al_2O_3, Ga_2O_3, In_2O_3, Sb_2O_3, Fe_2O_3 will influence glass-electrode properties in a generally similar way" and, moreover, that "this influence is somewhat different for the oxides La_2O_3, Nd_2O_3, and Y_2O_3." He suggests that the development of cation selectivity is due to the presence of B^{III} and Ga^{III} in fourfold coordination in such glasses, a view in accord with that advanced in reference 32 and in Section IV. In summarizing the Russian work, Shul'ts (176) states that "the dependence of electrode properties upon their chemical composition is determined by the latter's influence on the energy state of the alkali metal ions and hydrogen ions in the glass," from which it can be seen that the Russian workers interpret the dependence of electrode selectivity upon chemical composition of glass, in a manner similar to that expounded in Section IV. These authors formulate the energies in terms of an ion-exchange process, but neglect the possibility of diffusional contributions to the potential and assume quite literally that the measured potential selectivity constant directly represents the ion-exchange equilibrium constant. In reading their papers, one should, therefore, realize that wherever an "ion-exchange constant" is described, it corresponds to the potential selectivity constant, K^{pot}, and not the true ion-exchange equilibrium constant, K. Shul'ts discusses the various states of oxygen in glass and concludes that differences in "acidity" between SiO^- and $AlOSi^-$ sites causes the "step" form of the electrode potentials in glasses with small amounts of M_2O_3 oxides, as has already been discussed in Section II-3-D.

Other laboratories have also been concerned with the effects of composition on glass-electrode sensitivities. Lengyel and Csakvari (93) have studied the effects on the "alkaline error" of replacing SiO_2 by 12 mole-% of the oxides GeO_2, P_2O_5, TiO_2, PbO, ZnO, BeO, and La_2O_3 in a glass of base composition 72 mole-% SiO_2, 6.4 mole-% CaO, 21.4 mole-% Na_2O. They concluded that the strongest cation sensitivities resulted from additions of Al_2O_3, B_2O_3, and ZrO_2. Tendeloo et al. (186) and Mans and Kateman (107) have recently reported in detail on the properties of potassium–silicate glass electrodes containing BeO_2 (which should have cation-selective sites of type $[Be^{II}O_4]^{2-}$). They find that a glass (K_2O 21, BeO 6, SiO_2 73 mole-%) responds satisfactorily to K^+ and Na^+, but not to Ca^{2+}, and give a decreasing selectivity sequence for their glass of H^+, Ag^+, Rb^+, K^+, NH_4^+, Na^+, Li^+, $C_3H_7(NH_3)^+$. Savage and Isard (158) have characterized many details of the properties of cation-sensitive silicate glasses containing Al_2O_3 and B_2O_3.

In view of the results outlined in Section IV, all of the above findings are understandable in terms of the "anionic field strength" produced by these replacements; and many of the observations can now be seen to have been foreshadowed by Perley's systematic studies (142) of the effects of small additions (2 mole-%) of various oxides on the pH error of Li_2O–Cs_2O–BaO silicates. Perley found increasingly larger "alkaline errors" when the following oxides were added to glass: La_2O_3, Pr_2O_3, CeO_2, Nd_2O_3, TeO_3, P_2O_5, Mn_2O_3, TiO_2, CoO, Co_2O_3, ZrO_2, Cb_2O_5, Ta_2O_5, ThO_2, As_2O_5, UO_2, B_2O_3, Cr_2O_3, WO_3, SeO_2, V_2O_5, Al_2O_3, MoO_3, and Tl_2O_3. Many of the elements Perley found to lead to the largest "alkaline errors" are exactly the ones one expects, from the considerations of Section IV, to produce substantial cation sensitivity when added in larger amounts.

B. ELECTRODE PROPERTIES AND DURABILITY

Savage and Isard (158) have studied in detail many important properties of Na_2O–Al_2O_3–SiO_2 and Na_2O–B_2O_3–SiO_2 glasses for the purpose of establishing relationships between electrode potential and durability of glass. They note that such relationships are not only of theoretical importance, but would be of use technologically. They have examined the time course of electrode potentials in Na^+, Li^+, and K^+ solutions and find that the steady response is reached in periods ranging from a few minutes to more than an hour, depending upon experimental conditions. They observe that leaching an electrode in distilled water at 60°C. for 48 hr. produces an extremely sluggish response.

C. LOW-TEMPERATURE STUDIES

LePoutre et al. (97) have examined the low-temperature behavior of Na^+-selective glasses of NAS 11-18 and LAS (Electronics Instruments Ltd. BH 68) types. They used either mercury or alcoholic NaCl solutions on the inside of the electrode and found that they could measure potentials reproducibly at temperatures as low as −40°C.

2. Applications

Glass electrodes specific for cations should be useful wherever a direct measurement of ionic *activity* is desired, whether this be in a simple solution or in a complex ionic mixture, *in vitro* or *in situ*. The electrodes offer unique advantages over other methods when high sensitivity, nondestructive, continuous, or *in situ* recording of ionic activity is desired. Glass electrodes may also be used to estimate ionic *concentration*, provided proper account is taken of activity coefficients, or empirical standardization procedures are used. Alternatively, the solution in question can be serially diluted and concentrations evaluated by extrapolation to infinite dilution.

Cation-selective glass electrodes have been proved to respond reversibly to many cations (32,163, see also Section II) and to be indifferent to most anions (13,36,37) although certain anions such as fluoride (13) have been reported to affect the electrode response. The electrodes are also unaffected by the presence of oxidizing or reducing substances, or of protein (36,37,123); although unusually high concentrations of protein or amino acids may themselves produce particular responses because of their cationic groups (cf. Sec. II-6-D).

A. COMMERCIALLY-AVAILABLE GLASS ELECTRODES

Glass electrodes selective for various cations are now available commercially. Tubing and electrodes of Na^+-selective NAS 11-18 and K^+-selective NAS 27-4 glass are made by the Corning Glass Works; Electronics Instruments Ltd. makes Na^+- and K^+-glass electrodes of both dip and flow-through types from somewhat different compositions; and the Beckman Instrument Company also makes both Na^+- and K^+-selective electrodes, the former (78178) being a lithium aluminosilicate and the latter (78137) being a sodium aluminosilicate of approximately NAS 27-4 composition. The properties of NAS 11-18 and NAS 27-4 glasses are described in Section II, as well as in 32,36–38, 44–52,55,56,70,84,98,123,124,148–151,158,163,177; references 22, 111–118 give the characteristics of the Na^+-selective compositions made by Electronics Instruments Ltd., and the properties of the Beckman electrodes are summarized in references 5, 9–11,13,125, 181. The general procedures to follow in using such electrodes are similar to those outlined in the previous sections. It should be recalled that electrodes such as the Beckman 78137 type require aging in aqueous solutions to develop their maximum K^+ selectivity.

B. GENERAL ELECTRODE PROPERTIES

(1) **Precision and Accuracy.** (a) Na^+ *Electrodes.* Most Na^+-selective electrodes are sufficiently Na^+ specific relative to K^+ that they can be used for the direct measurement of Na^+ without need to correct for K^+. Friedman (49) has recently reviewed high-precision applications, emphasizing biological uses. Mattock (115) reports response times of 2–7 min. (faster in more concentrated solutions) for E.I.L.–Na^+ electrodes, and suggests wiping the electrodes dry rather than rinsing them with water to obtain the fastest response. He concludes that the practical discrimination level for Na^{+*} electrodes of the dip type is of the order of 0.01 to 0.02 pNa^+ (2–4.5% in terms of concentration); while Friedman (49) using flow-through electrodes finds that Na^+ concentration can be measured much more precisely (to values approaching the 0.2% level of accuracy), a finding substantiated by the results of Portnoy (148) and Garrels (53) in other applications. Consistent with the above, Hyman (76) concludes that readings can usually be reproduced to 0.5 mv. and, with extra care, to about 0.02 mv. Friedman and Bowers (51) also report that with flow-through electrodes steady potentials are reached for Na^+- and

* $pNa^+ = -Log_{10} a_{Na^+}.$

K^+-selective electrodes within 10–20 sec. (*sic*); although they recommend waiting 2 min. for taking readings because NAS 11-18 glass responds transiently to traces of K^+ (cf. Ref. 51, Fig. 4).

(*b*) *K^+ Electrodes.* Glass electrodes have not been as extensively studied for the measurement of K^+ as for Na^+ measurement, and often require a simultaneous measurement of Na^+ because of their lower selectivity (i.e., only 10 to 1 in favor of K^+ over Na^+). Friedman (49) and Portnoy (148) have both reported accuracies for K^+ approaching those for Na^+. Mattock (115,116) has reported that the practical range of usefulness of E.I.L.'s K^+-selective BH 115 glass electrode (which has a selectivity constant for K relative to Na of about 7 to 1) is from MK to 4 p.p.m. He finds that the response time is about 2 min. to reach the 0.01–0.02 pK^+ level of accuracy, except when the K^+ concentration is less than 10^{-3} where it becomes 3–4 minutes. (See also the recent studies by Mattock and Uncles, Ref. 118a.) Many practical aspects of K^+ measurement are discussed in the papers by Portnoy et al. (148–152), Khuri et al. (84,85), Friedman et al. (44–51), Hinke (69,70), and Lev et al. (100–102).

(*c*) *Measurement of Ag^+.* Mattock and Uncles (118) have reported on the analytical possibilities of using Na^+-sensitive electrodes for the measurement of Ag^+. Defining pAg in concentration terms as $-\log C_{ag^+}$, they found the electrode response to be linear over the pAg range 0–5 and still apparent at pAg 5 (corresponding to approximately 0.1 p.p.m. of Ag), which is in agreement with the results of Section II-5-A. They note that the speed of electrode response to Ag^+ was better than to Na^+ and that drying and wetting of the electrode did not affect the response time adversely. Budd (13) also has reported on the usefulness of the Ag^+ response of the two commercially available Beckman electrodes. Budd's results are in agreement with Mattock's findings. In addition, Budd reports that the electrode is poisoned neither by cyanide nor sulfide, and is affected adversely only by fluoride or concentrated alkali. He notes that there is very little effect from as much as a thousandfold excess of Na^+ over Ag^+, and that K^+ has no measurable effect upon the measurement of Ag^+.

(*d*) *Measurement of NH_4^+.* Mattock (115,116) has noted that the BH 115 electrode can be used for the measurement of NH_4^+ probably down to the range of 10 p.p.m. (Sec. II-5-C).

(*e*) *Measurement of Tl^+.* Mattock (115,116) has reported a limited Tl^+ response of the Na^+-selective BH 68 glass, but the reproducibility is poor. He suggested that a measurement of Tl^+ might be useful in the determination of the relative amount of Tl (I) in the presence of Tl (III). Since, from Figure 30, BH 68 can be seen to be one of the less selective glasses for Tl^+, compositions lying further toward the right of this figure should be more appropriate for the measurement of Tl (I). For further details on Tl^+ response, see Section II-5-B.

(f) *Measurement of Li^+.* Mattock and Uncles (118) have commented upon the possible usefulness of the Na^+-selective BH 68 glass for the measurement of Li^+. Their results, with which the observations of Section II-4-C 4 are in agreement, led them to conclude that over the range pLi 0–4 the Li^+ response was certainly good enough for purposes of measurement.

(g) *Measurement of Divalent Cations.* Of the glasses described in this paper, only those lying to the extreme right of Figures 36 and 37 are likely to be of interest for the measurement of divalent cations; and none of the present electrodes have sufficiently high selectivities to be of practical usefulness for the measurement of Ca^{2+} activity in fluids such as blood. The most promising developments for divalent cation electrodes are due to Garrels et al. (54) and to Truesdell and Pommer (196). Garrels et al. have reported that electrodes made from glass membranes, glued with thermoplastic cement to a supporting stem, can have a substantial response to Ca^{2+} ion. They find that the development of sensitivity to divalent cations is apparently dependent upon the ratios of the monovalent, divalent, and trivalent oxides in the glass, rather than upon their specific nature. Most of the compositions which they report to have substantial divalent selectivities appear to contain relatively large amounts of divalent oxides, which distinguishes them from the glasses characterized in Section II. Truesdell and Pommer have studied cemented membranes of a phosphate glass and report it to have a significant selectivity for alkaline earth cations. Since the electrical resistance and speed of response of their electrode is strongly influenced by prior conditioning, they conclude that "this electrode is practical only if calcium activities must be known, even at the price of considerable inconvenience."

(2) **Comparison with Flame-Photometer.** Friedman (49) states that in his experience the NAS 11-18 electrode will "outperform flame-photometry by a wide margin" in the measurement of Na^+; and Mattock (116) notes good agreement in the results of a number of authors who have compared C_{Na^+} measured by glass electrodes with C_{Na^+} measured by the flame-photometer. Many other compari-

sons of electrode and flame-photometer measurements have been carried out and will be referred to below in relation to particular applications. In particular, the studies by Moore and Wilson (123), Khuri et al. (84,85), Bower (9–11), and Taulli (181) should be noted.

(3) **Liquid Junction Potentials.** Hyman (76) has studied the liquid junction potentials of various reference electrodes in solutions in which part of the water has been replaced with dextrose or ethyl alcohol. He suggests that a mixed KCl–KNO_3 bridge solution may be more useful than the usual saturated KCl solution. Hyman also presents evidence, from studies of $NaCl$ solutions with several types of salt bridge, in support of the usual assumption that the activity coefficients of Na^+ and Cl^- are equal to each other and to the mean activity coefficient of $NaCl$ in moderately concentrated solutions.

A number of authors have successfully used a glass electrode as a reference electrode for another type of glass electrode to eliminate the liquid junction potential (Garrels, 53). Khuri (personal communication), in measuring the pH of arterial blood, has used an NAS 11-18 glass as a reference electrode for his pH glass electrode and confirmed the usual assumption that a saturated KCl–calomel reference electrode eliminates the liquid junction potential in blood.

(4) **Computer Solutions for Cation Analysis with Glass Electrodes.** Friedman and Bowers (51) have recently used a Na^+ and K^+-electrode pair to obtain simultaneous measurements of Na^+ and K^+ activities, using an analogue computer to process the information obtained from the glass electrodes. They find that sodium and potassium activities can be read directly and continuously. The computer solution is quite general and can be modified to suit any similar electrode pair. Their calculation involves the linearization of the exponential electrode response using a function generator adjusted to cover a preselected range of values. The assembly is capable of high precision and reproducibility. It should be noted that since a single calomel electrode served as a common reference to both glasses, the electrodes were, in effect, pitted against each other and the liquid-junction potential eliminated in this manner.

C. ELECTRODE CONSTRUCTION

(1) **Microelectrodes.** The earliest method of constructing and using microelectrodes of Na^+ and K^+-selective glasses was published

by Hinke (69,70). Subsequent to this work, Khuri et al. (84,85) have published a simpler method of microelectrode construction using internal insulation to localize the electrode response to the electrode tip but find it desirable to supplement the internal insulation by an additional polystyrene external insulation. With such a design Khuri (personal communication) has successfully made and used electrodes of NAS 11-18 and KAS 20-5 glass having a tip diameter of less than 2 μ. Still more recently, Lev (98) has made Na^+ and K^+ microelectrodes with an active length of 3 μ and tip diameters as small as 0.6 μ, and applied these to the study of ionic activities inside single fibers of frog skeletal muscle.

(2) **Flow-through Electrodes.** Extensive studies on flow-through electrodes have been carried out by Friedman and his colleagues (44–52) and by Portnoy et al. (148,149). Such electrodes generally yield more precise results than dipping electrodes. Friedman notes that "streaming potentials" can give rise to difficulties in flowing systems, and he has used constant flow conditions to avoid this problem. However, Portnoy et al. (149) have concluded that some of the difficulties described by Friedman arise from the reference electrode and suggest alternative methods for minimizing the effects of flow. They report that the "streaming potential" can be reduced to less than 50 μv. over a wide range of flow rates.

D. APPLICATIONS IN NONLIVING SYSTEMS

(1) **General Analytical Measurements.** (a) *The Measurement of Ionic Activity in Systems in which Cation Binding or Association Occurs.* Geyer and Frank (55,56) have studied the binding of K to tetraphenylboron; and have characterized the use of the electrode as an indicator for the direct titration of K with Ca tetraphenylboron. They have also carried out K titrations using Na tetraphenylboron and K-selective electrodes of the NAS 27-4 type. Mattock (116) has reported no success in the latter titration, presumably because of the replacement in the solution of K^+ by Na^+ with an increasing Na^+ interference as the titration proceeds. However, the simultaneous use of an Na^+-selective electrode should circumvent this difficulty. Rechnitz et al. (154a,b) have carefully studied the use of a cation-sensitive glass electrode to follow the precipitation titration of K, Rb, Cs, NH_4, and Ag with Ca tetraphenylboron titrant, and

report errors of considerably less than 1%. Rechnitz and his co-workers have recently extended these studies to the malate system (154c), as well as to mixed solvents (154,154d). In a similar application, Tomicek and Pulpan (193) have used Na^+-sensitive glass electrodes for identifying the equivalent point of the Na^+ titration with zinc uranylacetate.

Shedlovsky et al. (163) have used Na^+-responsive electrodes to examine the behavior of aqueous solutions of mixed colloidal electrolytes (Na alkyl sulfates). From their measurements, they were able to calculate the extent of dissociation of Na^+ counterions by the micelles and to infer the presence of strong interaction below the critical micelle concentration. A similar study has been carried out by Stanley (as quoted by Isard in Ref. 77) in Na^+ solutions of paraffin chain salts and dyestuffs.

Palaty (138) has used Na^+-sensitive glass electrodes in the evaluation of formation constants for the Na^+ chelates of ethylenediaminetetraacetic acid. He finds the glass-electrode method very suitable for this purpose and more precise than the classical "pH shift" method. Palaty finds a dependence of the stability constant on pH, noting that this has not been previously observed because the "pH shift" method is insensitive in the case of weak chelates. Garrels (53) has used Na^+ electrodes to demonstrate the existence of the $NaCO_3^-$ complex ion and to measure its dissociation constant.

(b) *Soil or Clay Suspensions and Extracts. Na^+ Measurement.* Bower (9–11) has studied the usefulness of Na^+-selective electrodes in measuring the salinity of waters, soil water extracts, and slurries of salts and clay, noting that information on the Na^+ content of soil water is important because of the adverse effect of Na^+ on plant growth. He has compared the results of glass electrode measurements with those obtained by flame-photometry and finds the agreement between the methods to be sufficiently good to justify the use of the electrode for most practical purposes. The principal advantage cited for the electrode over the flame-photometer is the elimination of the need to filter the sample. Bower also analyzes the "suspension effect" and attributes it to the KCl-salt bridge since it is a function of the KCl concentration of the bridge. Pommer (145–147) has applied Na^+ sensitive glass electrodes to the measurement of Na^+ activities in clay suspensions and to the analysis of the mixed acid properties of H-Montmorillonite. Komarova and Kryukov (87) have used Na^+-

sensitive glass electrodes in studies of Na^+ activity in solutions containing humic acids. They report differences between the Na^+ activities in moist soils and in the solutions isolated from them, but have not analyzed the origins of these in detail. Di Gleria and Katalin (20,21) have also compared the Na^+ values measured by glass electrodes in various soil solutions with results obtained using the flame-spectrophotometer and found good agreement.

Taulli (181) has used Na^+-responsive glass electrodes for determining Na^+ concentration in acidic silica sol systems after dilution and pH adjustment. Glass electrodes offer an advantage in this system because the colloidal silica clogs the atomizer of the flame-spectrophotometer. Taulli compares the use of glass electrodes with existing methods for sol systems and concludes that the electrometric measurement is considerably easier. He finds that at the proper pH levels the electrode responses are linear with respect to Na^+ in aqueous solutions having a maximum Na^+ concentration of 100 p.p.m. and reports that the average per cent deviation between the electrometric method and other methods, including the flame-spectrophotometer, is 5.7 in the analysis of silica sols over the range from 12–334 p.p.m. of Na^+.

K^+ Measurement. Mortland (125) has used the Beckman 78137 electrode to estimate the exchangeable K^+ level of acid soils. He notes that, even without correcting for Na^+ contamination, the simplicity of use of a moderately K^+ sensitive electrode may make it valuable in soil testing where extreme accuracy is not necessary.

(c) *Analysis of Natural Waters.* Goremykin and Kryukov (61) have published a paper on the use of glass electrodes in determining the Na^+ in natural waters. They compared the analysis by the glass electrode with determinations using zinc uranylacetate and found agreement to within a few per cent between the two methods. Bower (9,10) has successfully used cation-responsive glass electrodes for estimating the quality of irrigation water. Mattock (116) summarizes unpublished observations by West and Pursey, who have compared the analysis by glass electrodes and by flame-photometer in natural waters whose sodium content varies from 4–3000 p.p.m. These authors note that independent measurements made by two different types of glass electrodes may agree well even when the flame-photometer results differ for unknown reasons. Siever et al. (177) have used Na^+-sensitive glass electrodes of NAS 11-18 composition to determine Na^+ activity in water extracted from samples of muds from the ocean bottom. They find salinities higher than ocean water at the same location and suggest that the salinities may be either "paleosalinities" or the result of a semipermeable membrane phenomenon in the mud layers.

(d) *Continuous Industrial Measurements.* Mattock (116) notes that specific Na^+ measurements offer advantages in checking salinity levels (traditionally studied by means of conductivity measurements) and notes that Na^+ electrodes have been successfully used to monitor Na^+ levels in boiler feed waters, which normally have an alkaline pH and are, therefore, a particularly favorable situation for continuous measurement at low Na^+ levels. He notes that a significant response has been found to Na^+ in concentrations as low as 0.002 p.p.m.! (cf. the recent report by Gurney (63a) on the defection of O to 10-ppb of Na^+ in steam and condensate.) Mattock also describes the use of electrodes for studies of ion exchange breakthrough, where Na^+ detection at the 1 p.p.m. level is feasible. He also summarizes a variety of applications in which conventional flame-photometry is inconvenient or inaccurate. The studies of Bishop and of Bevington and Davis are cited as examples of the analysis of Na^+ in foods and beers. Good agreement was found between electrode, flame-photometric, and chloride titration analyses. Advantages of the electrodes cited are that no preliminary measurement is necessary to identify the approximate sodium level, as is often required with flame-photometry when the concentration varies widely, and that it is unnecessary to ash the sample.

(e) *Metallurgical Applications.* Chernyak (15) has used an Na^+-glass electrode for the determination of the Na^+ content in an aluminum alloy after treating the alloy with $HgCl_2$ and subsequently electrodialyzing the $Al(OH)_3$ precipitate obtained.

(2) **Analyses of Biological Fluids.** Cation-sensitive glass electrodes have been used for the analysis *in vitro* of Biological Fluids and extracts as well as for the analyses *in vivo* reported in part E. Any analysis capable of being carried out *in vivo* can generally be done *in vitro*, and the converse is often also true.

(a) *Determination of Na^+ in Serum, Plasma, Whole Blood, Urine, and Cerebrospinal Fluid.* Moore and Wilson (123) have characterized the use of Na^+-selective glass electrodes in the measurement of Na^+ activity in urine, serum, cerebrospinal fluid, whole blood, and plasma and have compared their results with analyses by flame-photometric methods. They find that the Na^+ activity in these fluids is linearly related to the Na^+ concentration and have calculated empirical activity coefficients for expressing the electrode data in terms of the more conventional Na^+ concentration for each fluid. Concentrations, so calculated, agree with the flame-photometer values to within about 2%. They also find that protein, erythrocytes, urea, and uric acid have no adverse effect on the electrode response. Moore and Wilson report that the average difference between duplicate determinations of Na^+ concentration by flame-photometer is 0.8 meq./l., while the average difference between duplicate activity determinations by the glass electrode is better, being 0.3 meq./l. In their Table I they carry out an estimate of replicate variability by analysis of variance, giving values representing the 95% confidence limits for the true value of any given individual sample. They find, for urine, a mean Na^+ concentration (meq./l.) of 109.8 ± 2.34 (2 S.D.) by flame-photometer, whereas by the electrode the Na^+ activity is found to have a mean value of 77.6 ± 0.87 (2 S.D.). For serum, they find the Na^+ concentration value by flame-photometer to be 141.5 ± 2.07, whereas by the electrode the Na^+ activity is 109.8 ± 0.42. For cerebrospinal fluid, the Na^+ concentration value by flame-photometer is 141.7 ± 2.25, while the activity value by the electrode is 105.4 ± 0.96. It can be seen from these results that the determinations by the glass electrodes have less than half the variability of the determinations by flame-photometer. Moore and Wilson conclude that Na^+ activity (or concentration) can be determined rapidly in urine, serum, cerebrospinal fluid, whole blood, and plasma with a high degree of accuracy and reproducibility using glass electrodes.

(b) *The State of Na^+ and K^+ in Bile.* Diamond (22) has measured Na^+ activity in bile using glass electrodes and has compared this with the sodium concentration determined by flame-photometer. He reports an activity coefficient for Na^+ of 0.56 ± 0.07 at a concentration level of approximately 3.3 M and notes that this is lower than that in NaCl solutions of the same concentrations. More recently, Moore and Dietschy (124) have studied more extensively the state of Na^+ and K^+ in bile, and report that the activity coefficients of both Na^+ and K^+ in bile, and in solutions of bile salts, are lower than those for NaCl solutions at corresponding concentrations. Their results are interpreted as indicating

Na$^+$ association, probably through micelle formation.   Dietschy and Moore (23) have used these calculated activity coefficients in interpreting the bioelectric potentials observed across the gall bladder wall.

(c) *Protoplasmic Extracts.*   Na$^+$ and K$^+$ glass electrodes have been applied to detect Na$^+$ and K$^+$ binding in extracts of brain by Ungar and co-workers (198–201), who suggest that proteins of the resting cell absorb K$^+$ preferentially, but that in the excited state the preference is altered to favor Na$^+$.

(d) *Nucleic Acid Solutions.*   Lev and Vorobyev (102) have used glass electrodes to study changes in the apparent activity coefficients of Li$^+$, Na$^+$, and K$^+$ in solutions of desoxyribonucleic acid during heat denaturation.

(e) *ATP and Creative* PO$_4$.   Mullins and Noda find the activity coefficient of K$^+$ in 0.14M K$_4$ATP and K$_3$ creative PO$_4$ to be 0.57 and 0.60, respectively (125a).

E. APPLICATIONS IN LIVING SYSTEMS

(1) **Measurements of Intracellular Ionic Activities.**   One of the unique, and potentially most interesting, applications of cation-sensitive glass electrodes is to the measurement of intracellular ionic activities.   The pioneering work on this subject was carried out by Hinke (69,70), who made microelectrodes of Na$^+$ and K$^+$-selective glasses and used these to assess the activities of Na$^+$ and K$^+$, initially in crab muscle and later in the axoplasm of the giant squid axon.   By measuring Na$^+$ and K$^+$ activities inside the squid axon before and after stimulation, Hinke was also able to calculate the net fluxes of these ions across the membrane.   He found Na$^+$ to enter at a rate in good agreement with previous measurements made using radioactive isotopes.   Hinke also studied intra-axonal activities as a function of distance from the injured end of the axon and found the Na$^+$ content to increase and the K$^+$ content to decrease as one approached closer to the injury, the sum of Na$^+$ and K$^+$ remaining constant.   These changes also correlated with spatial changes in resting and action potentials observed as the injured end was approached.   In addition to the above studies *in situ*, Hinke determined Na$^+$ and K$^+$ activities on extruded axoplasm and found the activities to be slightly higher in extruded axoplasm than *in situ*.   He also analyzed the Na$^+$ and K$^+$ content of extruded axoplasm by flame-photometer and, by comparing activity and concentration, calculated that, in axoplasm, Na$^+$ has a

lower activity coefficient than K^+. He concluded that some 30% of axoplasmic Na^+ was "bound." This result was similar to his previous observation in muscle that the concentration of Na^+ is 3 times greater than its measured activity, while the concentration of K^+ is twice as great as its measured activity. Recently, Lev (98) has carried out observations on Na^+ and K^+ activities within single frog muscle fibers in which, although he finds no evidence of K^+ binding, about 70% of intracellular Na^+ appears to be bound.

Baker et al. in collaboration with Keynes (83) have published glass-electrode measurements on activities of Na^+ and K^+ in the solutions they used for perfusing the squid giant axon.

(2) **Measurements Within Single Kidney Tubules.** Khuri et al. (84) have used Na^+ and K^+ microelectrodes to measure Na^+ and K^+ in glomerular and proximal tubular fluid from single amphibian kidney tubules. Measurements were made not only on samples collected by micropuncture, but also by using cation electrodes placed *in situ*. Khuri et al. found a ratio 1.00 ± 0.02 for Na^+ in glomerular fluid relative to serum, while the ratio of tubular to glomerular Na^+ is 0.99 ± 0.01, confirming previous measurements with the flame-photometer. However, the K^+ concentration in fluid collected from the most distal portion of the proximal tubule was found to be nearly twice as concentrated as that in the glomerulus, also in agreement with previous observations obtained using flame-photometer. Khuri et al. have recently extended these observations to the single proximal tubules of the rat (85).

(3) **Continuous Analyses in Artery or Vein.** Friedman et al. (44–52) have pioneered the measurement of plasma Na^+ and K^+ continuously in the blood vessels of living animals. These authors have been concerned with the relationship between blood pressure and plasma Na^+ and K^+ concentration levels. Friedman et al. have developed not only refined methods for continuous measurement in the living animal, but also very precise techniques for the analysis *in vitro* of extremely small samples. Much of this work has recently been summarized by Friedman (49) in a paper which provides many useful technical details. Sugioka (180) has also been concerned with the measurement of Na^+ and K^+ in blood vessels.

(4) **Analyses at the Surface of the Cerebral Cortex.** Meyer and associates (122) and Portnoy et al. (150–152) have studied the changes in Na^+ and K^+ in the cerebrospinal fluid at the cortical surface as a

function of a number of physiological variables, with somewhat different results. Portnoy et al. suggest that the differences are due to bioelectric potentials directly recorded in the work of Meyer et al.

(5) **Determination of Na⁺ in Sweat—A Diagnostic Test for Cystic Fibrosis.** Goldbloom and Sekelj (57) have carried out a study in which Na^+ activity is measured by a glass electrode at the surface of dry or moist skin without the prior induction of sweating. The authors report that the method clearly separates normal children from those with cystic fibrosis of the pancreas.

(6) **Possible Ion Binding in Disease States.** Friedman et al. (50) note occasional striking divergences between flame and electrode measurements of Na^+ in hospital patients, despite good correspondence between the two methods with normal subjects. They suggest that "a detailed clinical investigation of ion binding as a factor in disease might be profitable, especially now that the electrode instrumentation is available and the procedure quite feasible."

Acknowledgment

The author thanks Miss Mary Hogan and Mrs. Carole Alcorn for their able technical assistance and Drs. M. Nordberg, E. Perl, and R. Wolbach for reading the manuscript and for their many valuable suggestions.

References

1. Aleshin, S., and I. Gorb, *Dokl. Moskov. Sel'shokhoz. Akad.*, **32**, 505 (1958).
2. Akerlöf, G., *J. Am. Chem. Soc.*, **52**, 2353 (1930).
3. Anderson, O. L., and D. A. Stuart, *J. Am. Ceram. Soc.*, **37**, 573 (1954).
4. Bates, R. G., *Electrometric pH Determination. Theory and Practice*, Wiley, New York, 1954, p. 331.
5. "Laboratory Cationic Electrodes," Beckman Instruction Manual 1154-A, 1962.
6. Belijustin, A. A., and M. M. Shul'ts, *Vestn. Leningr. Univ.*, **4**, 149 (1963).
7. Bernal, J. D., and R. H. Fowler, *J. Chem. Phys.*, **1**, 515 (1933).
8. Born, M., and A. Landé, *Ber. Physik. Ges.*, **20**, 210 (1918).
9. Bower, C. A., *Soil Sci. Soc. Am. Proc.*, **23**, 29 (1959).
10. Bower, C. A., *Trans. 7th Intern. Congr. Soil Sci.*, **2**, 16 (1960).
11. Bower, C. A., "Studies on the Suspension Effect with a Sodium Electrode," *Soil Sci. Soc. Am. Proc.*, **25**, 18 (1961).
12. Bronsted, J. N., *J. Am. Chem. Soc.*, **42**, 761 (1920).
13. Budd, A. L., *J. Electroanal. Chem.*, **5**, 35 (1963).
14. Charles, R. J., *J. Appl. Physics*, **32**, 1115 (1961).
15. Chernyak, R. S., *Zavodsk. Lab.*, **27**, 536 (1961).

16. Conti, F., and G. Eisenman, "The Nonsteady State Membrane Potential of Ion Exchangers with Fixed Sites." *Biophys. J.*, in press.
17. Conti, F., and G. Eisenman, "The Steady-State Properties of Ion-Exchange Membranes with Fixed Sites," to be published.
17a. Crank, J., *The mathematics of diffusion*, Oxford, New York, 1956.
18. Cremer, M., *Z. Biol.*, **47**, 562 (1906).
19. Cruickshank, E. H., and P. Meares, *Trans. Faraday Soc.*, **53**, No. 418, 1299 (1957).
20. Di Gleria, J., and D. Katalin, *Agrokem. Talajtan*, **9**, 261 (1960).
21. Di Gleria, J., and D. Katalin, *Pflanzenernaehr. Düng., Bodenk.*, **91**, 202 (1960).
22. Diamond, J., *J. Physiol. (London)*, **161**, 442 (1962).
23. Dietschy, J. M., and E. W. Moore, *Diffusion Potentials and Potassium Distribution Across the Gallbladder Wall*, in press.
24. Dole, M., *J. Am. Chem. Soc.*, **53**, 4260 (1931).
25. Dole, M., *J. Chem. Phys.*, **2**, 862 (1934).
26. Dole, M., *The Glass Electrode: Methods, Applications, and Theory*, Wiley, New York, 1941.
27. Doremus, R. H., "Diffusion in Noncrystalline Silicates," in J. D. KcKenzie, Ed., *Modern Aspects of the Vitreous State*, Vol. II, Butterworths, London, 1962.
28. Doremus, R. H., "Exchange and Diffusion of Ions in Glass," *J. Phys. Chem.*, **68**, 2212 (1964).
29. Douglas, R. W., and J. O. Isard, *Trans. Soc. Glass Technol.*, **33**, 289 (1949).
30. Dubrovo, S. K., and Yu. A. Shmidt, *Zh. Priklad. Khim.*, **32**, 742 (1959).
31. Eisenman, G., "On the Elementary Atomic Origin of Equilibrium Ionic Specificity," in A. Kleinzeller and A. Kotyk, Ed., *Symposium on Membrane Transport and Metabolism*, Academic Press, New York, 1961, p. 163.
32. Eisenman, G., *Biophys. J.*, **2**, *Part 2*, 259 (1962).
33. Eisenman, G., *Boletin Inst. Estud. Med. Biol. Mex.*, **21**, 155 (1963).
34. Eisenman, G., *On the Origin of the Glass Electrode Potential* (to be published).
35. Eisenman, G., "A Physical Basis for Specific Ion Differences Observed in Chemical and Biological Phenomena," in L. O. Peachey, Ed., *1st A.I.B.S. Conference on Cellular Dynamics*, in press.
35a. Eisenman, G., Ed., *Glass Electrodes for H⁺ and Other Cations: Principles and Practice*, Marcel Dekker, New York, in press.
36. Eisenman, G., D. O. Rudin, and J. U. Casby, *Science*, **126**, 831 (1957).
37. Eisenman, G., D. O. Rudin, and J. U. Casby, "Glass Electrode for Measuring Sodium Ion," U. S. Patent, 2,829,090 (1957).
38. Eisenman, G., D. O. Rudin, and J. U. Casby, "Glass Electrode for Measuring Potassium Ion," U. S. Patent 3,041,252 (1962).
39. Eisenman, G., and G., Karreman, "On the Origin of the Potential of Cation-Responsive Glass Electrodes," Kendall Award Symposium of *Am. Chem. Soc.*, Washington, D. C., March, 1962. (Summarized in News Report, "Glass Electrode Potential Analyzed," *Chem. Eng. News*, **40**, 52 (1962).
40. Evstrop'ev, K. S., and N. V. Suikovskaya, *Compt. Rend. Acad. Sci. USSR*, **4**, 421 (1934).

364   GEORGE EISENMAN

41. Faick, C. A., J. C. Young, D. Hubbard, and A. N. Finn, *J. Res. Natl. Bur. Std.*, **14**, 133 (1935).
42. Fajans, K., *Radioelements and Isotopes: Chemical Forces and Optical Properties of Substances*, McGraw-Hill, New York, 1931, p. 125.
43. Fajans, K., "Polarization", in *Encyclopedia of Chemistry*, Clark and Howley, Ed., Reinhold, New York, 1957, p. 763.
44. Friedman, S. M., J. D. Jamieson, J. A. M. Hinke, and C. L. Friedman, *Proc. Soc. Exp. Biol. Med.*, **99**, 727 (1958).
45. Friedman, S. M., J. D. Jamieson, M. Nakashima, and C. L. Friedman, *Hypertension*, **8**, 156 (1959).
46. Friedman, S. M., J. D. Jamieson, J. A. M. Hinke, and C. L. Friedman, *Am. J. Phys.*, **196**, 1049 (1959b).
47. Friedman, S. M., J. D. Jamieson, M. Nakashima, and C. L. Friedman, *Science*, **130**, 1252 (1959).
48. Friedman, S. M., and C. L. Friedman, *Anat. Rec.*, **138**, 129 (1960).
49. Friedman, S. M., "Measurement of Sodium and Potassium by Glass Electrodes," in D. Glick, Ed., *Methods of Biochemical Analysis*, Vol. 10, Interscience, New York, 1962, p.71.
50. Friedman, S. M., S. L. Wong, and J. H. Walton, *J. Appl. Physiol.*, **18**, 950 (1963).
51. Friedman, S. M., and F. K. Bowers, *Anal. Biochem.*, **5**, 471 (1963).
52. Friedman, S. M., M. Nakashima, and C. L. Friedman, *Circulation Res.*, **13**, 223 (1963).
53. Garrels, R. M., Personal communication.
54. Garrels, R. M., M. Sato, M. E. Thompson, and A. H. Truesdell, *Science*, **135**, 1045 (1962).
55. Geyer, R., and H. Frank, *Z. Anal. Chem.*, **179**, 99 (1961).
56. Geyer, R., and H. Frank, *Sonderdruck Freiberger Forschungshefte*, **267**, 421 (1962).
57. Goldbloom, R. B., and P. Sekelj, *Application of a Sodium Electrode to the Skin in the Diagnosis of Cystic Fibrosis of the Pancreas*, in press.
58. Goldman, D. E., *J. Gen. Physiol.*, **27**, 37 (1943).
59. Goldman, R. G., and D. Hubbard, *J. Res. Natl. Bur. Std.*, **48**, 370 (1952).
60. Goldschmidt, V. M., *Skrifter Norske Videnskaps-Akad. Oslo. I. Mat.-Naturv. Kl.*, **1926**, 7.
61. Goremykin, V. E., and P. A. Kryukov, "Potentiometric Method of Determining Sodium Ions by Means of a Glass Electrode With a Sodium Function," *Izv. Akad. Nauk, SSSR Otdel. Khim. Nauk*, **1957**, No. 11, 1387.
62. Gotoh, F., Y. Tazaki, K. Hamaguchi, and J. S. Meyer, *J. Neurochem.*, **9**, 81 (1962).
63. Gross, P., and O. Halpern, *J. Chem. Phys.*, **2**, 136 (1934).
63a. Gurney, W. B., Beckman Reprint R-6212.
64. Haber, F., and Z. Klemensiewicz, *Z. Physik. Chem. (Leipzig)*, **67**, 385 (1909).
65. Hanns, M., *Bull. Soc. Chim. France*, **11**, 2658 7455 (1963).
66. Harned, H. S., and B. B. Owen, *The Physical Chemistry of Electrolytic Solutions*, 2nd Ed., Reinhold, New York, 1950.
67. Helfferich, F., *Discussions Faraday Soc.*, **21**, 83 (1956).

68. Helfferich, F., *Ion Exchange*, McGraw-Hill, New York, 1962.
69. Hinke, J. A. M., *Nature*, **184**, 1257 (1959).
70. Hinke, J. A. M., *J. Physiol.* (*London*), **156**, 314 (1961).
71. Hodgkin, A. L., and B. Katz, *J. Physiol.* (*London*), **108**, 37 (1949).
72. Horovitz, K., *Z. Physik.*, **15**, 369 (1923).
73. Horovitz, K., *Z. Physik. Chem.* (*Leipzig*), **115**, 424 (1925).
74. Hughes, W. S., *J. Am. Chem. Soc.*, **44**, 2860 (1922).
75. Hubbard, D., M. H. Black, S. F. Holley, and G. F. Rynders, *J. Res. Natl. Bur. Std.*, **46**, 168 (1951).
76. Hyman, E. S., *Anal. Chem.*, **34**, 365 (1962).
77. Isard, J. O., *Nature*, **184**, 1616 (1959).
78. Izmailov, N. A., and A. G. Vasel'ev, *Zh. Fiz. Khim.*, **29**, 1866 (1955).
79. Izmailov, N. A., and A. G. Vasel'ev, *Zh. Fiz. Khim.*, **29**, 2145 (1955).
80. Izmailov, N. A., and A. G. Vasel'ev, *Zh. Fiz. Khim.*, **30**, 1500 (1956).
81. Jenny, H., *J. Phys. Chem.*, **36**, 2217 (1932).
82. Karreman, G., and G. Eisenman, *Bull. Math. Biophys.*, **24**, 413 (1962).
83. Keynes, R. D., as acknowledged in Baker, Hodgkin, and Shaw, *J. Physiol.*, **164**, 330 (1962).
84. Khuri, R. N., D. A. Goldstein, D. L. Maude, C. Edmonds, and A. K. Solomon, *Am. J. Physiol.*, **204**, 743 (1963).
85. Khuri, R. N., W. J. Flanigan, and D. E. Oken, "Micropuncture Study of K Concentration in Proximal Tubule Using Glass Electrodes," Communication to Federation of Chemical Research, Atlantic City, April 28, 1963.
86. Koltunov, Y. B., *Biofizica*, **8**, 619 (1963).
87. Komarova, N. A., and P. A. Kryukov, *Colloid J.* (*USSR*), **21**, No. 2, 175 (1959).
88. Landquist, N., *Acta Chem. Scand.*, **9**, 595 (1955).
89. Latimer, W. M., *The Oxidation States of the Elements and their Potentials in Aqueous Solutions*, 2nd ed., Prentice-Hall, Englewood Cliffs, N. J., 1952.
90. Lees, J., "New Types of Glass Electrodes," *Proceedings of the 8th Symposium on the Art of Glassblowing*, Chicago, 1963, p. 47.
91. Lengyel, B., *Z. Physik. Chem.* (*Leipzig*), **167**, 295 (1933).
92. Lengyel, B., and E. Blum, *Trans. Faraday Soc.*, **30**, 461 (1934).
93. Lengyel, B., and B. Csakvari, *Acta Chim. Acad. Sci. Hung.*, **25**, 369 (1960).
94. Lengyel, B., and B. Csakvari, *Proc. Inst. Gen. Chem., Budapest*, 369 (1960).
95. Lengyel, B., B. Csakvari, and Z. Boksay, *Acta Chim. Acad. Sci. Hung.*, **25**, 225 (1960).
96. Leonard, J. E., "Glass Electrodes for the Direct Measurement of Sodium Ion Activity in Aqueous Solutions," Beckman Reprint R-6148, 1959.
97. LePoutre, G., P. Chieux, and D. Bouthors, Personal communication.
98. Lev, A. A., *Nature*, **201**, 1132 (1963).
99. Lev, A. A., "On Measuring the Activities of Cations in Sea Urchin Eggs with Glass Microelectrodes," *Cytology* (*USSR*), in press.
100. Lev, A. A., "Determination of Activity and Activity Coefficient for Potassium Ions in the Frog Muscle Fibers with Cation-Sensitive Glass Microelectrodes," *Biophysics* (*USSR*), in press.
101. Lev, A. A., and E. P. Buzhinsky, *Cytology* (*USSR*), **3**, 614 (1961).

102. Lev, A. A., and V. I. Vorobyev, *Biophysics* (*USSR*), in press.
103. Ling, G. N., *A Physical Theory of the Living State*, Blaisdell, New York, 1962.
104. Long, A. O., and J. E. Willard, *Ind. Eng. Chem.*, **4**, 916 (1951).
105. Mackay, D., and P. Meares, *Kolloid-Z.*, **171**, 139 (1960).
106. Manegold, E., *Z. Ver. deut. Ing. Beih. Verfahrenstech.*, **5**, 145 (1940).
107. Mans, A. E., and I. Kateman, *Rec. Trav. Chim. Pays-Bas*, **81**, 917 (1962).
108. Marshall, C. E., *J. Phys. Chem.*, **48**, 67 (1944).
109. Materova, E. A., V. V. Moiseev, and S. P. Shmitt-Fogelevich, *Akad. Nauk, SSSR*, **33**, 893 (1959).
110. Materova, E. A., V. V. Moiseev, and A. A. Belijustin, *Akad. Nauk, SSSR*, **35**, 1258 (1961).
111. Mattock, G., "Glass Electrodes Responsive to Sodium Ions," Electronic Instruments, Ltd., Technical Bulletin TDS-Elect.-9 Issue 1, 1960.
112. Mattock, G., *pH Measurement and Titration*, Heywood, London, 1961.
113. Mattock, G., Personal communication, 1961.
114. Mattock, G., *Acta IMEKO Budapest*, **1** (1961).
115. Mattock, G., *Analyst*, **87**, 930 (1962).
116. Mattock, G., *Anal. Chem. Proc. Int. Symp.*, **59**, 247 (1963).
117. Mattock, G., "Laboratory pH measurement," in C. N. Reilley, Ed., *Advances in Analytical Chemistry and Instrumentation*, Vol. 2, Interscience, New York, 1963.
118. Mattock, G., and R. Uncles, *Analyst*, **87**, 977 (1962).
118a. Mattock, G., and R. Uncles, *Analyst*, **89**, 350 (1964).
119. Meyer, K. H., and J. F. Sievers, *Helv. Chim. Acta*, **19**, 649 (1936).
120. Meyer, K. H., and J. F. Sievers, *Helv. Chim. Acta*, **19**, 665 (1936).
121. Meyer, K. H., and J. F. Sievers, *Helv. Chim. Acta*, **19**, 987 (1936).
122. Meyer, J. S., F. Gotoh, Y. Tazaki, and K. Hamaguchi, *Trans. Am. Neurol. Assoc.*, **86**, 17 (1961).
123. Moore, E. W., and D. W. Wilson, *J. Clin. Invest.*, **42**, 293 (1963).
124. Moore, E. W., and J. M. Dietschy, *Na and K Activity Coefficients in Bile and Bile Salts Determined by Glass Electrodes*, in press.
124a. Morey, G. W., *The Properties of Glass*, 2nd Ed., Reinhold, New York, 1954.
125. Mortland, M. M., *Quarterly Bulletin of the Michigan Agricultural Experiment Station, Michigan State University*, **43**, 491 (1961).
125a. Mullins, L. J., and K. Noda, *J. Gen. Physiol.*, **47**, 117 (1963).
126. Murray, R. W., and C. N. Reilley, *Anal. Chem.*, **34**, 313 (1962).
127. Murray, R. W., and C. N. Reilley, *Anal. Chem.*, in press.
128. Nernst, W., *Zeits. f. Phys. Chem.*, **2**, 613 (1888).
129. Nernst, W., *Zeits. f. Phys. Chem.*, **4**, 129 (1889).
130. Nicolskii, B. P., *Acta Physicochim. URSS*, **7**, 597 (1937).
131. Nicolskii, B. P., and T. A. Tolmacheva, *Zh. Fiz. Khim.*, **10**, 504 (1937).
132. Nicolskii, B. P., and T. A. Tolmacheva, *Zh. Fiz. Khim.*, **10**, 513 (1937).
133. Nicolskii, B. P., M. M. Shul'ts, E. A. Materova, and A. A. Belijustin, *Akad. Nauk SSSR*, **140**, 641 (1961).
134. Nicolskii, B. P., M. M. Shul'ts, and A. A. Belijustin, *Dokl. Akad. Nauk. SSSR*, **144**, 844 (1962).

135. Nicolskii, B. P., and M. M. Shul'ts, *Zh. Fiz. Khim.*, **36**, 1327 (1962).
136. Nicolskii, B. P., and M. M. Shul'ts, *Vestn. Leningr. Univ.*, **4**, 73 (1963).
137. Nicolskii, B. P., M. M., Shul'ts, and A. A., Belijustin, *Vestn. Leningr. Univ.*, **4**, 86 (1963).
138. Palaty, V., *Can. J. Chem.*, **41**, 18 (1963).
139. Parfenov, A. I., M. M. Shul'ts, T. N. Nekrosova, and I. P. Polozova, *Vestn. Leningr. Univ.*, **4**, 126 (1963).
140. Pauling, L., *The Nature of the Chemical Bond*, 2nd ed., Cornell University Press, Ithaca, New York, 1940.
141. Pauling, L., *General Chemistry*, 2nd ed., W. H. Freeman, San Francisco, Calif., 1958.
142. Perley, G. A., *Anal. Chem.*, **21**, 394 (1949).
143. Planck, M., *Ann. Phys. und Chem.*, **39**, 161 (1890).
144. Planck, M., *Ann. Phys. und Chem.*, **40**, 561 (1890).
145. Pommer, A. M., "Sodium-Sensitive Glass Electrodes in Clay Titrations," Geological Survey Research, Short papers in the Geological Sciences, 1960, No. 229, p. B502, 1960.
146. Pommer, A. M., "Measurement of Sodium Activities in Clay Suspensions with Cationic-Sensitive Electrodes, Short papers in the Geological and Hydrologic Sciences, Article 284, C-373, 1961.
147. Pommer, A. M., "Relation Between Dual Acidity and Structure of H-Montmorillonite," Geological Survey Professional Paper 386C., C.1., 1963.
148. Portnoy, H. D., L. M. Thomas, and E. S. Gurdjian, *Talanta*, **9**, 119 (1962).
149. Portnoy, H. D., L. M. Thomas, and E. S. Gurdjian, *J. Appl. Physiol.*, **17**, 175 (1962).
150. Portnoy, H. D., L. M. Thomas, and E. S. Gurdjian, *Surg. Forum*, **13**, 430 (1962).
151. Portnoy, H. D., L. M. Thomas, and E. S. Gurdjian, *Neurology*, **14**, 324 (1964).
152. Portnoy, H. D., L. M. Thomas, and E. S. Gurdjian, *Arch. Neurology*, **8**, 597 (1963).
153. Quittner, F., *Ann. Physik*, **85**, 745 (1928).
154. Rechnitz, G. A., *J. Chem. Ed.*, **41**, 385 (1964).
154a. Rechnitz, G. A., S. A. Katz, and S. B. Zamochnick, *Anal. Chem.*, **35**, 1088 (1963).
154b. Rechnitz, G. A., and S. B. Zamochnick, *Talanta*, **11**, 1061 (1964).
154c. Rechnitz, G. A., and J. Brauner, *Talanta*, **11**, 607 (1964).
154d. Rechnitz, G. A., and S. B. Zamochnick, *Talanta*, **11**, 979 (1964).
155. Reilley, C. N., *Anal. Chem.*, **32**, 185 (1960).
156. Robinson, R. A., and R. H. Stokes, *Electrolytic Solutions*, 2nd ed., Academic, New York, 1959.
157. Rossini, F. D., D. D. Wagman, W. H. Evans, S. Levine, and I. Jaffe, "Selected Values of Chemical Thermodynamic Properties," Circular of the Natl. Bur. of Std., No. 500. U. S. Govt. Printing Office, Washington, D. C., 1952.
158. Savage, J. A., and J. O. Isard, *Phys. Chem. Glasses*, **3**, 147 (1962).
159. Schiller, H., *Am. Physik.*, **74**, 105 (1924).

160. Schwabe, K., and H. Dahms, *Naturwissenschaften*, **47**, 351 (1960).
161. Schwabe, K., and H. Dahms, *Silikat Tech.*, **11**, 583 (1960).
162. Schwabe, K., and H. Dahms, *Elektrochem.*, **65**, 518 (1961).
163. Shedlovsky, L., C. W. Jakob, and M. B. Epstein, *J. Phys. Chem.*, **67**, 2075 (1963).
164. Shul'ts, M. M., *Vestn. Leningr. Univ.*, **13**, 80 (1953).
165. Shul'ts, M. M., and L. G. Azo, *Vestn. Leningr. Univ.*, **10**, 153 (1955).
166. Shul'ts, M. M., and A. I. Parfenov, *Vestn. Leningr. Univ.*, **13**, 118 (1958).
167. Shul'ts, M. M., and A. A. Belijustin, *Vestn. Leningr. Univ.*, **3**, 116 (1962).
168. Shul'ts, M. M., A. I. Parfenov, N. V. Peshekhonova, and A. A. Belijustin, *Vestn. Leningr. Univ.*, **4**, 98 (1963).
169. Shul'ts, M. M., N. V. Peshekhonova, T. A. Kopuntsova, and L. P. Shandalova, *Vestn. Leningr. Univ.*, **4**, 104 (1963).
170. Shul'ts, M. M., N. V. Peshekhonova, T. A. Kopuntsova, and L. P. Shandalova, *Vestn. Leningr. Univ.*, **4**, 114 (1963).
171. Shul'ts, M. M., N V. Peshekhonova, and G. P. Shevina, *Vestn. Leningr. Univ.*, **4**, 120 (1963).
172. Shul'ts, M. M., V. S. Bobrov, and I. S. Bukhareva, *Vestn. Leningr. Univ.*, **4**, 134 (1963).
173. Shul'ts, M. M., A. I. Parfenov, Chen' De-yuim, T. G. Bondarenko, and J. J. Mekhrjushev, *Vestn. Leningr. Univ.*, **4**, 155 (1963).
174. Shul'ts, M. M., A. I. Parfenov, and N. P. Panfilova, *Vestn. Leningr. Univ.*, **4**, 143 (1963).
175. Shul'ts, M. M., and V. S. Bobrov, *Vestn. Leningr. Univ.*, **4**, 166 (1963).
176. Shul'ts, M. M., *Vestn. Leningr. Univ.*, **4**, 174 (1963).
177. Siever, R., R. M. Garrels, J. Kanwisher, and R. A. Berner, *Science*, **134**, 1071 (1961).
178. Sokolov, S. I., and A. G. Pasuinskii, *Zhus Fiz. Khim.*, **3**, 131 (1932).
179. Stephanova, O. K., M. M. Shul'ts, E. A. Materova, and B. P. Nicolskii, *Vestn. Leningr. Univ.*, **4**, 93 (1963).
180. Sugioka, K., Personal communication, 1961.
181. Taulli, T. A., *Anal. Chem.*, **32**, 186 (1960).
182. Tendeloo, H. J. C., and A. J. Voorspuij Z., *Rec. Trav. Chim.*, **55**, 227 (1936).
183. Tendeloo, H. J. C., and A. J. Voorspuij Z., *Rec. Trav. Chim.*, **61**, 531 (1942).
184. Tendeloo, H. J. C., and A. J. Voorspuij Z., *Rec. Trav. Chim.*, **62**, 784 (1943).
185. Tendeloo, H. J. C., *Discussions Faraday Soc.*, **1**, 293 (1947).
186. Tendeloo, H. J. C., A. E. Mans, I. Kateman, and F. H. van der Voort, *Rec. Trav. Chim. Pays-Bas*, **81**, 506 (1962).
187. Tendeloo, H. J. C., and F. H. Van Der Voort, *Rec. Trav. Chim. Pays-Bas*, **79**, 640 (1960).
188. Teorell, T., *Proc. Soc. Exp. Biol. Med.*, **33**, 282 (1935).
189. Teorell, T., *Proc. Natl. Acad. Sci.*, **21**, 152 (1935).
190. Teorell, T., *Trans. Faraday Soc.*, **33**, 1086 (1937).
191. Teorell, T., *Z. Elektrochem.*, **55**, 460 (1951).

192. Teorell, T., "Transport processes and electrical phenomena in ionic membranes," in J. A. V. Butler and J. T. Randall, Eds., *Progress in Biophysics and Biophysical Chemistry*, Vol. 3, Pergamon, New York, 1953.
193. Tomicek, O., and R. Pulpan, *Chem. Listy*, **49**, 497, C.11261 (1955).
194. Trebge, E., and R. Fischer, *Silikat Technik*, **10**, 351 (1959).
195. Truesdell, A. H., *Nature*, **194**, 77 (1962).
196. Truesdell, A. H., and A. M. Pommer, *Science*, **142**, 1292 (1963).
197. Truesdell, A. H., "Study of Natural Glasses Through their Behavior as Membrane Electrodes," Thesis, Harvard University, Dept. of Geology, 1962.
198. Ungar, G., *Cytologia*, **1**, 627 (1959).
199. Ungar, G., and D. V. Romano, *Fed. Proc.*, **18**, 162 (1959).
200. Ungar, G., and D. V. Romano, *Proc. 21st Intern. Congr. Physiol. Sci.*, 278 (1959).
201. Ungar, G., *Excitation*, C. C Thomas, Springfield, Illinois, 1963.
202. Walton, H. F., "Ion Exchange Equilibria," in F. C. Nachod, Ed., *Ion Exchange, Theory and Application*, Academic, New York, 1949.
203. Weyl, W. A., *Soc. Glass Technol. Monograph*, **1951**, 541.
204. Weyl, W. A., "A New Approach to Surface Chemistry and to Heterogeneous Catalysis," Penna. State College Mineral Industries Expt. Station Bulletin 57, 1961.
205. Weyl, W. A., and E. C. Marboe, *The Constitution of Glasses*, Vol. II, Interscience, New York, in press.

Manuscript received by Publisher June 16, 1964.

Recent Advances in Time-of-Flight
Mass Spectrometry

DONALD C. DAMOTH, *The Bendix Corporation, Cincinnati, Ohio*

The use of a mass spectrometer to determine the qualitative and quantitative nature of compounds is widely appreciated. In the last two decades hundreds of instruments have been employed for this purpose. Recently, new techniques have been developed to further extend the range of samples which may be analyzed. Not only stable gases and volatile liquids but also nonvolatile materials and even solids may now be vaporized and analyzed.

A mass spectrometer is an instrument for the measurement of the mass and abundance of ionized particles and sometimes neutral particles. The mass of the particles identifies the sample and the abundance of a particular mass-to-charge ratio (m/e) peak is a determination of the amount of material represented by that mass. Of considerable secondary importance, the abundance of the several peaks in the spectrum (cracking pattern) of a compound further serves to identify that compound, because many compounds may have the same mass number or atomic weight.

One of the most fruitful areas of employment of mass spectrometry is now being opened. That is the study of the time dependence of the abundance of the various "peaks" in a mass spectrum representing various components of a sample. This is made possible by the ability of the time-of-flight mass spectrometer to measure the abundance of several mass peaks simultaneously during very short time intervals (10 μsec.).

Several principles for separating different m/e particles have been advanced. These are the magnetic deflection, r.f. (radio frequency), time-of-flight, omegatron, and quadrupole mass spectrometers. The magnetic deflection and time-of-flight types are the most widely used because these are the only types which have demonstrated resolution in excess of 100 in a practical laboratory configuration. Magnetic deflection instruments have been widely employed since about 1940, the time-of-flight since 1958.

Gas and liquid analysis, including isotope ratio analyses, thermal ionization analysis, particularly of radioactive materials, and Knudsen cell effusion studies were principal applications which broadened the use of mass spectrometry. The last ten years have witnessed an applications growth in mass spectrometry that is impressive and gratifying. The TOFMS (time-of-flight mass spectrometer) has been an important part of this development. Mass spectrometry has expanded its capabilities to the extent that practically every laboratory in the world is at least contemplating its use. The principal barrier to more widespread use of mass spectrometry is the cost. Laboratory units other than modest gas analyzers run upwards from $25,000. The complexity of the units range from a few man months of effort to engineering marvels that take many tens of man years and hundreds of thousands of dollars to construct.

The TOFMS has been employed in a wide variety of applications for several basic reasons. The linear ion trajectories and time separation of the various m/e particles places the critical portions of the configuration in the electronic circuitry rather than in the mechanical arrangement. Thus, modification of the mechanical configuration to accommodate new experiments can be accomplished simply without destroying the performance characteristics of the instrument. The mechanical simplicity also markedly reduces the cost of the unit, since the electronic complexity is cheaper to manufacture. The time separation of the various m/e particles allows collection of several different masses on each of the 10–100 thousand cycles per second. Separation of the mass peaks by geometric means does not permit such multiple channel output collection except in certain highly specialized configurations. The fast response of the instrument makes it unique in its capabilities in the field of reaction kinetics.

The output of a complete mass spectrum each 10–100 μsec. makes possible the determination of a reaction profile for reactions of as little as 100 μsec. duration. This fast reaction capability has led to a common misconception that the only widespread use of the instrument is in the field of reaction kinetics. Actually, over 75% of the more than 200 time-of-flight mass spectrometers in use would still be employed as they are if the fast reaction capability did not exist. The reason for this is the versatility of the instrument, as we shall see later on in this treatise.

The last general review of the state of the art of time-of-flight mass spectrometry was by Harrington in 1960(1); at that time the analog output (electrical recording) system had been introduced. The first versions of the direct inlet system and the Knudsen cell furnace had been applied. Since that time, the resolution, sensitivity, and range of application of this type of instrument have increased markedly.

Since there have been extensive changes in every aspect of this instrument, it is more practical and lucid to describe the present instrument and characteristics, pointing out the improved aspects, rather than to specify improvements over previous performance characteristics. This will be no disadvantage to those already familiar with the instrument, as they will recognize the improvements as such, and it will be a distinct advantage to those unfamiliar with the instrument, as it will present a complete picture.

This treatise, then, is organized on this basis.

I. INTRODUCTION TO TIME-OF-FLIGHT MASS SPECTROMETRY

The essential features of a time-of-flight mass spectrometer are an evacuated tube containing a source of ions, a means for accelerating a closely spaced group of ions uniformly, a drift region, and a sensitive fast-response detector. A means of translating the events of the mass spectrometer cycle which occurs in a few tens of microseconds into a practical time base is required outside the tube.

A simplified schematic of the TOFMS is shown in Figure 1. (All the TOF mass spectrometers referred to in this treatise are Bendix models, or users, adaptations of these.) The cycle of operation is started each 100 μsec. by a stable oscillator. In the pulsed electron

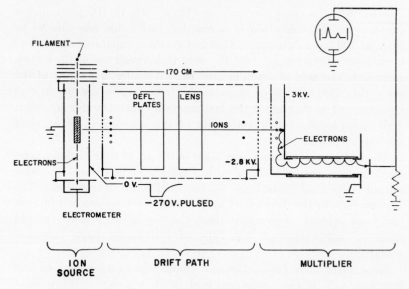

Fig. 1. Schematic drawing of time-of-flight mass spectrometer.

beam mode, the ionizing electron beam passes through the ionization region for 0.25–2 μsec. Then the electron beam is biased off and the ions formed are pulsed out by the drawout grid. The second grid is a focusing grid at an intermediate potential. The third grid is the main accelerating electrode and is usually operated at about 3000 v. As the ions pass through grid 3, they enter into a region bounded by a screen at the potential of grid 3. This is a nominally field-free drift region.

Inside the screen are deflection plates to position the most intense part of the ion "beam" on the detector. There is also a simple lens to focus the "beam" on the detector. The distance from the ionization region to the detector has increased from 40 cm. in the first time-of-flight instruments to about 170 cm. in the latest instruments. The increased length gives increased actual resolution, but in addition, it makes the recorded resolution better, because at a given ion energy with a longer flight path the ion bunches will be farther apart and this eases the requirements on the output system. The ions separate according to their various mass/charge ratios as they fly from the source to the multiplier under equal energy pulses. The lighter ions arrive at the detector first and as successively heavier ions reach the detector the time between bunches becomes less because the velocity is inversely proportional to the square root of the mass. The mathematics are developed in a paper by Wiley and McLaren (2).

The detection system for such an instrument must have some unusual capabilities. First, it must have very high gain, capable of detecting single ion inputs. Second, it must have very fast response characteristics to respond to the closely spaced ion bunches. Frequency response beyond 100 megacycles is required. These capabilities as well as several other desirable aspects were satisfied by the magnetic electron multiplier with gated output developed by Bendix. In addition to the multiplier, development of very fast response recorders and oscilloscopes has improved the readout of information from the TOFMS.

The vacuum system associated with the TOFMS has been developed to provide efficient operation and also to reduce the background pressure to increase the usable sensitivity. High sensitivity in a mass spectrometer requires that extraneous gases be eliminated, just as high-sensitivity electronics requires curtailment of extraneous electrical signals. The pumping speed of the vacuum system in the TOFMS is high compared to most laboratory mass spectrometers because of the frequent requirement to accommodate large gas throughputs such as in fast reaction studies or molecular beam work with differential pumping for continuous sampling from high pressures.

The various inlet systems are essential parts of the mass spectrometer. All samples must be converted to a gaseous ionized state before they can be analyzed. Various fundamental properties and interactions of ions and molecules in the gaseous state both ionized and un-ionized can likewise be studied. Consequently, the inlet systems play a basic part in the ability of the mass spectrometer to perform useful work. Fortunately, the TOFMS is capable of accepting a multitude of inlet systems.

II. OPERATION OF THE ION SOURCE AND ION OPTICS

In any mass spectrometer, but particularly in the time-of-flight type, the ion source operation is critical. The ion formation and drawout in the TOFMS are especially critical because the linear

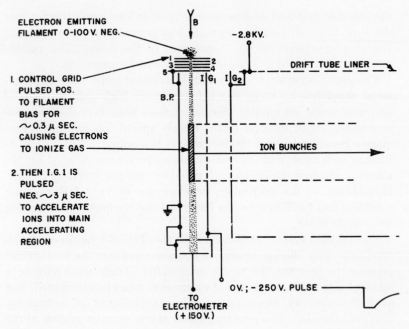

Fig. 2. Operation of time-of-flight mass spectrometer with pulsed ionization.

trajectory of the ions does not reject ions which are not being measured. Therefore, it is necessary to maintain focusing conditions throughout the mass spectrum to insure a satisfactory signal/noise ratio. If ions leave the source with improper energy or at the wrong time, they become "noise." This is a rigorous case to maintain, but the benefit is that widely differing masses can be observed simultaneously when it is met.

Until 1961 the necessary focusing properties were attained with the pulsed mode two-grid source. Focusing is attained because the ions are drawn out of the source immediately after formation. The configuration is shown in Figure 2. The emitting filament is usually 0.005-in. diameter tungsten wire, but 0.007-in. rhenium may be used to reduce poisoning of the filament in samples with large percentages of available oxygen. The filament is resistance heated with either a.c. or d.c. drive. It was originally postulated that a.c. drive was superior because the electrons could be drawn from the filament during the portion of the current cycle during which there was negligible voltage drop across the filament to reduce the energy spread of the electron beam for ionization potential studies. This has not been confirmed to date, and good ionization potential studies are being made without observing this condition.

As indicated in Figure 2, five electron gun slits are currently being use. In normal analytical work, the first slit is used as the control grid, and the second through fifth slits are at zero potential with respect to the ionization region. The configuration for ionization potential measurement will be discussed later. A trap current regulator has been incorporated to keep the ionizinge lectron beam current constant and thereby improve the stability of the sensitivity. This regulator senses the current reaching the trap anode and adjusts the bias between the filament and control grid to keep the trap current constant. The addition of the trap current regulator was one of the most significant advances in improving the quantitative accuracy of the TOFMS.

In 1961, Dr. Martin Studier of Argonne National Laboratories developed an improved mode of operation for continuous sources of ions. The pulsed mode described above is not capable of good signal/noise ratio and focusing properties except with pulsed ion generation. If the electron beam is not pulsed, but left on throughout the 100-μsec. cycle, poor resolution and a high level of random ions result. Studier discovered and improved a continuous mode of operation similar to that shown in Figure 3 while using the TOFMS for thermal ionization studies (3).

The outstanding features of this mode are the absence of a pulse on the control grid, the coupling of part of the drawout pulse to the "backing plate" and the use of d.c. bias on the first ion grid or drawout grid. The control grid, or first electron slit, is operated slightly positive with respect to the filament, providing a constant stream of electrons into the source. These generate ions throughout the cycle. At the beginning of a cycle the ions are drawn out by the pulse on the first grid. The electron beam is deflected from passing through the effective ionization region by the drawout pulse. During the falloff of the drawout pulse the delayed pulse applied to the "backing plate" attracts the ions, preventing them from leaving the source as defocused "noise." A similar result is achieved in later model instruments by using a rectangular drawout pulse with no pulse on the backing plate.

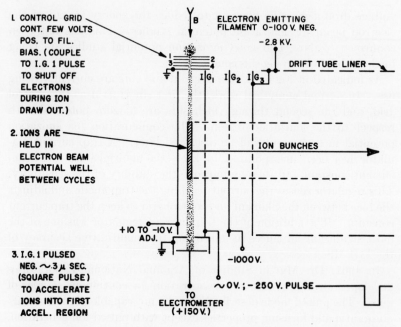

Fig. 3. Operation of time-of-flight mass spectrometer with continuous ionization.

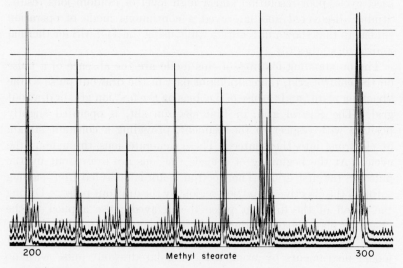

200   Methyl stearate   300

Fig. 4. Mass spectrograph of methyl stearate in continuous mode operation.

It is interesting to discuss at this point the difference in results of the pulsed and continuous modes, as they are called. The pulsed mode is relatively easy to adjust with only a single electrical control, the drawout pulse (focus pulse) amplitude, plus the electron beam collimating magnet position. The continuous mode adds the bias on the drawout grid and the coupling to the backing plate. The additional controls are not of enough additional complexity to cause difficulty, but the matter of balancing the noise level versus the resolution with the added controls takes a bit more "feel" on the part of the operator to get optimum performance.

The results, however, are well worth the effort. In the pulsed mode the resolution is quite dependent on the initial energy of the ionized species. Resolution (1% adjacent peak height interference) values from 100 to over 600 are obtained for ions of different initial energies on the same instrument. Using the continuous mode, the resolution is markedly inproved for the peaks which displayed the effects of larger initial energies. Figure 4 illustrates the resolution obtained in continuous mode operation on an organic species. Resolution in excess of 300 is common for hydrocarbons and, again, for some species exceeds 600. Equally important, a sensitivity increase of 10 to 100 times is observed in the continuous mode, due to the longer duty cycle. This is particularly valuable in making fast scans because the number of ions intergrated while scanning a peak is usually the limiting factor in determining the sensitivity or accuracy.

The most reasonable explanation yet advanced for the resolution increase observed with the continuous ionization mode attributes the effect to a trapping action in the potential well of the electron beam (3). In the pulsed mode, the ions are formed over a relatively short period of time ($\sim 0.3 \mu$sec.), then immediately pulsed into the drift region. If the ions have an average initial velocity of appreciable magnitude along the axis of the drift tube, some of them will arrive at the detector ahead of the center of the bunch and others behind. This time-of-flight spread is observed as broadened peaks at the output and results in a decrease in resolution. Such species as the CCl_3^+ radical from CCl_4 show this effect markedly. Other ions, principally inorganic parent ions, show little broadening.

One method for compensating this effect is "time-lag focusing." This simply is the insertion of a delay between ion formation and ion drawout. Figure 5 illustrates how this causes energy focusing.

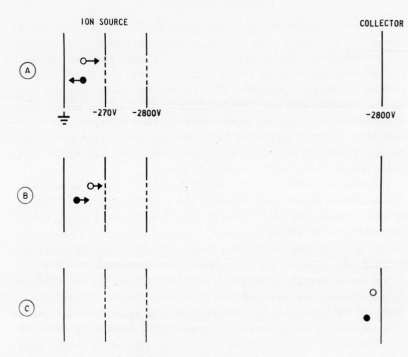

Fig. 5. Time-lag energy focusing.

Figure 5A illustrates the conditions at the time of ion formation; one ion has a velocity toward the detector, another one away from the detector. The solid circle represents the average or center of the group. By delaying the ion drawout, Figure 5B, the ions are allowed to move in the direction of their velocities. At some appropriate time the ions are drawn out by applying a voltage suddenly to the drawout grid. The ion nearest the drawout grid falls through the least potential and thus is accelerated to a lower velocity than the ion farther from the grid. The ion with a velocity away from the detector can just overtake the ion with a velocity toward the detector in the middle of the bunch, or at the average position, just as the bunch arrives at the detector, Figure 5C. The correct time delay for any given set of conditions is determined empirically. The disadvantage of this technique is that it is highly selective, that is, mass and energy dependent. Thus, it is practical for investigating a range of about

20 atomic mass units but is not suitable for general scans, particularly fast scanning.

In the continuous ionization mode, the electron beam is "turned on" for a large fraction of a cycle, e.g., 50–75 μsec. During that time, the electrons are constantly making new ions. The efficiency is such that the depletion of the number of molecules available for ionization is not significantly altered during this period. By the same token, the number of multiple hits, that is, an ionized particle being hit by a second electron, is negligible.

The conditions of the electron beam are such that a "potential well" is probably formed due to warping of the electric field between the drawout grid and the backing plate by the concentrated charge of the electron beam. This potential well is a trap for the lower energy ions, but the higher energy ions can escape from the trap or well. Most of the ions which escape from the well are attracted to the backing plate by a slight bias. Under proper operating conditions only the well-behaved low initial energy ions are pulsed out, resulting in a spectrum of improved resolution.

As mentioned before, the 170-cm. drift path length contributes to the increased resolution of the TOFMS. The longer path helps in two ways. First, the actual time separation between the ion bunches of different masses is increased. Since the peaks are now "spread out" in time, the frequency response requirements on the output systems are reduced, causing a more complete portrayal of the mass separation by the oscilloscope and analog output. Second, it is highly probable that the actual relative separation of the ion bunches is increased by the longer flight path. Whichever effect predominates, a net increase in resolution is obtained.

The increase in resolution gained by lengthening the drift path is attained at the expense of a slight decrease in sensitivity. If the system were perfect, the ions would not spread in the radial direction to any significant extent. However, a certain amount of radial spreading is caused by non-uniformity in the accelerating fields. One major cause of this in time-of-flight mass spectrometers has been warpage of the fine etched nickel mesh grids due to the electrostatic attraction between the grids. This was partially alleviated by operating the number 2 ion grid at an intermediate potential (e.g., 500 v.) and has been helped considerably by improving the grid mountings.

In the matter of ion optics, two other important improvements have been added. One is voltage stability of the ion deflection plates; until recently the stability of the voltage divider circuits to which the deflection plates are attached was insufficient. Normal drift in the deflection plate voltages caused some loss of quantitative reproducibility by shifting the position of the ion "beam." This condition has been corrected by improving the voltage dividers, reducing the length of the deflection plates, and making provision to short the deflection plates to the drift tube liner.

The other improvement is the recognition of the importance of properly compensating the magnetic fields in the ion source region. For normal use, a magnetic field of 150–200 gauss is employed in the ion source to collimate the electron beam. The direction of the magnetic field coincides with the direction of the electron beam and translates the radial motion of the electrons to a circular motion, greatly reducing the spreading of the electron beam. This causes a slight dispersion of the ions according to their m/e values, since the ions must traverse the magnetic field in leaving the ion source. A magnetic field of opposite polarity has always been used to compensate for this dispersion. However, in the first years of the program the compensation was not always properly done. New techniques have been devised to insure proper compensation. This is important because with standardized reproducible compensation, standardized spectra may be taken with confidence.

Another development is the operation of the ion source without a collimating magnetic field for the electron beam. This is particularly significant for studying charged particle interactions in the ion source. Although the magnetic field free operation is not quite as good as that obtained with the field at the time this is written, it is satisfactory for much work where it is desired and further development will certainly bring improvement.

Other ion source configurations such as the nude source, the ion–molecule reaction source, and the enclosed source are discussed in Section VI.

The TOFMS has been shown to be capable of being used for ionization and appearance potential measurements by several methods (4,5). The first efforts to accomplish this were carried out in conjunction with Dr. David White of Ohio State University in 1960 (6). The changes necessary to permit ionization potential measurements were minor. Addition of the five-slit electron gun, keeping these slits clean, operation of the control grid so it does not go more than a few volts positive with respect to the filament, operation of the trap anode at a few volts positive with respect to the ionization region rather than 150 v. positive, and operation of the number 2 ion grid at a low negative potential to reduce field peek-through into the ionization region are the necessary changes. Another important improvement for ionization potential work was the addition of an electrostatic shield behind the filament to prevent the ground potential at the wall of the source housing from disturbing the electron energy spread.

The pulsed ionization mode is nearly ideal for this type of measurement because the ionization region is bounded by ground potential electrodes, resulting in minimal normalization of the results. The continuous ionization mode has not yet been assessed to determine its capability in ionization potential measurements. The trap current regulator is not used during ionization potential measurements. It has been determined that anomalous results are obtained when attempt is made to keep the trap current constant either with the electronic regulator or by adjusting the filament drive. Excellent results are obtained by allowing the indicated trap current to change naturally.

III. THE MAGNETIC ELECTRON MULTIPLIER AND ANALOG OUTPUT

The ion detection system in the time-of-flight mass spectrometer must be capable of detecting very small amounts of charge (unit charge) with an extremely fast time constant (greater than 100 mc. response). The magnetic electron multiplier with a time-gated output is capable of the required degree of performance. It operates in a magnetic field and the electron paths are well defined by the combination magnetic and electric fields. Figure 6 shows the multiplier operation in schematic form.

The ions strike the cathode with 3000 e.v. energy (depending on the model) and dislodge secondary electrons. These electrons describe cycloidal motion and the fields are adjusted for optimum cycloid dimensions. As soon as the electrons leave the ion impact region, they are directed between the resistive plates of the multiplier. Here the voltages are adjusted so that the equipotential lines are directed

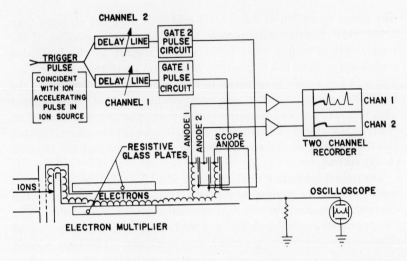

Fig. 6. Recording output system.

down into the lower (dynode) strip. The electrons strike the glass strip with several tens of volts of energy as the cycloidal motion directs, dislodging, on the average, 1.3–1.4 secondary electrons for each primary. Forty to sixty cycloids insure adequate gain.

The stability or reproducibility and hence the quantitative accuracy of the mass spectrometer depends on the stability of the multiplier gain. The multiplier gain is a function of the voltages applied to the elements of the multiplier. The stability of the multiplier power supply has been increased to 1 part in 100,000, which has minimized these factors in the instrument stability.

The amplified current is caused by the signal electrons but comes from the dynode strip. There is an upper limit to the amount of current which may be drawn from that strip. If the output current goes to high, the amplification becomes nonlinear. This effect prevents achievement of a much larger dynamic range in the TOFMS without readjusting the multiplier gain. The noise characteristics of the multiplier and output system permit measurement of partial pressure to below 1×10^{-12} Torr. The upper pressure limit of operation is above 5×10^{-4} Torr. This constitutes a dynamic range in excess of 5×10^{8}. If the multiplier gain is set to measure the lowest pressure, the output would be severely nonlinear at the highest pres-

sure.   The maximum range which can be measured on a single multiplier gain setting has been 10^6.

The limits of the dynamic range usable on a single multiplier gain
setting are determined on the upper end by the saturation effect
in the multiplier and on the lower end by the noise in the electrometer
amplifier.   The saturation effect in the multiplier is due to charge
depletion on the surface of the dynode strip as the amplified "bunch"
of electrons proceeds down the strip.   Due to the high resistance (10^7
ohms) of the conductive film on the strips, the return of the electrons
is not instantaneous.   The charge depletion causes a decrease in the
field between the dynode and field strips and a short-term reduction
of multiplier gain.   The charge in a single "bunch" of electrons must
be nearly 10^{-11} coulombs to have an appreciable effect, so that at
10 kc/sec. the saturation becomes detectable at 0.5–1 $\times$ 10^{-7} amp.
for a single peak.

The lower limit of the usable dynamic range is determined by the
amplifier noise.   This has been reduced from about 1 $\times$ 10^{-13}
amp. to less than 1 $\times$ 10^{-14} amp.   This has increased the dynamic
range to 10^7.

To increase the dynamic range where one large peak is the primary
cause of multiplier saturation such as in gas chromatograph effluent
identification without removal of the carrier gas, the pre-dynode
gating feature (peak eliminator) has been developed.   This is simply
a pulsing circuit with an adjustable time delay (0–20 μsec.) capaci-
tively coupled to the "Z plate" at the front end of the multiplier.   A
negative going pulse is applied to the Z plate, cutting off the electron
transit and deadening the multiplier for the width of a mass peak at
a selected time.   Thus a peak such as m/e 4 can be gated out before
passing through the multiplier causing saturation.   The selectivity
is such that it can gate out mass 40 without losing masses 39 or 41.
This extends the practical range of sensitivity in gas chromatograph
effluent identification by 10 to 100 times.

At the output end of the multiplier, the current pulses pass into the
gating region.   If a pulse is not diverted into one of the analog gate
channels, it proceeds to the last gate channel, which delivers the
current to the oscilloscope load resistor.   The current develops a
voltage across this 100-ohm resistor.   The voltage heights of the
output pulses are in the millivolt range.

If one of the preceding gate electrodes is pulsed negatively, it diverts the electron beam into that channel. The gate is maintained at the negative potential only long enough to collect the current pulse due to a single mass peak on each cycle of the instrument. The width or time duration of the electrical pulse applied to the gating electrode determines in part how well the true separation of the mass peaks is translated into the analog output. Since the gating action occurs as a gradual function of the gate voltage over a 0 to -100 v. range, and since the pulses have time durations of less than 10^{-7} sec., a perfectly instantaneous gate turn on and turn off is not obtainable. The pulses must have an approximately trapezoidal or triangular shape, whereas the ideal shape is rectangular. Recent advances in electronic circuitry provide more nearly rectangular shape gate pulses and consequently better recorded resolution.

The gating process is repeated on each cycle and the series of current pulses due to a particular mass is delivered to the current pickup electrode of that channel and then to the input of an electrometer circuit. The electrometer circuit integrates the current pulses and passes them on to a recorder after amplification.

The linear ranges of the electrometer amplifier have been extended to cover a range of 10^7. An innovation is the incorporation of a logarithmic amplification feature covering a range of 10^5. This is very useful for survey work but is not as quantitatively accurate as the linear amplifiers. It takes some acclimation to become accustomed to a mass spectrum presented on a logarithmic plot, but once one becomes familiar with it, it is easier to use than the multiple sensitivity traces in the familiar 1, 3, 10, 30, 100 sequence.

Scanning is achieved by changing the relative time at which the gate electrode is pulsed on during each cycle. If it takes one second to scan over a peak, there have been 10^4 discrete changes in timing of the gate pulse during the scan at a 10 kc./sec. repetition rate. The gate literally "jumps" along. The increments are small enough so that they constitute a continuous scan for all practical purposes.

Several aspects of this gating feature of the multiplier are important. Several gate channels may be employed. The maximum number has been chosen as six plus the oscilloscope channel, as it could not be foreseen that more channels would be needed in a significant number of applications. Six peaks may be monitored simultaneously; or six scans of the mass spectrum may be performed simultaneously; or any combination of these. However, the same peak may not be gated into two channels concurrently.

The maximum scan rate provided has been increased and the fastest rate now provided covers the scan range of 0–900 atomic mass units in 1.5 sec. Several years ago, this would have been useless, but with the increases in the number of ions such as provided by the Studier continuous mode, this scan rate can now be utilized. The matter of the ion statistics affecting the mass spectrum has been a point requiring frequent clarification among users of fast-scanning mass spectrometers. Rapid scan rates together with high-performance detectors now bring the operation of a mass spectrometer into the range wherein the scan rate is not limited by the frequency response of the detector as much as it is by the statistical variation in the number of a particular mass of ions reaching the detector during the period that that peak is being scanned. Those people familiar with slow scanning instruments who observe the jagged aspect of peaks developed on a fast scan for the first time frequently refer to the instability of the peak heights as noise, believing it to be an instrument malfunction, when it is actually a manifestation of a basic physical principal.

It is well to point out here that when any mass spectrometer manufacturer claims fast scanning it is implicit that the fastest scans are usable only at greater partial pressures in the source, that is, on larger amplitude peaks. The smaller the peak the lower the scan rate must be to obtain a useable peak shape. On some time-of-flight mass spectrometers a maximum scan rate of 1.5 sec. from 0 to 900 atomic mass units is provided, but this is useful only on the top two or three orders of magnitude of sensitivity. Below about 0.1% the scan rate must be reduced proportionately to the reduced level of output to obtain useful results.

To permit the fastest possible scans the analog scanner plug-ins can be gauged to permit scanning up to six parts of the mass spectrum concurrently. For instance, the scanners can be set to scan the ranges 1–12, 12–35, 35–90, 90–150, 150–250, 250–400 atomic mass units, and can all be started with one switch. This is finding application in capillary gas chromatograph effluent identification since capillary gas chromatography peaks frequently last only about one second.

Another development is the "total output intergrator" plug-in, originally suggested by Langer and Gohlke (7). This device integrates the whole mass spectrum on every tenth cycle of the mass spectrometer. It may be adjusted to intergrate only after a given mass such as m/e 35. The addition of this device makes the mass spectrometer the detector as well as the fraction identifier for gas chromatography. This arrangement constitutes an ionization detector of about 10^6 dynamic range with a linearity of $+5\%$.

By triggering the external start scan and automatic recyclic scanning features with the total output integrator, semiautomatic analysis is obtained successfully by using a gas chromatography–TOFMS combination. This is particularly useful on the programmed temperature capillary gas chromatographs where 50–200 components must be separated and identified.

IV. THE VACUUM SYSTEM

Since a mass spectrometer presumes a vacuum system as an integral part of its nature, the rapid developments in the field of high-vacuum technology have had a direct bearing on the field of mass spectrometry. In a turn-about-is-fair-play vein, the mass spectrometer has played an important role in the advance of high-vacuum at any stage of development. The fact that the mass spectrometer can do this means that the limitation in sensitivity of the laboratory mass spectrometer will usually be the background or high-vacuum residuals. The improvement of the vacuum system associated with the TOFMS then lies in two areas, reduction of background and improvement of convenience of operation.

Two basically different types of pumping systems are utilized on the TOFMS—the mercury diffusion pumps and the sputter-ion pump. The diffusion pump system will be examined first, then the ion pump, then the two will be compared. Certain applications are better performed with one type or the other, but many are handled well by both.

The three-stage metal mercury diffusion pump has proven to be a reliable means for producing the high vacuum necessary in mass spectrometers. The most popular pumping system is that in the Bendix Model 12-107 TOFMS using a 4-in. diffusion pump. The original separate cold trap and water-cooled baffle have been replaced by an inproved one-piece liquid nitrogen cold trap and Freon-cooled chevron baffle. The liquid nitrogen cold trap is based on a design by Rauh (8). The conductance of the trap and baffle is in excess of 40 liters/sec. for nitrogen, delivering an unbaffled pumping speed to the mass spectrometer ion source of about 40 liters/sec. The liquid nitrogen consumption has been halved to about 0.5 liter/hr. The chevron baffle is cooled with a Freon compressor and maintains a mercury partial pressure in the analyzer of about 1×10^{-6} Torr with no liquid nitrogen in the cold trap. The mass spectrometer may be operated and left pumped down for extended periods without any coolant in the cold trap. Addition of liquid nitrogen to the cold trap reduces the mercury partial pressure in the analyzer to the 10^{-9} Torr range. The pumping speed for condensibles of the new cold trap is much more constant because the coolant reservoir surface that faces into the analyzer remains at a constant temperature until the coolant level is very low. The pumping speed changes less than 1% when the coolant level decreases over a one-hour period.

The 6-in. pump and large liquid nitrogen trap with a pumping speed of about 125 liters/sec. have been retained in the Bendix Model 14-107. Unfortunately, the chevron cold trap used in this unit is not as efficient as that on the Model 12-107, so liquid nitrogen must be maintained in the cold trap during operation. The liquid nitrogen consumption rate of this trap is about 1 liter/hr. Models 3012 and 3015 have vacuum systems resembling that on the 12-107 except that the plumbing is on a 6-in. diameter bias instead of 4. This provides pumping speeds of about 100 liters/sec. when required. A scaled-up version of the chevron baffle similar to that on the 12-107 is used, permitting operation without liquid nitrogen.

Sputter-ion (electrical discharge–getter pumps) are now being used to pump many mass spectrometers. About 20% of the time-of-flight mass spectrometers have been built with this type of pump. They pump by a combination of physicochemical gettering and plastering of gas molecules under layers of sputtered material. The vacuum system is roughed down to about 10^{-3} Torr with a mechanical pump isolated from the system by a molecular sieve trap, then the sputter-ion pump is turned on and the mechanical pump may be turned off. The convenience of the sputter-ion pump then becomes apparent, for it is silent and requires no water or liquid nitrogen and very little attention. The vacuums achieved with these pumps are equal or superior to all but the finest diffusion pump systems.

Why, then, are they not used on all systems? Because of several drawbacks. Least significant are greater weight and higher cost (about double). The poor pumping of inert gases such as helium and argon and the reduction in pumping speed of all gases in the 10^{-5} to 10^{-3} Torr range are serious shortcomings for certain applications.

For example, in gas chromatograph effluent sampling, the helium or argon carrier gas is pumped slowly, and the input rate to the mass spectrometer must be reduced, resulting in a loss of sensitivity. This can be overcome by use of special techniques. The reduced pumping at higher pressure rules out this type of pump in shock tube or fast reaction studies where large gas loads must be pumped.

In general, sputter-ion pumps are preferable for residual gas analysis and general analysis where the instrument is to be used on an occasional basis. The diffusion pumps are preferable for gas chromatograph effluent identification, fast reaction studies, and sampling from high-pressure sources for line-of-sight sampling. Most other cases are less obvious and must be considered carefully.

Whichever type of pump is used, it has been found that one of the major sources of instability in the TOFMS is the variation in pumping speed. For analytical work a pumping baffle is used between the source region and pump. This reduces the pumping speed out of the source region and reduces the effect of pump speed variations by the ratio of the pumping speeds with and without the baffle.

A primary source of hydrocarbon background in the analyzer was found to be the backstreaming of forepump oil vapors through the mercury diffusion pump. This has been reduced by over two orders of magnitude by incorporation of a molecular sieve trap in the line connecting the mechanical pump to the diffusion pump. Evidence of the effectiveness of this device is the absence of the characteristic mass 149 peak in the background.

A persistent source of air leaks in the instrument has been reduced by the use of Fusite electrical feed through construction in the source and multiplier headers. This type of header is molded as a single unit, rather than having individual feedthroughs soldered into a machined header. Although not completely immune to leaks, the incidence of air leaks has been reduced to a reasonable level by this change.

The Phillips GD-2 cold cathode discharge gage vacuum monitor has been retained immediately above the cold trap in the Model 12-107. In the 14-107, 3012, and 1015, a Bayard-Alpert type ionization gage is employed. The gages are primarily used as vacuum monitors and overpressure protect devices. Their off–on reliability is good, but they are unsatisfactory as a means of calibrating a mass spectrometer. The gages should not be stationed in the ion source region for routine applications, since they cause extensive molecular rearrangement of the sample for many hydrocarbons due to the discharge or hot filament.

V. READOUT SYSTEMS

The oscilloscope and the analog system are two separate types of readout on the TOFMS. The oscilloscope output has sufficient sensitivity and frequency response so that the mass spectrum produced on each cycle of the instrument can be read out as a separate entity. The analog output, on the other hand, does not have as high a frequency response but has greater sensitivity and accuracy.

The oscilloscope output is used for short time duration studies and for qualitative work in general usage. The oscilloscope has reasonable accuracy (better than $\pm 10\%$) from 100% down to about 0.5% of the maximum readings. The detection limit is about 0.001% on the oscilloscope. Below 0.5% the accuracy decreases, because below this level the sample partial pressure in the ion source is no longer a linear function of the peak height on the oscilloscope. This is so because as the sample pressure in the source diminishes, the number of ions generated decreases. At some pressure, there will be on the average, only one ion of a given mass reach the multiplier on each cycle. Below this pressure, there will not be a fraction of an ion on each cycle, but rather on some cycles there will be an ion and on other cycles there will be none. The manifestation of this on the oscilloscope under visual observation is that from maximum signal (about 10^3 ions/cycle) down to about 10 ions per cycle, the peak height is linear with sample partial pressure, while below about one ion per cycle the "intensity" of the peak varies with pressure. Figure 7 shows an oscilloscope presentation of an air spectrum. The m/e 28 (N_2^+) and 32 (O_2^+) peaks are multiple ion/cycle, 40 (A^+) is about 1 ion/cycle, and 44 (CO_2^+) is less than 1 ion/cycle.

Visual perception of changes in the oscilloscope pattern is most useful in the range from 10 sec. to a few tenths of a second. Faster time-scale observation requires the use of photographic techniques. Time correlations of various peaks down to about 10^{-3} sec. may also be performed with a multiple-channel analog output.

Photographing the oscilloscope pattern is simple with the usual cameras available, especially those with Polaroid backs. Simple

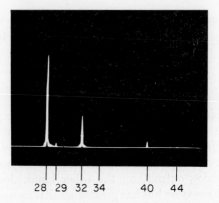

28 29 32 34   40   44

Fig. 7. Air spectrum on oscilloscope.

traces or repetitive traces of the same pattern may be photographed
without complications. In fast reaction studies, however, it is necessary to get information on successive spectra as little as 10 μsec.
apart. This may be accomplished with a camera which moves the
film past the focal point at a very high rate of speed ($\sim$ 0.1 mm./μsec.).
This results in the successive sweeps of the oscilloscope trace being
recorded at slightly different positions on the film. These spectra
may be read from the film and the data analyzed. This recording
technique gathers the maximum information in the shortest time,
since it records the whole spectrum as seen on the oscilloscope on
each cycle of the instrument. On the negative side, these techniques
are costly, requiring an expensive high-speed camera, very sensitive
film, and careful development for each shot. Moreover, the data
reduction process is tedious and long.

An easier and more adaptable method of recording fast reaction
data has been developed. In 1960, the author reported a new technique called Z-axis gating developed by the author and J. Betts (9).
Then in 1963, Lincoln reported an excellent system incorporating Z-
axis gating and a new technique called light-streak recording (10).

This method uses two oscilloscopes with standard cameras. One
oscilloscope is the dual-beam type which is practically two scopes in
one. Each beam is set up to monitor a single mass peak on each
cycle of the mass spectrometer. When the reaction is run, two components are thus monitored for abundance on each cycle with the
oscilloscope and the results are already plotted in bar graph form on

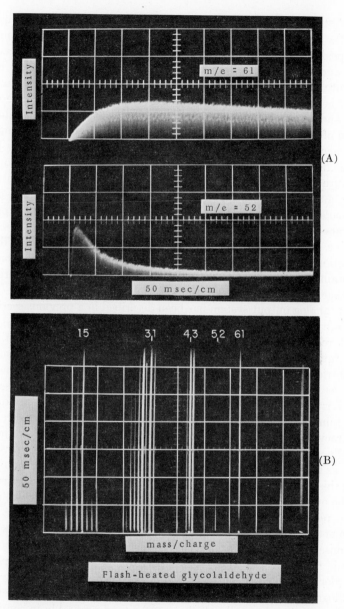

Fig. 8. Time-resolved raster display. (Time starts at bottom.) 10 kc. rate. Sample heated by a single flash from a xenon flash tube.

the photograph as in Figure 8A. The other oscilloscope is set up so that the displacement on the horizontal axis is a function of the mass of a peak as normally done. The vertical axis, however, is the time axis, and the distance from the top or bottom of the display is a measure of time. The amplitude variation signal due to the mass peaks is applied to a control element in the oscilloscope cathode ray tube and varies the brightness of the cathode ray spot. The abundance of a wide range of mass peaks may thus be roughly monitored, for when the reaction is run, a series of vertical light streaks is left on the film as in Figure 8B. The intensity of the streaks is a rough measure of their abundance, the horizontal location indicates the mass, and the relative time of increase or decrease of abundance of a particular peak is indicated by the vertical distance where the peak appears more or less intense. This technique is easier and less expensive to operate than the moving film camera technique, and data reduction is simplified. The loss is that full quantitative capability is obtained only on two mass peaks. This, however, is not a serious drawback and is more than offset by the advantages.

The analog output system has been described in a previous section. The output of the analog system is normally presented on a strip-chart recorder. The type of recorder chosen is a function of the scan rate and accuracy level desired. Single and multiple-pen potentiometric servo recorders are now available with a response time of 0.25 sec. These have a claimed accuracy of ±0.25% of full scale, which is about as good as can be obtained without special techniques. The minimum time necessary to scan from mass 10 to 200 with full accuracy is 4 min. This is a long scan, but this type of recorder is usually used at slower scan rates over a much shorter range of masses, such as in isotope ratio determinations. The type of record obtained with this type of recorder is well known: colored ink on white paper.

The other end of the scale of recorders is the oscillographic or light-beam recorder. This type of recorder employs a small mirror galvanometer about the size of a matchstick which can have a frequency response of many thousand cycles per second. This is sufficient to permit recording the whole mass spectrum in 1 sec. This type of recorder has linearity of 1–2%, which is adequate for most work. Oscillographic recorders can be obtained with 36 galvanometers, but four or six are usually all that can be used profitably in conjunction with the mass spectrometer. Using a suitable preamplifier between the analog system and the recorder, several galvanometers can be set up to scan the same spectrum at different levels of sensitivity simultaneously such as the familiar $1:3:10:30:100$ sequence. This is useful in survey work. Other galvanometers can record the outputs of other analog channels in practically any manner desired. The only difficulty is in unscrambling the traces on the paper. Since the paper is photosensitive and light activated, all the traces are the same color. Thus, care must be taken in setting up schemes where many channels are recorded simultaneously to permit deciphering the data. A logarithmic scale has been devised for this recorder to match the logarithmic electrometer range in the analog amplifier.

New types of paper have been developed for the oscillographic

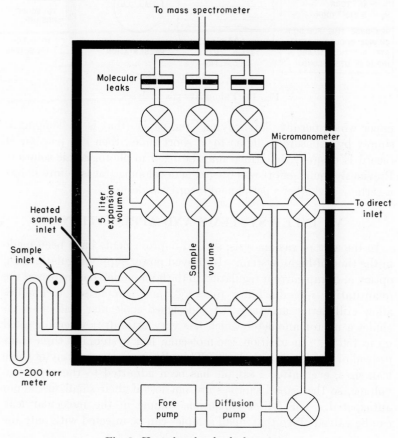

Fig. 9. Heated molecular leak system.

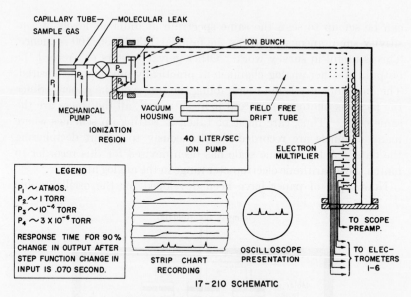

Fig. 10. Pulmonary gas analyzer.

paper which permit "latensifying" the paper (that is, developing it simply by exposure to light) for a short time; then if a permanent record is desired, that trace may be fixed in photographic solution. Previously, much effort was wasted in developing traces before it was ascertained whether a permanent record was desired.

VI. INLET SYSTEMS AND APPLICATIONS

In the area of gas analysis, several improvements have been made in the time-of-flight system. Improved power supply regulation, ion optics, and trap current regulation in the later models has increased the quantitative reproducibility to ±1%, and comparison techniques allow still better accuracy. A redesigned molecular leak inlet includes a micromanometer which has very little drift when operated up to 150°C. In addition, the molecular leak system has three leaks instead of the usual single leak. This allows selection of any of three leak sizes, even after a sample has been admitted to the expansion volume, so that small samples are not lost if their small size is not anticipated. The 5-liter expansion volume in the molecular leak can be valved off so that small samples can be injected with only the

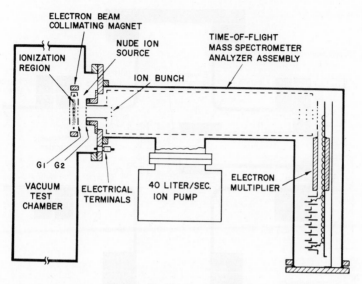

Fig. 11. Residual gas analyzer.

manifold volume ($\sim$ 40 cc.) acting as a reservoir. This results in being able to analyze gas samples of 1 Torr cc. with good accuracy. The schematic of this molecular leak system is shown in Figure 9.

Continuous sampling and analysis of gases from several atmospheres pressure to 10^{-4} Torr is possible with a new configuration of inlet and analyzer as shown in Figure 10. The atmospheric pressure gas is drawn through the capillary to the intermediate region at about 1 torr pressure. From there, the gas passes through a molecular leak into the source region at about 1×10^{-4} Torr. Pressures below atmospheric may be sampled by enlarging or removing the leaks. With this system, several gas components may be sampled simultaneously with a total system response time of less than 70 msec. This configuration is finding application in pulmonary research and simulated space cabin atmosphere analysis.

From 10^{-4} to 10^{-12} Torr, the configuration shown in Figure 11 provides a new approach to the analysis of vacuum residuals in large space chambers. The "nude" source projecting into the high-vacuum region obviates the problem of trying to bring "nothing" into the mass spectrometer. The source can be cantilevered into a high-vacuum tank to project past cryopanels to get true composition

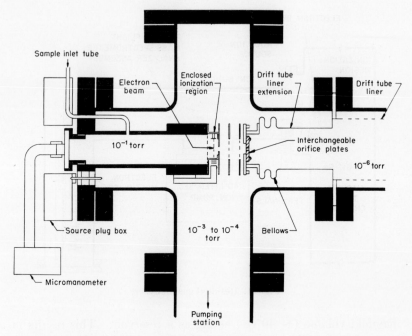

Fig. 12. Time-of-flight mass spectrometer ion-molecule reaction source.

analyses in the working high-vacuum region. At very low partial pressures the multiple-channel output can be used to monitor several pertinent peaks simultaneously. This is helpful because scan times become quite long at low pressures.

Melton and Hamill (11) have confirmed that ion–molecule reaction mechanisms can be studied with the standard TOFMS ion source. Also, the excitation efficiency curves of reactions such as

$$Ar^* + Ar \rightarrow Ar_2^+ + e^-$$

can be studied effectively by the retarding potential difference method and using the multiple channel output.

The investigation of ion–molecule interactions in the pressure range from 10^{-6} to over 10^{-1} Torr is made possible by the ion source configuration shown in Figure 12. The enclosed ionization region permits obtaining high pressure in that region while maintaining a pressure of about 3×10^{-4} Torr in the source housing and about 1×10^{-5} Torr in the drift tube by utilizing separate pumping on the source and drift tube. An innovation by the author, a micromanometer attached to the source, measures the pressure in the ionization region accurately. By introducing the gas into the chamber behind the ionization region, significant pressure gradients are avoided. This is apparently the first configuration to permit accurate measurement of the pressure in the interaction region.

Ionization with high-energy particles is being investigated by Schuler and Stuber (12). They have investigated ionization by M.E.V.-range protons by attaching the TOFMS to a van de Graaf accelerator. By also ionizing with k.e.v.-range electrons, they compare the ionization process caused by dissimilar mass particles at similar velocities.

A special TOFMS is being used by Hunt et al. to study metastable ions (13). The instrument has several sets of retarding grids in the drift tube to effect these studies. By retarding the ions at different times in their transit from the source to the multiplier, the metastable lifetimes can be bracketed if they are in a suitable range.

Methods of sampling from plasmas and flames have been developed. O'Halloran and Fluegge built an apparatus to sample ions and/or neutrals from a plasma at 11,000°K (14). It utilizes triple differential pumping and samples for only a few tenths of a second per run. The interesting feature is an extremely fine nozzle to which the shock wave attaches, apparently causing sampling through the shock wave, allowing investigation of the true properties of the species in front of the shock wave. It is also applicable to sampling directly from rocket exhaust permitting *in situ* investigation of the reaction products.

Milne and co-workers (15) are developing an apparatus for line-of-sight sampling of neutral species from flames at atmospheric pressure. They report polymers of common air constituents by sampling supersonic molecular beams from atmospheric pressure.

Scheurich has sampled positive and negative ions from flames at atmospheric pressure (16). Profiles of ions from different areas of the flame were obtained.

Diesen and Felmlee have achieved good results in experiments sampling shock waves in various atmospheres (17). They use a longitudinal shock tube terminating in the fast reaction chamber of the TOFMS source. Bauer (18) is designing an apparatus to sample shock waves through differentially pumped nozzles with the nude source near the exit nozzle to minimize boundary layer effects.

Wacks has a generator for manufacturing free radicals and sampling those with good efficiency (19). He has also investigated surface-catalyzed decompositions.

The interaction of halogens with metal surfaces at high temperatures has been investigated by McKinley (20,21). His apparatus permits identification of reaction products and short-lived intermediates. It permits measurement of their formation rates as a function of surface temperature and gas pressure.

Lincoln (10) and Friedman (22) have investigated the products of flash-pyrolyzed reactions. Lincoln examines the short-lived species and Friedman examines those which persist up to 10 sec.

Rauh (23) and White (6) pioneered Knudsen cell thermodynamic equilibrium studies with the TOFMS. They each built a furnace of their own design. The Bendix Knudsen cell furnace design (Fig. 13) was patterned after features of those designs and incorporates additional features such as the isolation valve which permits sample changing without venting the spectrometer. Stable temperatures in 2500°C. are achieved routinely now by virture of differential pumping and input power regulation. Studies at cell pressures from 0.1 to below 10^{-5} Torr are feasible.

The need to discriminate between primary species from the Knudsen cell and secondary species at the same mass due to molecular fragmentation in the ionization process by ionization potential measurements led to an investigation of this type of measurement. As described in Section II, a few minor changes in the mechanical configuration and operating configuration brought this type of operation to an excellent status. Variations of the R.P.D. method of Fox et al. (24) and the Schiff method (25) are popular typically as described by Glick and Llewellyn (26).

Battles has developed a variation of the Knudsen cell to allow insertion of various gases into the cell at elevated temperatures to study the interaction of the gases and the vapors arising from the normally solid samples (27). Appropriate reactions must be chosen to be commensurate with the normal operating pressures of the cell.

A device for the study of the vapors liberated by solids and liquids at temperatures from ambient to 750°C. at pressures from 10^{-9} to 10^{-4} Torr has been developed. The device originally developed by Damoth and Saari (9) utilized a sliding piston entering the mass spectrometer through a vacuum lock to position a crimped filament below the ion source. Current through the filament heated it

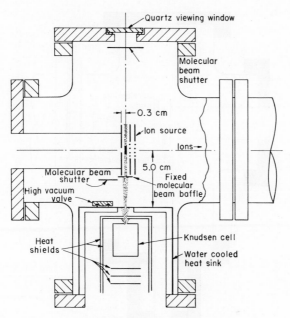

Fig. 13. Knudsen cell operation.

and vaporized the sample on the filament. Biemann and McClosky (28) modified the sample holder to position it nearer to the ionization region. This configuration was further modified to include a thermocouple to measure the sample temperature accurately as shown in Figure 14. This device has found application in the qualitative examination of materials that are too involatile to introduce through a molecular or viscous leak system. It is also useful for determining decomposition temperatures and products. Gohlke used a similar system and an earlier version of the total output integrator in a variation of differential thermal analysis, which he called mass spectrometric thermal analysis (7). An advantage of the direct inlet system for introducing low-volatility samples into the ionization region is that only the minimal amount of sample necessary to make the analysis is vaporized. The unvaporized sample is withdrawn in the crucible. Sample clearing times are reduced by orders of magnitude.

Studier uses a thermal ionization source to study minute amounts of radioactive material (3). Because of the oscilloscope output he was

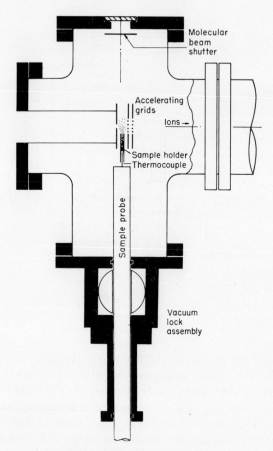

Fig. 14. Direct inlet system.

able to ascertain the cause of many discrepancies in such analyses done previously.   The direct inlet system can be modified to permit rapid changing of thermal ionization samples.

Ebert developed a sophisticated manifold for connecting a packed column gas chromatograph to a TOFMS (29).   It provides a means for holding sections of the gas chromatograph effluent stream at a fixed leak rate throughout the duration of a scan to eliminate the modulation of the mass spectrum by the sample concentration envelope.   Alternate paths allow elimination of the carrier gas for sensitivities in excess of 0.1 p.p.m. by freezing the sample rapidly, pumping off the carrier gas, revaporizing the sample and admitting it to the mass spectrometer. In principle, this "dynamic trapping" technique is similar to earlier methods of identifying gas chromatograph fractions by collecting various fractions in glass vessels as they are eluted from the gas chromatograph, then introducing each via a molecular leak system. The dynamic trapping system has several advantages. First and most important, it is faster and can keep up with any packed column set up, allowing scanning of most fractions on a single run. Second, it is more sensitive, since the sample is not transferred from one vessel to another. Such sample transferring can cause trace constituents to be lost or obscured. Third, it is simpler because the apparatus is designed for the job. Fourth, higher molecular weight compounds may be handled due to the optimized geometry and bake-out oven on the later manifold systems.

McFadden et al. (30) connected the output of capillary gas chromatographs directly into the TOFMS. The fast scan capabilities of the TOFMS permit scan durations short enough to obtain spectra of many capillary gas chromatograph fractions, even though many of these have durations at the output of less than 1 sec. The sample clearing time must also have a time constant of little more than a second to avoid overlap of fractions. The open construction and fast pumping at the TOFMS source are assets in this respect.

One of the simplest sampling devices has proven to be one of the most powerful. Many compounds which are relatively stable at atmospheric pressure or above tend to decompose when introduced into a molecular leak or other inlet system which reduces the sample to an intermediate pressure before admitting it to the mass spectrometer. The simple needle valve, admitting the sample from a high-pressure container directly into the high vacuum of the mass spectrometer, minimizes the chance of sample decomposition before analysis. A notable case is the use of a straightforward arrangement to identify XeF_4 and XeO_4 by Chernick, Studier, et al. (31,32).

VII. PERFORMANCE CHARACTERISTICS

Delineation of the performance characteristics of the time-of-flight mass spectrometer requires more than a simple listing of numbers. Some explanation is required because of the differing applications and modes of operation. A small amount of explanation of the

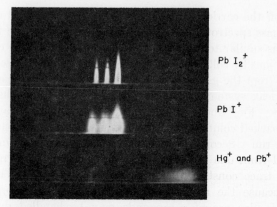

Fig. 15. Effects of large, random initial-ion energies.

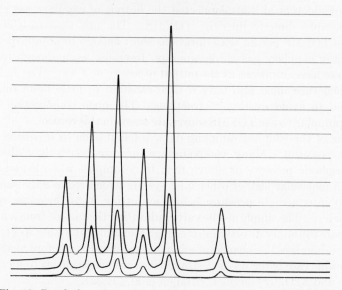

Fig. 16. Resolution of mercury isotopes in continuous mode operation.

meaning of the performance values will prevent some misunderstanding.

The resolution of TOFMS operated in the pulsed ionization mode with a 100-cm. drift path was specified as 200 for a long time due to the separation of the mercury isotopes on the oscilloscope output.

Actually, in the pulsed mode, the resolution depends on the initial energy of the ions as previously described and varies from about 100 for some organic patterns to about 500 for low initial energy inorganics. With the pulsed mode and the 170-cm. drift path, the resolution similarly may be described as varying from about 150 to 600. Even this description can be in error. Figure 15 shows the spectra of PbI_2^+, PbI^+, and Pb^+ obtained in the pulsed mode with a 170-cm. path. The effects of dissociation energy are obvious. With the continuous ionization mode and 170-cm. path, the resolution is about 250–600. A typical value for organic species is 300. Figure 16 shows the resolution of the mercury isotopes obtained in the continuous mode. (The resolution of the TOFMS is defined as that mass, M, at which, when a peak of mass $M + 1$ of equal height is introduced, the peak height or amplitude of M will be increased by 1%.)

The quantitative reproducibility of any mass spectrometer depends on a number of factors such as the type of sample and method of introduction, partial pressure in the ion source, the presence or absence of other compounds, the previous history of the instrument, and the operating environment. The previous values quoted for the 12–107 (± 2–5%) and the values currently quoted for the 3012 and 3015 (± 1%) are for samples introduced via a stable molecular leak system, containing no unusual "quirks" and with the instrument operating in a reasonably well-controlled environment after being turned on for at least 24 hr. to stabilize. For isotope ratio analysis ± 0.1% may be obtained with careful work, while in fast reaction studies ± 5–10% may be expected. It is implicit that the quantitative reproducibility decreases as the limit of sensitivity (accuracy = ± 100%) is approached.

The sensitivity of a mass spectrometer is perhaps the most difficult parameter of all to define satisfactorily. That is because it depends on the scan rate, the background, interferences (e.g., N_2^+ and CO^+ at m/e 28), molecular weight, method of inlet, and other factors. The only satisfactory method of specifying this elusive number seems to be to list it in the terminology or units applicable to a particular type of analysis and under reasonably typical conditions. In general, useful qualitative or quantitative work can be done at about one order of magnitude higher concentrations than bare detection. The values quoted, then are for a level about $10\times$ above detection.

For the direct inlet and molecular leak inlet, the sensitivity can be specified as an input rate of 1×10^{-14} mole/sec. for identification. An input rate of this value requires 10–100 sec. to develop a usable scan. Thus 10^{-13}–10^{-12} mole of sample is required for a favorable case. As much as 10^{-10} mole may be required in an unfavorable case where a lengthy, detailed scan would be required or where background is high.

In the case of gas chromatograph effluent identification, the ratio of the stream split must be taken into account. For example, if a simple splitter valve is used to deliver 0.1% of the output of a packed column gas chromatograph to the mass spectrometer, the sensitivity becomes about 10^{-10}–10^{-8} moles. However, if a manifold system is used to eliminate the carrier gas as mentioned in Section VI, the full sensitivity applies.

In the Knudsen cell inlet system, the sensitivity is better than 10^{-5} Torr in the cell. This number depends directly on the area of the effusion hole of the cell. The larger the hole the greater the sensitivity. This number is for a 0.01-in. diameter hole.

For residual gas analysis, the sensitivity is about 1×10^{-12} Torr in the ionization region. To yield true composition readings at ultra high vacuum, the nude source must project into the high-vacuum region.

In pulmonary gas measurement, the sensitivity to N_2 or CO in O_2 is limited to 0.1–1.0% due to the m/e 28 peak that is generated with large amounts of O_2. The sensitivity to O_2 and CO_2 in N_2 is about 0.01%. With the sputter-ion pumped instruments (e.g., Model 17–210P), helium and argon wash-in studies are limited due to the poor pumping of these pumps on noble gases.

Frequent reference is made to the low duty cycle (0.3–1.0%) of the ionizing electron beam in the pulsed mode of the TOFMS. There are factors which mitigate this situation. First, the instantaneous current is usually about 75–500 μamp. with average ionizing beam currents of 0.25–2.0 μamp. Second, in the continuous ionization mode, the duty cycle is at least 50% with average trap currents of 10–50 μamp. Third, the ions due to all masses are transported to the multiplier (ion detector) on every cycle of the instrument. In mass spectrometers with geometric ion separation, all the ions formed except those of one particular m/e ratio are continuously being lost.

The fact that the ions of all masses are collected on every cycle makes possible the repetition rates of 10–100 kc./sec. on the oscilloscope output. But of course, these high repetition rates mean that the scanning speed is so high that the sensitivity on the oscilloscope output is not as high as on the analog output. The sensitivity on the oscilloscope output is two to three orders of magnitude less than on the analog output.

As was mentioned previously, the maximum analog scan rate has been increased to 50 μsec./sec. That is the analog conversion of mass spectrometer time to real time. This permits scanning the mass range from 0 to 900 amu in 1.5 sec. The resolution of the instrument is not reduced at this scan rate, because this is merely a translation of the basic high-frequency operation of the instrument to a slower speed.

The sensitivity, however, is reduced at the fast analog scan rates. Maximum sensitivity is achieved at a scan rate of about 1000 sec. for 12 to 200 amu. Sensitivity is reduced in proportion to scan time, so the sensitivity is reduced by about 10^3 for a 1-sec. scan rate. This factor is not peculiar to the time-of-flight mass spectrometer. It is true in any mass spectrometer. The scan rate in the TOFMS is multiplied by simultaneous scanning with several analog channels. Increase of the scan rate in this manner does not reduce the sensitivity.

The capability for ionization potential measurements is such that determinations can be made with a precision of ±0.05 e.v. in some cases. In general, it may be stated that ionization potential measurements can be made with an accuracy consistent with the current state of the art and the ability to interpret the results.

The spectral cracking patterns have been found to be in general agreement with the cracking patterns in the API tables (33,34).

Most of the patterns in those tables were run with magnetic mass spectrometers with ion sources operated at a nominal 250°C. The TOFMS ion source usually operates at a much lower temperature (50°C.) and some slight differences in the patterns will be noticed due to this factor. However, the unit may be operated to 200°C. with a bake-out oven around the source end if desired. The improvement of the magnetic field compensation procedure as mentioned earlier has also helped to make the patterns more reproducible.

VIII. PREDICTIONS AND CREDITS

If anyone could predict a large number of the uses for which an instrument concept could be used and also delineate the advantages and disadvantages of each, he would be an excellent candidate for an applications engineer's job. One of the biggest hazards to making such predictions is the possibility of other instrumentation being developed which will do a job faster, easier, better, or cheaper. Some applications to which the time-of-flight mass spectrometer will probably be put are spelled out below and reasons for these are given which tend to support such predictions.

Probably the biggest area as yet left untouched is the employment of the TOFMS to assist in optimizing chemical process streams by instantaneous comparison of parameters by means of continuous sampling and multiple channel readout. Mass spectrometry is still too expensive and unreliable for process control but this could come, too.

Another likely field for the TOFMS is the microprobe analysis of solids via laser vaporization. The rapid multiple-channel output is a prime factor here, as well as the open geometry.

Rapid, routine analysis for certain elements via thermal ionization is also probable. A variation of the direct inlet probe, plus the multiple-channel readout, hold promise for rapid analysis.

More application of Langmuir vaporization apparatus at high temperatures right in the source region may be expected, because of the better sensitivity than Knudsen cell configurations.

The basic instrumental parameters will be improved, increasing the utility of the TOFMS in existing applications as well. The sensitivity will be improved by orders of magnitude, by reducing the background, by increasing the number of ions formed, by increasing the ion transmission efficiency, and by improving the multiplier efficiency.

The stability will be improved gradually. It is expected that stability of $\pm 0.1\%$ short term and $\pm 0.5\%$ over 8 hr. will be obtained.

The resolution will gradually be improved to about 1000. It is unlikely that any increase in resolution to compare with the double focusing magnetic instruments will be achieved.

The 100 kc./sec. repetition frequency appears to be a practical limit due to spectrum overlap. The analog scan rates can be increased if the sensitivity permits.

These improvements and a great many of those already achieved have and will be due to the ingenuity of the users of the time-of-flight mass spectrometer. The following list of references names some of those who have helped to advance the state of the art. Many others who are not listed here have also contributed. The Bendix Corporation is grateful for the many suggestions and ideas which have been given so generously.

References

1. Harrington, D. B., in C. F. Clark, ed., *Encyclopedia of Spectroscopy*, Reinhold, New York, 1960.
2. Wiley, W. C., and I. H. McLaren, *Rev. Sci. Instr.*, **26**, 1150 (1955).
3. Studier, M. H., *Rev. Sci. Instr.*, **34**, 1367 (1963).
4. Kiser, R. W., and E. J. Gallegs, *J. Phys. Chem.*, **66**, 947 (1962).
5. Hamill, W. H., and C. E. Melton, *J. Chem. Phys.*, **41**, 546 (1964).
6. White, D. O., A. Sommer, P. N. Walsh, and H. W. Goldstein, "Application of the Time-of-Flight Mass Spectrometer to the Study of Inorganic Materials at Elevated Temperatures," *Advances in Mass Spectrometry*, Vol. 2, R. M. Elliott, Ed., MacMillan, New York, 1963.
7. Langer, H. G., and R. S. Gohlke, *Anal. Chem.*, **35**, 1301 (1963).
8. Rauh, E., Argonne National Laboratories, private communication.
9. Damoth, D. C., "Recent Improvements in the Time-of-Flight Mass Spectrometer," Eight Annual ASTM Committee E-14, Conference on Mass Spectrometry, Atlantic City, June 1960.
10. Lincoln, K. A., *Rev. Sci. Instr.*, **35**, 1688 (1964).
11. Melton, C. E., and W. H. Hamill, *J. Chem. Phys.*, **41**, 1469 (1964).
12. Schuler, R. H., and F. A. Stuber, *J. Chem. Phys.*, **40**, 2035 (1964); [Erratum, **41**, 901 (1964)].
13. Hunt, W. W., Jr., and K. E. McGee, *J. Chem. Phys.*, **41**, 2709 (1964).
14. O'Halloran, G. J., and R. A. Fluegge, "Plasma Analysis with the Bendix Time-of-Flight Mass Spectrometer," Eleventh Annual ASTM Committee E-14 Conference on Mass Spectrometry, San Francisco, May, 1963.
15. Greene, F. T., and T. A. Milne, *J. Chem. Phys.*, **39**, 3150 (1963).
16. Scheurich, J., Texaco Experiment, Inc., to be published.
17. Diesen, R. W., and W. T. Felmlee, *J. Chem. Phys.*, **39**, 2115 (1963).
18. Bauer, S. H., Cornell University, private communication.
19. Wacks, M., *J. Phys. Chem.*, **68**, 2725 (1964).
20. McKinley, J. D., Jr., *J. Chem. Phys.*, **40**, 120 (1964).
21. McKinley, J. D., Jr., *J. Chem. Phys.*, **40**, 576 (1964).
22. Friedman, H. L., "Products of Flash Pyrolysis of Phenol-Formaldehyde by Time-of-Flight Mass Spectroscopy," Eleventh Annual ASTM Committee E-14 Conference.
23. Ackermann, R. J., and E. G. Rauh, *J. Chem. Phys.*, **36**, 448 (1962).
24. Fox, R. E., W. M. Hickam, T. Kjeldaas, Jr., and D. J. Grove, *Rev. Sci. Instr.*, **26**, 1101 (1955).
25. Cloutier, G. G., and H. I. Schiff, *J. Chem. Phys.*, **31**, 793 (1959).
26. Glick, R. A., and J. A. Llewellyn, *J. Chem. Phys.*, in press.
27. Battles, J., Argonne National Laboratories, private communication.
28. Biemann, K., and J. A. McClosky, *J. Am. Chem. Soc.*, **84**, 2005 (1962).

29. Ebert, A. A., *Anal. Chem.*, **33**, 1865 (1961).
30. McFadden, W. H., R. Teronishi, D. R. Black, and J. C. Day, *J. Food Sci.*, **28**, 316 (1963).
31. Chernick, C. L., et al., *Science*, **138**, 136 (1962).
32. Huston, J. L., M. H. Studier, and E. N. Sloth, *Science*, **143**, 1162 (1964).
33. American Petroleum Institute Research Project 44, *Catalog of Mass Spectral Data*, A and M Press, College Station, Texas.
34. Kiser, R. W., and E. J. Gallegos, *J. Phys. Chem.*, **65**, 1177 (1961).

Manuscript received by Publisher April 6, 1964.

Organic Analysis with Ultraviolet-Visible Absorption Spectroscopy

Lloyd N. Ferguson, *Howard University, Washington, D. C.*

I. INTRODUCTION

The construction of commercial instruments for chemical laboratory work, following World War II, set in motion two related developments. Spectroscopy, in its several forms, grew to become the most widely used experimental tool in pure and applied chemistry, and our fundamental knowledge of molecular structure rapidly increased through the use of spectroscopy. Almost every theoretical or experimental problem can use spectroscopy to an advantage. Thus, it enables chemists to make delicate but probing studies of intramolecular environments, it facilitates the characterization of complex molecules, and it provides quick, accurate analyses of chemical mixtures for guidance in research and process control.

The more recent advent of nuclear magnetic resonance and mass spectroscopy to the battery of physical techniques used for chemical and structural analysis has attracted the attention of many chemists, and the versatility of n.m.r. spectroscopy justifies this interest. Nevertheless, the use of ultraviolet-visible spectroscopy for chemical analysis is still indispensable.

There is an abundance of material in the periodical literature and there are many books on ultraviolet-visible spectroscopy. The biannual reviews of *Analytical Chemistry* (1964, 1962, etc.) present exhaustive cataloging surveys of the use of spectroscopy for analysis of a large variety of constituents, and colorimetry for functional group analysis is included in almost every chapter of the *Organic Analysis* volumes. As a chapter in the *Advances* series, this review will summarize the applications of ultraviolet-visible spectroscopy to organic analysis and emphasize its use as a diagnostic tool for the elucidation of molecular structure.

II. THEORETICAL BACKGROUND

1. Classification of Electronic Absorption Bands

The absorption of light from the ultraviolet-visible region of the spectrum produces changes in the electronic energy of molecules according to the relationship

$$E_e - E_0 = \frac{hC}{\lambda} = \frac{286 \times 10^3}{\lambda} \text{ kcal./mole}$$

where E_e and E_0 are the energies of an excited state and the ground state of the molecule, h is Planck's constant, C is the velocity of light, and λ is the wavelength of the absorbed light. Thus, the smaller is the transition energy $E_e - E_0$, the longer the wavelength of light absorbed.

Several types of electronic transitions may occur. One type, called an $N \rightarrow V$ or $\pi \rightarrow \pi^*$ transition, is identified with the process

$$C{=}C \xrightarrow{h\nu} \overset{\mp}{C}{-}\overset{\pm}{C}$$

in which the excited state closely resembles one of the polar structures. Naturally, the less energy required for this transition, i.e., the more polarizable the electrons involved, the longer is the wavelength of the $N \to V$ band. Accordingly, the position of this band for all multiple bonds ($>$180 mμ) is at longer wavelengths than for single bonds ($<$150 mμ). A second type of transition, designated $n \to \pi^*$, involves a shift of a nonbonding lone-pair electron to an empty antibonding molecular orbital. The corresponding absorption bands are of much longer wavelength than for $N \to V$ transitions and of very low intensity. For example, the $N \to V$ and $n \to \pi^*$ bands for the C$=$C and C$=$O groups have the following optical constants (1):

Bond	$\pi \to \pi^*$ band		$n \to \pi^*$ band	
	λ_{max}, mμ	ϵ	λ_{max}, mμ	ϵ
C$=$C	185	8000	230	2
C$=$O	188	900	275	22

The relative magnitudes of these transitions can be understood in terms of a diagram of the energy levels of the molecular orbitals involved (2). Normally, the energy required to remove electrons from a molecule increase in the order: nonbonding, π,σ. However, the relative energies of the electrons in the antibonding levels are reversed (see diagram). Thus, the transition energies decrease and the absorp-

Potential energy ↑

Antibonding σ^*
Antibonding π^*
Nonbonding
Bonding π
Bonding σ

tion band wavelengths increase in the order, $\sigma \to \sigma^*$, $\pi \to \pi^*$, $n \to \pi^*$, with the $\sigma \to \sigma^*$ bands lying in the far ultraviolet (ca. 150 mμ). In fact, it was recognized early in the history of organic chemistry that colored substances possess multiple bonds and the unsaturated groups were given the name *chromophore*. The color-producing or chromophoric power of some common multiple bonds is in the order:

$$C{=}C < C{=}N < C{=}O < N{=}N < C{=}S < N{=}O$$

Similar transitions may occur in a conjugated system but at longer wavelengths. Thus, the $\pi \rightarrow \pi^*$ transition for an α,β-enone system

$$C=C-C=O \xrightarrow{h\nu} {}^+C-C=C-O^-$$

produces a band near 220 mμ and at high intensity. The $n \rightarrow \pi^*$ band appears at longer wavelengths too, but still at low intensity.

	$\pi \rightarrow \pi^*$ band		$n \rightarrow \pi^*$ band	
Compound	λ_{max}	ϵ	λ_{max}	ϵ
$CH_3-CH=CH-CHO$	217 mμ	16,000	321 mμ	20

Aromatic rings exhibit two types of absorption bands referred to as *primary* and *secondary* bands in the American School and K and B bands in the British School. The secondary band is identified with transitions to polar excited states, e.g.,

in which X is a substituent, and the direction of polarization of electrons depends on the nature of X (3). The primary band is associated with a forbidden transition and, therefore, is of low intensity. The spectral constants for these bands, for several monosubstituted benzenes, are given in Table I, and the several types of electronic absorption bands just discussed are summarized in Table II.

A second important feature of an absorption band is its intensity. We saw that the wavelength of absorbed light is a function of the *energy* of the transition from ground to excited state. The intensity of the absorption band, usually reported as the absorptivity, is a function of the *probability* of the transition and of the magnitude of the transition moment. Absorption takes place when the transition is accompanied by a polarization of the molecule. The absorption intensity, then, is dependent on the magnitude of the transition moment, which in turn is related to the length of the chromophoric system. This polarization is sometimes expressed as the *oscillator* strength, f

$$= f \, 4.32 \times 10^{-9} \int \epsilon d\nu \simeq 0.5 \Delta\nu \cdot \epsilon$$

TABLE I
Spectral Constants for the Principal Bands of Monosubstituted Benzenes (4)

Substituent	Primary band		Secondary band	
	λ_{max}, mμ	ϵ	λ_{max}, mμ	ϵ
H	203.5	7,400	254	204
$^+NH_3$	203	7,500	254	160
CH_3	206.5	7,000	261	225
Cl	209.5	7,400	263.5	190
Br	210	7,900	261	192
OH	210.5	6,200	270	1,450
OCH_3	217	6,400	269	1,480
CN	224	13,000	271	1,000
COOH	230	11,600	273	970
NH_2	230	8,600	280	1,430
$COCH_3$	245.5	9,800		
CHO	249.5	11,410		
NO_2	268.5	7,800		

TABLE II
Classification of Electronic Absorption Bands

Electronic transition	Band terms	Characteristics
$N \rightarrow T$ or $\pi \rightarrow \pi^*$	Chromophore and primary bands	In general, electron-donor *and* electron-acceptor groups, and also increased polarity of solvent, produce bathochromic shifts. Examples: π,π^* conjugation $\quad h\nu$ $$C{=}C{-}C{=}O \rightarrow {}^+C{-}C{=}C{-}O^-$$ π,p conjugation $\quad h\nu$ $$R_2N{-}CH{=}CH_2 \rightarrow R_2\overset{+}{N}{=}CH{-}\overset{-}{C}H_2$$ π,σ conjugation $$CH_3{-}CH{=}CH_2 \rightarrow {}^+H\ CH_2{=}CH{-}\overset{-}{C}H_2$$
$n \rightarrow \pi^*$	$n \rightarrow \pi^*$ and secondary bands	In general, (i) electron-donor and increased solvent polarity produce blue shifts, (ii) are broad, and (iii) are of low intensity.

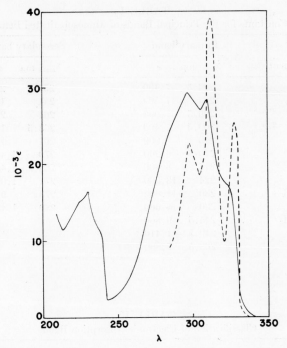

Fig. 1. Spectrum of *trans*-stilbene in alcohol at 20°C (solid line) and −130°C (5).

where ϵ is the molar absorptivity and $\Delta\nu$ is the range of the absorption band expressed in wave numbers.

2. Solvent and Temperature Effects

Electronic excitations are accompanied by vibrational and rotational changes. This produces a distribution of electronic transitions varying slightly in energy and, accordingly, the observed absorption band is an envelope of lines. As the temperature is lowered, the molecules fall more and more into the lower vibrational states and produce narrower groupings of transition energies. This appears as *fine structure* in the absorption spectrum as illustrated in Figure 1.

Solvent effects on spectra are quite complex and understood only in a qualitative way or at most to a semiquantitative degree. Various attempts have been made to correlate spectral shifts with certain properties of the solvent such as its polarizability, refractive index, or dielectric constant (6). Interactions between the solute and solvent, such as hydrogen bonding, obviously can affect spectra (7). Furthermore, solvent effects differ for different absorption bands. For example, increasing the polarity of the solvent has opposite effects on the $\pi \rightarrow \pi^*$ and $n \rightarrow \pi^*$ bands. The former shift to longer wavelength and the latter to shorter wavelengths as the solvent gets more polar. This is elegantly illustrated by the data for mesityl oxide in Table III.

TABLE III
Absorption Maxima of Mesityl Oxide in Various Solvents (8)

Solvent	Dielectric constant	Z value[a]	λ_{max}, mμ	
			$\pi \rightarrow \pi^*$ band	$n \rightarrow \pi^*$ band
Isooctane	0.2	60.1	230.6	321
Acetonitrile	37.5	71.3	233.9	314
Isopropyl alcohol	26	76.3	236.2	311.2
n-Butyl alcohol	17	77.7	237.2	311.1
Ethyl alcohol	25.8	79.6	236.4	310.5
Methyl alcohol	31	83.6	236.8	308.8
Ethylene glycol	41	85.1	240.1	307.4
Water	81	94.6	242.6	⌣302

[a] A measure of the solvent polarity as determined spectroscopically (9).

III. SOME STRUCTURAL PERTURBATIONS ON SPECTRA

The general procedure in using absorption spectra as an aid in the elucidation of molecular structure has been to determine empirically a few basic structure–spectra relationships from the spectra of compounds whose structures are well established. Then, these generalizations are used as a tool in the analysis for, or the characterization of, new organic substances. This same approach has been employed in the several forms of spectroscopy, n.m.r., infrared, Raman, etc., and will be used here for ultraviolet-visible spectroscopy.

Although the applicability and use of molecular-orbital calculations for interpreting spectra is rapidly expanding, the majority of chemists have no more than a reading familiarity with this technique. Consequently, the modern structural theory of organic chemistry is still the principal method of describing and interpreting the properties of organic molecules (3). This method uses the familiar valence-bond structural formulas and incorporates the effects of resonance, induction, hydrogen bonding, steric requirements, solvation, etc. Accordingly, the effects of these structural parameters on ultraviolet spectra will be discussed as a means of drawing correlations between spectra and molecular structure.

1. Resonance and Polarization

The wavelength of an ultraviolet-visible absorption band is determined by the energy difference between the excited and ground electronic states, and the effect of resonance and polarization on spectra depends on whether they produce a net stabilization of the ground state or of an excited state. For illustration, the principal resonance of benzene is among Kekulé (**1a**) and ionic (**1b**) forms. Forms **1a**

(a)   (b)

1

make the major contribution to the ground state and forms **1b** contribute chiefly to the excited states. Furthermore, the Kekulé resonance energy is the larger. As a result, resonance stabilizes the ground state more than the excited state. On the other hand, the dominant resonance of an isomer of benzene, fulvene, is among the

(a)   (b)

2

ionic forms (**2b**), which make the larger contribution to the excited state (see Fig. 2). This produces a net stabilization of the excited state, i.e., $E_1 - E_1' > E_0 - E_0'$. As a consequence, the electronic transition energies for benzene and fulvene, ΔE_B and ΔE_F, are of such magnitudes that benzene absorbs below the visible range (λ_{max}, 255 mμ), whereas fulvene is yellow (λ_{max}, 373 mμ). Similarly, the principal resonance of naphthalene is of the Kekulé type, produces a net stabilization of the ground state, and leads to absorption in the ultraviolet ($\lambda_{max} \sim 314$ mμ). In contrast to this, the major resonance of

E_1 ─────
E_1' ─────↑
          │ ΔE_B
E_0 ───|─
E_0' ──────
Benzene

E_1 ─────
E_1' ─────↑
          │ ΔE_F
E_0 ───|─
E_0' ─────
Fulvene

Fig. 2. Potential energies of excited and ground states of benzene and fulvene in absence of resonance (E_1, E_0) and with resonance stabilization (E_1', E_0'). ΔE represents the electronic transition energy.

an isomer of naphthalene, azulene, is among ionic forms **3b**, which make their principal contribution to the excited state. This leads to a very small transition energy and absorption in the visible (λ_{max}, 697 mμ). Thus, naphthalene is colorless, whereas azulene is blue.

(a)   (b)

3

Consequently, increased resonance among polar structures can produce a net stabilization of the excited state and bring about a bathochromic shift. (A change in absorption to longer wavelengths is called a *bathochromic* or *red-shift* and the reversed change is a *hypsochromic* or *blue-shift*.) Good examples are provided by phenol-phthalein **4** and indophenol **5**. Both compounds exhibit bathochromic shifts when placed in an acid or basic medium. In acid as well as base, two perfectly equivalent forms may be written for each compound, which increases the resonance energy. However, this resonance among ionic forms is even greater in the excited state and leads to absorption at longer wavelengths than in neutral solution (10).

Some molecules have a major conjugation in a single direction and they too fall in either the class where the net resonance stabilization is in the ground state, or the class in which resonance stabilizes chiefly the excited state. In the former class, for example, are the merocyanine dyes (11) and enolate ions (12), for which the transition

$$R_2N\text{—}(CH\text{=}CH)_n\text{—}CH\text{=}\overset{+}{N}R_2, \; R_2\overset{+}{N}\text{=}CH\text{—}(CH\text{=}CH)_n\text{—}NR_2$$
$$^-O\text{—}(CH\text{=}CH)_n\text{—}CH\text{=}O, \; O\text{=}CH\text{—}(CH\text{=}CH)_n\text{—}O^-$$

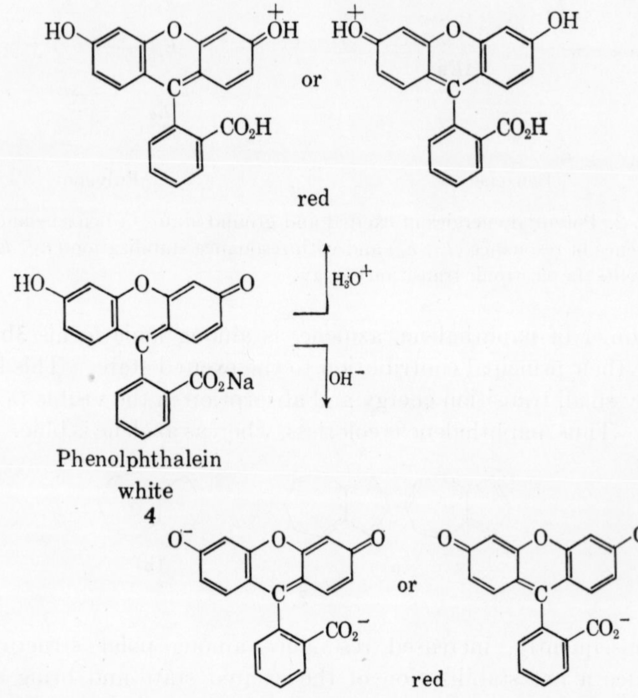

red

Phenolphthalein
white
4

or

red

energies decrease rapidly with increasing number of ethylenic groups
and λ_{max} varies linearly with n. The second class of linearly conjugated molecules consists of neutral polyenes for which the ionic reso-

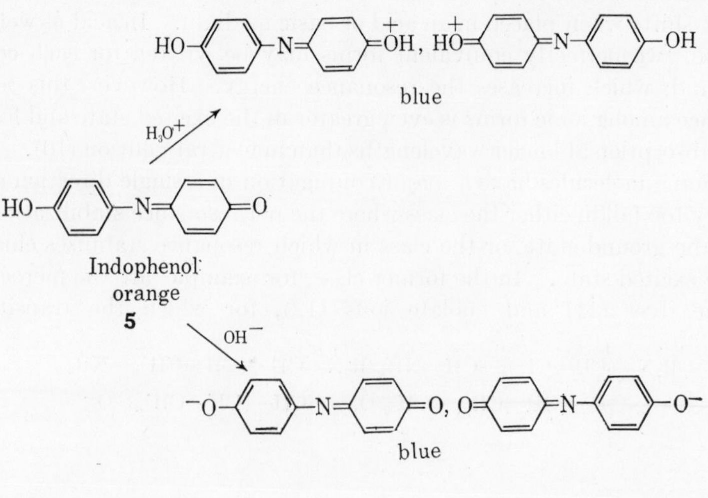

blue

Indophenol
orange
5

blue

nance forms make an increasing contribution to the excited states as n

R—(CH=CH)$_n$—R   R—(CH=CH)$_n$—CHO

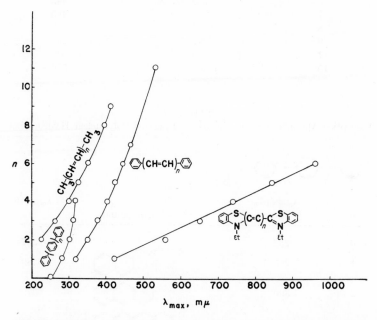

increases, and absorption occurs at longer wavelengths with λ_{max}^2 proportional to n. The spectral data for several series in this class are given in Tables IV and V and are diagramed in Figure 3.

Fig. 3. Variation of λ with n for some linearly conjugated molecules.

Since hyperconjugation is a form of resonance, the effects of hyperconjugation are similar to those of resonance. For instance, substitution of alkyl groups on a chromophoric system

$$H_3C—CH=CH_2, \quad {}^+H\ CH_2=CH—\bar{C}H_2$$

produces a bathochromic shift. The increase in λ_{max} is normally 5–10 mμ per alkyl group (cf. Section IV-3-A).

When a conjugated system is divided in half and the parts insulated from each other, the molecule will have an absorption band character-

TABLE IV

λ_{max} Values (in mμ) for Some Polyenes

n	CH_3—$(CH{=}CH)_n$—CH_3 (13)	C_6H_5—$(CH{=}CH)_n$— C_6H_5 (14)
1		319
2	227	352
3	263	377
4	299	404
5	326	424
6	352	445
7		465
8	395.5	
9	412.5	
11		530
15		570

TABLE V

Absorption Maxima of Some Linearly Conjugated Polynuclear Hydrocarbons

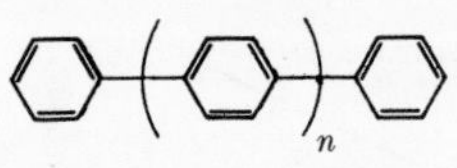

n	λ_{max} (15), mμ	Compound	λ_{max} (16), mμ
0	252		207
1	280	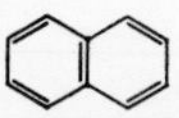	289
2	300	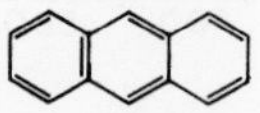	379
3	310	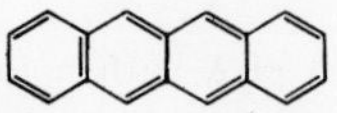	471
4	317.5	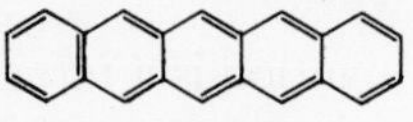	576

istic of the insulated chromophores, but approximately twice the normal intensity. For illustration, the molecules C_6H_5—$CH{=}N$—CH_2—CH_2—$N{=}CH$—C_6H_5 and C_6H_5—$CH{=}N$—CH_3 have essentially the same λ_{max} but the intensity of the former is twice that of the latter. Other examples are given in Table VI. When the two in-

TABLE VI
Spectral Constants for Some Single and Insulated Double Chromophoric Systems

Compound	λ_{max}, mμ	ϵ
$C_6H_5-CH=N-$⟨⟩	263	16,800
$C_6H_5-CH=N-$⟨⟩$-N=CH-C_6H_5$	267	33,800
$C_6H_5-CH=CH-$⟨⟩	295	26,300
$C_6H_5-CH=CH-$⟨⟩$-CH=CH-C_6H_5$	298	52,700
$CH_3-(CH=CH)_2-CHOH-C\equiv CH$	230	28,500
$CH_3-(CH=CH)_2-CHOH-C\equiv C-CHOH-$ $(CH=CH)_2-CH_3$	229	74,000
2-HO-5-CH_3-C_6H_3-N=N-⟨⟩-CH_3	380	14,000
[2-HO-5-CH_3-C_6H_3-N=N-⟨⟩-CH_2-]	380	32,000

sulated chromophores are dissimilar, the molecule may exhibit two absorption bands. For example, in an unsymmetrical benzophenone,

there is a cross conjugation between the benzoyl groups, and such compounds usually have two bands corresponding to the two cross-conjugated chromophoric systems. Thus, benzophenone and 4,4'-dimethoxybenzophenone each have one absorption band in the 240–280 mμ region, but 4-methoxybenzophenone has two bands, one characteristic of the C_6H_5CO group and one typical of the p-CH_3O—C_6H_4CO group.

The effect of substituents on the coplanarity of R and S in a conjugated system R—S can generally be discerned by comparing λ_{max} and ϵ values of the substituted and unsubstituted compounds. Usually there will be a marked increase or decrease of λ_{max} with a decrease in ϵ in both cases. With large steric interference to coplanarity of R and S, λ_{max} shifts to shorter wavelengths; this is the most common case for which several examples can be given.

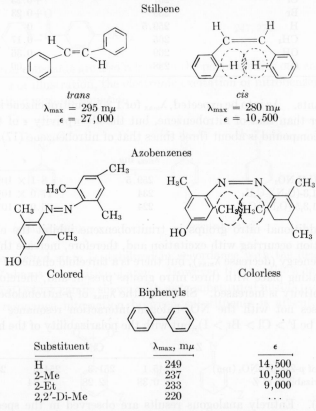

Stilbene

trans
$\lambda_{max} = 295$ mμ
$\epsilon = 27,000$

cis
$\lambda_{max} = 280$ mμ
$\epsilon = 10,500$

Azobenzenes

Colored

Colorless

Biphenyls

Substituent	λ_{max}, mμ	ϵ
H	249	14,500
2-Me	237	10,500
2-Et	233	9,000
2,2'-Di-Me	220	...

In these systems, the extended conjugation of the planar molecules is pinched off to varying degrees in the nonplanar compounds (*cis*-stilbene, di-*ortho*-substituted azobenzenes, or poly-*ortho*-substituted biphenyls), and absorption occurs at significantly shorter wavelengths. Two chromophoric systems R and S in the compound R—S may be insulated from each other by insertion of a saturated group between

R and S or by steric hindrance, as is found in a 2,2′,6,6′-tetrasubstituted biphenyl. As was shown in the previous section, if the two insulated chromophoric systems are identical, the absorption spectrum of the bis compound will be similar to that of the single chromophore, but have twice the intensity. For example, the bisazo dyes **7** and **8** have spectra closely resembling that of a twofold concentration of **6**. The completely conjugated compound **9**, on the other hand, absorbs at much longer wavelengths.

TABLE VIII

Spectral Constants for Some Bisazo Dyes (20)

Compound	λ_{max} (mμ)	ϵ	λ_{max} (mμ)	ϵ
6	380	14,000	330	27,000
7	380	32,000	335	60,000
8	375	30,000	335	54,000
9	550	43,000	470	30,000

When the steric hindrance is relatively small, λ_{max} may change very little but suffer a decrease in intensity. This occurs in many *ortho*-substituted benzene derivatives and some examples are provided in Table IX.

TABLE IX
Molar Absorptivities of Some Minor Sterically Hindered Compounds (21)

Hindrance to the NO_2 group		Hindrance to the NMe_2 group	
R in R-$C_6H_4NO_2$	ϵ (λ_{max} ~250 mμ)	R in R-C_6H_4-NMe_2	ϵ (λ_{max} ~250 mμ)
H	8900	H	15,500
2-Me	6070	2-Me	6,360
2-Et	5300	2-Et	4,950
2-i-Pr	4150	2-i-Pr	4,300
2-$tert$-Bu	1540	2,6-di-Me	2,240
2,4,6-tri-$tert$-Bu	830	2-$tert$-Bu	630

The hypsochromic effect (decreasing λ_{max}) of strain in the excited state is revealed by the C=N—N=C grouping. It contains two stronger chromophores than the C=C—C=C diene system but absorbs at shorter wavelengths.

$$CH_3O-\!\!\left\langle\bigcirc\right\rangle\!\!-CH=CH-CH=CH-\!\!\left\langle\bigcirc\right\rangle\!\!-OCH_3$$

λ_{max} = 363 mμ; ϵ 46,600

$$CH_3O-\!\!\left\langle\bigcirc\right\rangle\!\!-CH=N-N=CH-\!\!\left\langle\bigcirc\right\rangle\!\!-OCH_3$$

λ_{max} = 331 mμ; ϵ = 45,900

In the excited state of the chromophore

$$-CH=N-N=CH- \xrightarrow{h\nu} -\overset{\pm}{CH}-N=N-\overset{\mp}{CH}-$$

there is the strained N=N bond which destabilizes the excited state, i.e., increases E_e. On the other hand, when the C=N groups are turned around to give the N=C—C=N chromophore

$$-N=C-C=N- \xrightarrow{h\nu} -\overset{\pm}{N}-C=C-\overset{\mp}{N}-$$

there is no unusual strain in the excited state, and indeed the system exhibits a greater chromophoric power than the C=C—C=C group (144).

$$CH_3O-\!\!\left\langle\bigcirc\right\rangle\!\!-N=CH-CH=N-\!\!\left\langle\bigcirc\right\rangle\!\!-OCH_3$$

λ_{max} = 382 mμ; ϵ = 9470

Bathochromic shifts result when steric hindrance inhibits resonance in the ground state or when there is intramolecular strain in the molecule. For example, substitution of a methyl group into **10** is accompanied by a small blue shift, but introduction of the methyl group into the crowded molecule **11** produces a substantial bathochromic shift (22). In compounds of type **11**, steric hindrance which prevents co-

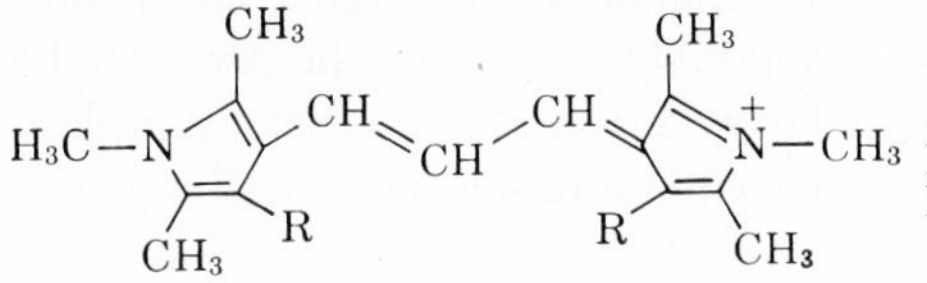

	λ_{max}, mμ	ϵ
R = H	536	6.3 × 10⁴
R = CH₃	534	7.6 × 10⁴

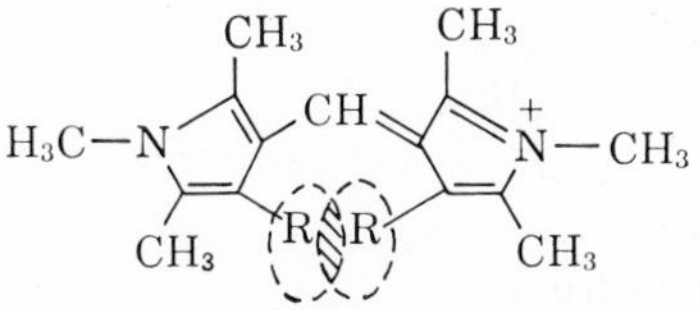

10

	λ_{max}, mμ	ϵ
R = H	446	3.5 × 10⁴
R = CH₃	479	1.25 × 10⁴

11

planarity of the conjugated system inhibits the ground state resonance

$$R_2N\text{---}(CH\text{=}CH)_n\text{---}CH\text{=}\overset{+}{N}R_2, \quad R_2\overset{+}{N}\text{=}CH\text{---}(CH\text{=}CH)_n\text{---}NR_2$$

and makes $E_e - E_0$ smaller, thereby increasing λ_{max}.

The bathochromic effect of intramolecular strain is exhibited by the alicyclic diene system.

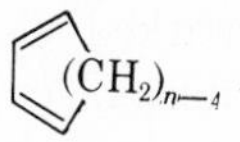

n	λ_{max} (mμ)	ϵ	References
5	238.5	3400	145
6	265	6030	146
7	248	7400	147
8	228	5600	148
10	215		149
12	230		150
13	232		150

Bond angle strain in $C_5\text{---}C_7$ rings decreases the thermodynamic stability of the ground states of the molecules and thereby decreases the transition energies $E_e - E_0$. As a result, λ_{max} is larger than that for an acyclic diene, e.g., 227 mμ for 1,4-dimethylbutadiene (Table IV). This bond angle strain apparently is absent in the C_8, C_{12}, and C_{13} rings. Hyperconjugation in the C_5 diene gives the ring some aromatic character and this ground state stabilization makes λ_{max} smaller than would be expected on the basis of bond angle strain. The two double bonds in the *cis,cis*-cyclodecadiene are not coplanar, as shown by the failure of the compound to undergo a Diels-Alder reaction. This nonplanarity effectively insulates the two double bonds, and accordingly, λ_{max} is below 215 mμ. Another example of the bathochromic effect of intramolecular strain is found in the spectra of the paracyclophanes.

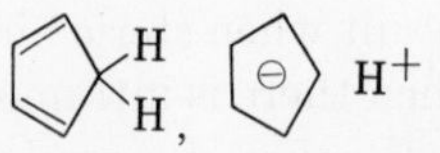

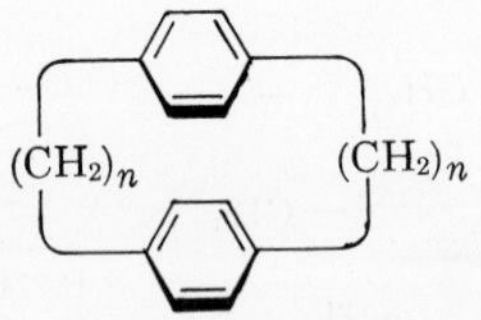

Paracyclophanes

As n gets smaller in these compounds, the benzene rings become increasingly strained and eventually lose their planarity when $n = 2$ (115). This strain is accompanied by a change in λ_{max} to longer wavelengths (114). The distorted benzene rings lose a part of their ground state Kekulé resonance energy which makes $E_e - E_0$ smaller and λ_{max} larger.

3. Hydrogen Bonding

Intramolecular hydrogen bonding has a marked visible effect on ultraviolet absorption spectra, whereas intermolecular hydrogen bonding has only a small effect. For instance, intramolecularly hydrogen bonded *ortho*-nitrophenols are deep yellow, but the corresponding *para* isomers are buff colored. The intramolecular hydrogen bond is also responsible for the yellow color of **12**, whereas its methyl ether is pure white. The bathochromic effect of intramolecular hydrogen

(a)   (b)

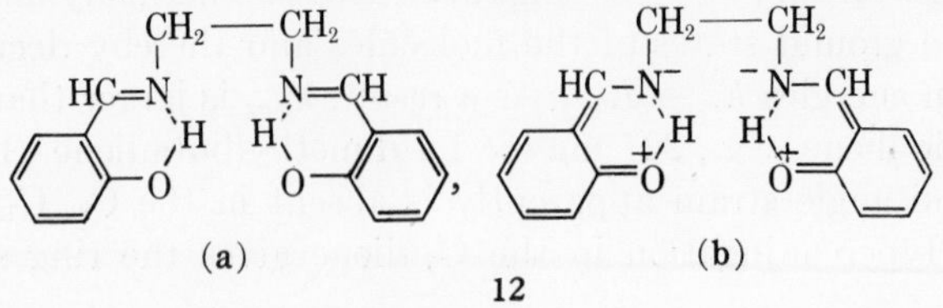

12

bonding can be attributed to an increase in the hydrogen bond strength in the excited state, as a result of resonance among dipolar structures such as 12b. This produces a net stabilization of the excited state, decreases the transition energy $E_e - E_0$, and leads to absorption at longer wavelengths. The bathochromic effect of intramolecular hydrogen bonding can be demonstrated in another way. Replacement of a methoxy group by a hydroxy group *para* to a carbonyl or nitro group produces a blue-shift, but when the substitution is made *ortho* to the carbonyl or nitro group, there is an accompanying bathochromic shift (23). This is illustrated by the data for benzaldehyde and nitrobenzene:

| Parent compound | | Wavelength of Primary Band in Hexane | | | |
| | | Substituent | | $\Delta\lambda$ | |
		OCH_3, mμ	OH, mμ	*Para*, mμ	*Ortho*, mμ
Benzaldehyde	4-	266.4	262.0	−4.4	
	2-	246.5	255.0		+8.5
Nitrobenzene	4-	292.0	287	−5.0	
	2-	248.3	271		+22.7

IV. SPECTRAL ANALYSIS

This section is the heart of this review. Herein is discussed the use of spectroscopy for making analyses for the presence of an organic compound or for working out the molecular structure of organic substances. We commonly identify objects by their colors and this is nothing more than qualitative, visible spectroscopic analysis. Many, many qualitative analytical procedures in the laboratory are based on the formation or disappearance of color in solution, or the appearance of a colored precipitate following a reaction with the sought constituent. The procedure is placed on a quantitative basis by measuring the intensity of color change because the intensity of color is directly related to the concentration of the colored constituent. Physical methods, particularly spectroscopy, offer certain advantages for quantitative analysis such as speed, accuracy, small-size sample needed, and often preservation of the sample. Spectroscopy is especially suited for studying equilibria because the measurements do not disturb the equilibria. Spectroscopy, in its several forms, is one of the most powerful techniques for the elucidation of molecular structure, and in this section we will discuss some of the various details which can be learned about molecules from their ultraviolet spectra.

1. Analytical Spectrometry

In spite of the marked successes of infrared and N.M.R. spectroscopy, ultraviolet-visible spectrometry continues to be the most widely used method of analysis. It is employed not only for the determination of most metal and nonmetal ions, but also for essentially every type of organic substance, including complex biological constituents. In this section, comments will be made first on general analytical procedures, then attention will be directed to accessories such as instruments, books, and collections of spectral data.

A. QUALITATIVE ANALYSIS

Qualitative spectroscopic analysis essentially consists of the identification of a substance or confirmation of the identity of a sample from its spectrum. An excellent example of one technique in the use of spectrophotometry for qualitative analysis was the determination of the structure of thiamine (24). Natural B_1 was split into two fragments, an acidic fragment and a basic portion by treatment with sodium sulfite. The hydrochloride of the latter was found to have a spectrum resembling that of 4-methylthiazole hydrochloride (Fig. 4). Also, when the basic fragment was treated with methyl iodide, the product had a spectrum almost identical to that of 4-methylthiazole ethiodide (Fig. 5), and when the basic fragment was oxidized it gave a product whose spectrum was identical to that of 4-methylthiazole-5-carboxylic acid (Fig. 6) (25). Thus, the spectra of the unknown basic fragment and the known 4-methylthiazole are similar both before and after chemical treatment, and indicate that the two samples have the same chromophoric system **13**.

The acidic fragment from the sodium sulfite cleavage of vitamin B_1 was found to be an aminosulfonic acid that loses ammonia upon hydrolysis to give an oxysulfonic acid. This reaction changed the absorption curve from one having a maximum at 245 mμ to one with maxima at 229 and 275 mμ, which is typical of the spectral changes exhibited by the hydrolysis of aminopyrimidines (26). Chemical work on the second cleavage product led to its identification as 2,5-dimethyl-4-aminopyrimidine (**14**).

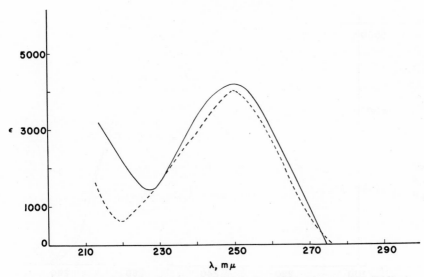

Fig. 4. Spectra of the hydrochloride of the basic degradation fragment (solid line) and 4-methylthiazole hydrochloride (dashed line) (25).

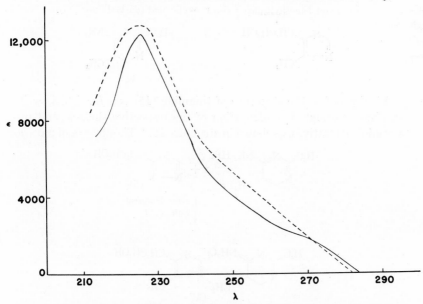

Fig. 5. Spectra of the methiodide of the basic degradation fragment (solid line) and 4-methylthiazole ethiodide (dashed line) (25).

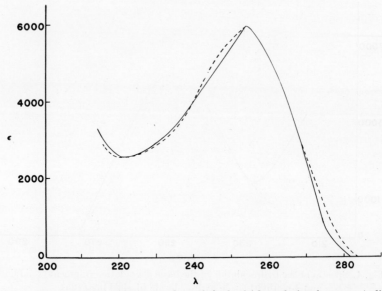

Fig. 6. Spectra of the oxidation product of the basic degradation fragment (solid line) and 4-methylthiazole-5-carboxylic acid (dashed line) (25).

Final proof of the structure of thiamine (**15**) was furnished by its synthesis through a condensation of the respective thiazole and pyrimidine derivatives, as shown in structure **15**. The spectra of natural

and synthetic thiamine are essentially identical (Fig. 7).

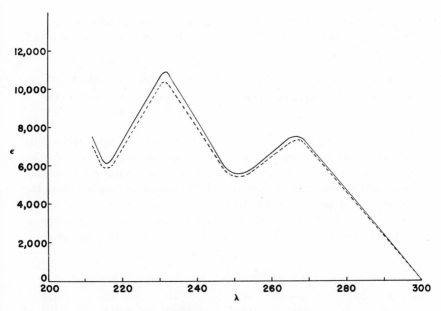

Fig. 7. Spectra of natural (solid line) and synthetic (dashed line) thiamine hydro-chlorides (24).

In this type of spectrophotometric qualitative analysis, identification is made on a basis of the shape of the absorption curves. Particular attention is given to the wavelength and absorptivity at maxima and minima in the curve. Caution must be exercised, however, in establishing an identity on one spectrum because several minor changes can be made in a molecule without significantly altering its ultraviolet spectrum. Similarity of spectra of a known compound and an unknown sample merely indicates that the two have similar chromophoric systems. For instance, replacement of the methyl group by an ethyl or isopropyl group in either chromophoric fragment of **15** would hardly be recognized from the spectra of the two compounds. There are several ways to verify that two samples with similar spectra are identical. One can measure the spectra in different solvents at different temperatures, and at high and low concentrations. Since impurities can affect shapes of curves, small differences in regions of low absorbance can usually be ignored. Alternately, as was done with the fragments from thiamine, one can measure the spectra before and after chemical reactions with the unknown. For

example, chemical methods led to the structure of penicillin as that of
16 or 17, where R is an alkyl group. Only by the use of physical

methods, e.g., infrared spectroscopy and x-ray diffraction, could a definite structure be assigned. Ultraviolet spectroscopy provided con-
firmatory evidence. Thus, an N-nitroso derivative was prepared and
its ultraviolet spectrum measured. If the substance had structure 16,
its nitrosation product would be an N-nitrosoamine, whereas if it had
structure 17 the derivative would be an N-nitrosoamide. A survey of
these two classes of model compounds showed that they are characterized by the following absorption bands:

	N-nitrosoamine		N-nitrosoamide		
λ_{max}, mμ	235	360	245	405	425
ϵ	7000	~85	~6000	~100	~100

Clearly, the two classes are distinguishable by their spectra. The
spectrum of the N-nitroso penicillin closely resembles that of the N-
nitrosoamide with absorption bands at 248, 405, and 425 mμ. This
confirms structure 17 as assigned from other physical data.

This type of qualitative analysis is impractical unless there is a
collection of spectra available for screening and comparison. An aid
in the screening process is to have a file of curve-shape indexes. One
curve-shape index was developed by Shurcliff (27) based on the number of maxima and wavelengths of the maxima, and also upon the
ratio of absorptivities at the several maxima. When the amount of
usage warrants it, the curve-shape index data should be developed in
one's own laboratory because the values are affected by changes in
solvent, temperature, pH, or other experimental conditions.

Not always can this procedure of identifying a compound by comparing its spectrum with that of a known compound be used. Very
often the problem is one of ascertaining the structure of a new substance or the constitution of a very complex structure. In these
cases, structure assignment is based on empirically drawn relationships between structure and spectra. This technique is discussed in
Section 3.

B. QUANTITATIVE ANALYSIS

The usual sequence of operations in quantitative analytical procedures, namely, sampling, preparation of sought constituent for measurement, and calculation of results, is followed as well in quantitative spectrophotometry. The second stage in this sequence may involve any number of processes, such as oxidation, reduction, precipitation, volatilization, extraction, dissolution, or complexation, to get the sought constituent in a known measurable form. Most research in this area has been concerned with attempts to improve methods for eliminating interfering substances, to acquire a better understanding of the structural, kinetic, and mechanistic features of the reactions involved, and to learn more about the spectral properties of species on which spectral measurements are to be made. Considerable searching has been made for organic reagents which have greater selectivity and/or sensitivity in analysis for inorganic or organic constituents (151). Chelates, for example, have revolutionized the practice of analytical spectrophotometry (152). They provide a high sensitivity as a result of their large molar absorptivities and stabilities, they can be exceptionally specific through the choice of chelating agent, or control of experimental conditions of pH, concentration, solvent, etc. Consequently, their versatility is almost unlimited.

One of the preliminary steps taken in the identification of an unknown organic compound, or the structure assignment of a new organic substance, is a determination of the common functional groups present in the molecule (153). Chemical, as well as physical techniques are used. Infrared and n.m.r. spectroscopy, and to a lesser extent ultraviolet and mass spectroscopy, are the principal physical methods employed. The chemical methods generally involve the formation of colored reaction products for the qualitative detection of a specific functional group (166). Sometimes the intensity of a given color test can be used for a quantitative measure of the functional group and the compound. However, a photometric titration (see Section IV-2) generally gives more accurate results. A recent review of qualitative functional group analysis appears in this *Advances* series (154).

Quantitative spectrophotometry makes use of the Bouguer-Beer law (28) in the form

$$\log I_0/I = a\,c = \log 1/T$$
$$A = a\,b\,c$$

where (29) A = absorbance = $\log 1/T$ = $\log I_0/I$

T = transmittance = I/I_0

I_0 = intensity of radiant energy incident on the sample.

I = intensity of radiant energy transmitted by the sample.

a = absorptivity

b = sample path length (in cm.)

c = concentration of solute (in g./liter)

On most modern spectrophotometers the absorbance and transmittance may be read directly on the instrument dials or are plotted on paper by automatic recorders as the spectrum is taken. Normally, the absorptivity at each wavelength is a constant for a given substance just as is its boiling point at each pressure. Failure of Beer's law for a substance, i.e., its absorptivity is concentration dependent, is an indication that the solute is undergoing some type of dissociation or association, or reacting with the solvent such that its absorbing capacity changes with concentration. Consequently, most quantitative analyses are conducted in concentration ranges where Beer's law does hold. Even so, certain empirical procedures have been developed for cases in which Beer's law does not hold for one or more components in a mixture (32). Under conditions where Beer's law is followed, the absorbance of a multicomponent system at each wavelength can be expressed as the sum of the individual absorptivities (i components).

$$A = a_1c_1 + a_2c_2 + \ldots a_ic_i \tag{1}$$

Hence, if the absorptivities are known for the pure components, one may analyze an i-component system by making absorbance measurements at i different wavelengths and solving the i simultaneous equations for the concentrations of the i components. The solution of i simultaneous equations is a formidable task for more than four equations even for an electric calculator. Obviously, an electronic computer is an asset (30), but in its absence various short cuts or approximation methods have been used (31). Also, a number of experimental techniques can be used to decrease the number of equations to be solved (32). For example, measurements can be made at wavelengths where one or more absorptivities are insignificant and, therefore, the corresponding a_ic_i terms could be neglected. As a result, many types of multicomponent mixtures have been analyzed with good accuracy and precision (33).

Quantitative analyses involving titration techniques are discussed in Sections IV-1-C and IV-2.

C. PROCESS CONTROL AND REACTION KINETICS

The general techniques of quantitative analytical spectrophotometry described in the preceding section are applied to dynamic systems as well. Thus, it is a useful tool for industrial process control, the detection of short-lived intermediates (34), the measurement of extremely fast reaction rates, or the study of regular reaction kinetics. It is a standard procedure for chemical plants to continuously monitor the composition of reaction mixtures by following the absorbances of certain constituents in the mixtures.

The study of reaction kinetics provides the most general means of learning something about reaction mechanisms, and of course, an analytical meter is needed to study the rates of reactions involved. Ultraviolet spectrophotometry is often used for this purpose by determining the concentration either of some product or a reactant involved in the reaction. For example, in a study of the kinetics and mechanism of the nucleophilic reactions of morpholine with the benzoyl halides,

$$\phi—C{=}O + R_2NH \rightleftharpoons \underset{\overset{|}{^+NHR_2}}{\overset{\overset{O^-}{|}}{\phi—\overset{k}{C}—X}} \overset{R_2NH}{\rightleftharpoons} \underset{\overset{|}{NR_2}}{\phi—C{=}O} + R_2NH_2X^-$$

the rate of reaction was followed by measuring the change in absorbance at the λ_{max} of each benzoyl halide (35). Thus, spectrophotometry provided a very easy measuring device for this study. Another very simple case is the measurement of the rate of iodination of aniline. The reaction can be followed by titration of unreacted iodine at successive time intervals or by measuring the absorbance of the reaction medium (at 525 mμ) as a function of time (36a). The two methods give comparable results. A somewhat more complex situation is one when there are two absorbing species. An example of such a case involves the isomerization of cis and trans-bisethylenediamine-dichlorocobalt(III) chloride. The rate of this process can be measured quite easily spectrophotometrically (36b). In other examples, the speed of oximation of ketones was measured spectrophotometrically (37), the rate of reduction of nitrobenzene to aniline was followed by measuring the nitrobenzene absorption at 265 mμ (38), and rate constants were determined for a number of reactions of the hydrated electron from absorption measurements at 578 mμ (165).

Ultraviolet-visible spectroscopy is used extensively in the study of enzymatic and biological reactions. Leonor Michaelis was the first to combine potentiometric, spectroscopic, and magnetic measurements to show that certain biological redox reactions occur in two one-electron steps and that free-radical intermediates may have a measurable lifetime (39a). In many such reactions, colored free-radical intermediates are produced momentarily and it is observed that the variation in light absorption at a chosen wavelength follows closely the change in magnetic susceptibility. The latter technique has recently been replaced by the sensitive electron paramagnetic resonance spectroscopy. In extremely fast reactions, in which the absorption band is only visible within a few seconds, a rapid scanning spectrophotometer is used (39b). This instrument plots a complete visible or ultraviolet spectrum 60 times a second on the screen of an oscilloscope from which continuous cinematographic records may be taken.

D. SPECTROSCOPY ACCESSORIES

Accessories, such as spectral catalogues, books, solvents, and specialized instruments, constitute an integral part of analytical spectrophotometry. Two types of bibliographic material are now available: collections of spectral curves and literature surveys of published data. In the first category, Project 44 of the American Petroleum Institute has issued curves for a number of years which now total over 900 spectra. Almost 700 spectra have been catalogued by Lang with literature references (40). There have been issued about 6000 spectra by the Sadtler Company (41). The American Society for Testing Materials issues spectral data on thousands of IBM punch cards (42). Name-formula index cards are available on which data are coded from the literature as well as from the API, Sadtler, and Lang collections. The Society for Applied Spectroscopy has announced a *Central Library of Spectroscopy* which will contain spectroscopic titles in Interlingua (43). The Friedel and Orchin collection of spectra (44) provides a useful service. Compilations of spectral data on special classes of substances are scattered in the literature (45).

An abundance of the second type of literature reference material has also become readily available in recent years. The *Organic Electronic*

Spectral Data series comprises a survey of approximately 70 journals over the years 1946 through 1959 (46). These compilations list wavelengths and intensities of band maxima; compounds are listed on a molecular formula basis with the *Chemical Abstracts* name. The solvent and references to the original literature are also given. A literature survey by Hershenson (47) provides a good complement to the Kamlet-Ungnade volumes. Hershenson only lists literature references. Gillam and Stern (48) offers a bibliography which covers most of the older literature.

The number of books on spectroscopy has grown rapidly in recent years with a burst appearing during the last four years. The *Encyclopedia of Spectroscopy* (49) takes up scattered and diversified topics in spectroscopy and several sections are of special interest to ultraviolet spectroscopists. The *Advances in Spectroscopy* series (50) contains reviews on all aspects of spectroscopy, and several chapters relate to the ultraviolet-visible range. Several very recent books (51), and others a little older (52), on molecular absorption spectroscopy, which includes ultraviolet, visible, and infrared spectroscopy, are each very useful in providing information on the theory, methods, and applications of absorption spectroscopy. These books are all on the same general topic, but each makes a valuable contribution to the field as a result of differences in organization and emphasis. They have enough diversity as to compliment one another.

A number of analytical reference and text books contain sections devoted to ultraviolet-visible spectrophotometry (53). These treatments are usually brief and merely give a sketch of the subject along with references for further study. Perhaps the most useful survey of the field is provided by the biannual reviews on *Ultraviolet Spectrometry* and *Light Absorption Spectrometry*, which are published in Analytical Chemistry, usually the April issue of the even years (1960, 1962, etc.). These reviews provide information and references chiefly on analytical spectrophotometry, including the theory, instrumentation, experimental techniques, and tables of photometric methods of analysis for metals, nonmetals, and organic substances, and also present sources of information on related fields. The coverage in these reviews on new instruments and modifications of commercial instruments, for instance, is very complete. One should consult these reviews for ideas of the variety of sought substances and reagents used in quantitative spectrophotometric analysis and for suggestions on experimental techniques. Thus, unusual solvent media such as poly-ethylene (54) or KBr, or temperature control devices have been reported for special problems. Mention should also be made here of the several relatively recent journals devoted to spectroscopy or analytical chemistry (with treatments on ultraviolet spectrophotometry: *Journal of Molecular Spectroscopy, Spectrochimica Acta, Applied Spectroscopy, Talanta,* and *Analytica Chimica Acta*).

2. Spectrophotometric Titrations

In addition to the study of reaction kinetics, spectrophotometric titrations are very useful to organic chemists for the determination of empirical formulas of complexes in solution and the measurement of dissociation constants. A wide variety of methods has been developed for the treatment of the experimental data but owing to the complexity of the problem, the most successful methods employ graphical techniques (155). Digital methods have been proposed (156) but even these methods are not completely satisfactory. The situation is that two substances X and Y are presumed to react reversibly to produce one or more association products in solution. At a given temperature and in a given solvent, the absorbance of the mixture at a fixed wavelength is determined by the initial concentration of X and Y, the values of the molar absorptivities, and the equilibrium constants for the equilibria involved. Of course, only the initial concentrations of X and Y are experimentally controlled. The problem is to determine values of the equilibrium constants.

Several graphical procedures are commonly used to deduce experimental values for the association constants (77). In the *method of continuous variations*, mixtures of different mole fractions of X and Y are prepared with a fixed total number of moles of X and Y. Then, the absorbance values for the solutions at a chosen wavelength are plotted against the mole fraction of one component, and the mole fraction of that component in the complex will correspond to the point of maximum absorbance (55). For example, in Figure 8 the absorbance of solutions of ferric ion and 4-hydroxy-biphenyl-3-carboxylic acid are plotted against the mole fraction of the latter, and the maximum in the curve indicates a formula of Fe_2R_3 for the complex, where R represents the organic moiety (56). The curve has a broad maximum which is the result of appreciable dissociation of the complex. Almost identical

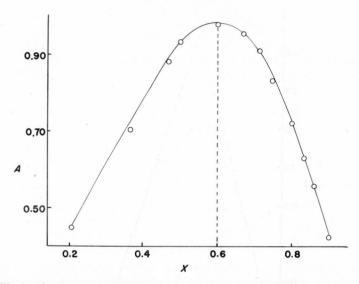

Fig. 8. Absorbance–mole fraction curve for solutions of ferric ion and 4-hydroxy-biphenyl-3-carboxylic acid at 375 mμ (56). X = mole fraction of organic reagent, A = absorbance of solutions.

curves were obtained when measurements were carried out at different wavelengths, which shows that the reagent forms only one complex with ferric ion. A similar curve is shown in Figure 9 for the copper–acetylacetone 1:1 chelate measured at 300 mμ (57). Care must be exercised with this method when there are competitive reactions occurring with either or both of the components because then one is subject to get unreliable results (58).

In the *slope ratio method* (59) the concentration of one component is varied, while the ionic strength and large excess concentration of the other component are held fixed. Then the slope of the line obtained when the concentration of the variable component is plotted against the absorbance gives the ratio of the components in the complex. In the *molar ratio method*, the absorbance is plotted against the molar ratio of X to Y at a fixed ionic strength (59). For illustration, the sharp break in the curve of Figure 10, in which absorbance is plotted against the molar ratio of *o*-phenanthroline to ferric ion, indicates the complex has the formula FeR_3, where R represents the organic component (59b). In the *logarithmic method*, generally the concentration of one component is held fixed and the log of the concentration of

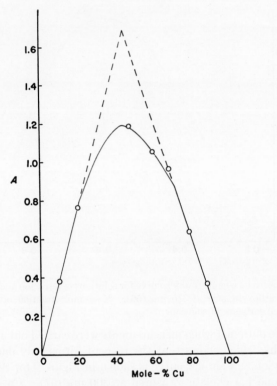

Fig. 9. Absorbance–mole fraction curve for the copper–acetylacetone system at 300 mμ (57).

this component is plotted against the log of a varying concentration of the second component (60). The slope of the line so obtained should correspond to the ratio of the components in the complex.

The choice of one or more of these methods for a given problem depends on certain factors such as how many different complexes are formed and the degree of overlap of the absorption bands of X, Y, and the complexes. Often, the techniques must be modified to suit the system. For instance, variations of the logarithmic method are frequently used to determine association constants between weak acids and bases in organic solvents (61), or ionization constants of very weak acids (62), or bases (63) in aqueous or non-aqueous media. In the latter case, modifications of the classical method of Flexser et al.

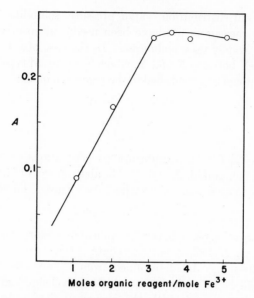

Fig. 10. Absorbance–mole ratio curve for solutions of ferric ion and orthophenanthroline at 590 mμ (59b).

are commonly used (64). This method is based on an equation of type (2)

$$pK_a = pH + \log \frac{e_2 - e_3}{e_1 - e_2} + \log f_{BH}^+ \tag{2}$$

in which e_1 and e_3 are the absorptivities at a given wavelength of the neutral and ionic species of the organic compound, e_2 is the observed absorbance in the buffer, and f_{BH}^+ is the activity coefficient of the ionic form of the organic compound (cation of an amine or anion of an acid). This activity coefficient can be calculated from the Debye-Hückel relationship.

One of the principal methods of studying charge-transfer (CT) complexes has been by ultraviolet-visible spectrophotometry. A large majority of CT complexes dissociate readily in solution and resist isolation. Consequently, physical methods are used for studying their stability and thermodynamic properties. Cryoscopic, im-

miscible solvent distribution, vapor pressure, solubility and electro-
motive force measurements have been used, but spectroscopy is by
far the most widely used technique. In the case of a 1:1 molecular
complex X—Y between X and Y, which is the usual type, an equilibrium constant can be established in the regular manner:

$$X + Y \rightleftharpoons X—Y$$

$$K_c = \frac{(C_{XY})}{(C_X)(C_Y)}$$

where C_{XY}, C_X, C_Y = equilibrium concentrations of the complex
X—Y and of compounds X and Y. The absorbance A of the mixture at
any wavelength for a 1-cm. cell is where the ϵ's are molar absorptivities

$$A = C_{XY}\epsilon_{XY} + C_X\epsilon_X + C_Y\epsilon_Y$$

at the same wavelength. Several graphical procedures have been used
for determining K_c from absorbance data (141). Then, enthalpy and
entropy values may be determined from K_c and its temperature
coefficient (78). In some instances, the wavelengths of the charge-
transfer bands are used, with the necessary theory, to deduce the
ionization potentials of the donor components (141).

In any event, several factors must first be considered in the spectrophotometric analysis of a multicomponent system, such as the absorption characteristics of all species present, the probable range of concentrations to be used, and the choice of a solvent or medium. Each
analytical problem must be examined from these standpoints on a
basis of available information, and a procedure adopted which seems
best for the situation.

One variation of these graphical techniques is a straightforward
titration in which absorptivities are measured as a means of obtaining
equivalence points. Such titrations are commonly called photometric titrations (157). Under suitable conditions a straight line is
obtained when the absorptivity is plotted against volume of titrant
added, and a fairly sharp break in the line occurs at the end point
(Fig. 11) (65).

Photometric titrations offer several advantages over other volumetric methods, particularly in applicability (66). Thus, photometric titrations may be used for colored or non-aqueous solutions, more
than one species may be determined with a single titration, the accuracy is usually high, and most organic functional groups may be
determined by at least one of the wide variety of reactions which may

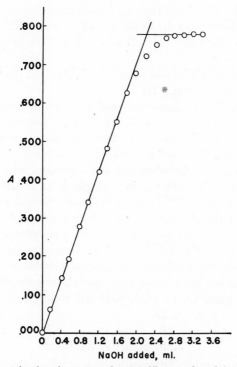

Fig. 11. Photometric titration curve for 2,4-dibromophenol in the presence of phenol (65).

be employed, such as acid–base neutralization, redox, precipitation, or complexation reactions, and with inorganic (158) or organic constituents (159). The following few examples will serve to illustrate the versatility of photometric titrations. Unsaturated compounds in automobile exhausts were determined by photometric titration with standardized bromate–bromide solutions (67). Alkaloids (68) and other weak bases (69) have been titrated directly in acetic acid with perchloric acid. One of the most common volumetric methods for primary and secondary amines involves the acetylation of the amine with excess acetic anhydride in pyridine and titration of the acid liberated. Hydroxy compounds interfere with this procedure. However, by photometric titration with acetic anhydride in pyridine, a direct titration can be made by measuring the absorbance of the amine, and hydroxy compounds do not interfere (70). Weak acids in alcohol solvents have been titrated with tetrabutylammonium hydroxide dissolved in alcohol and up to four phenols in a single mixture, for example, have been determined (71). Dienes (72) and aromatic hydrocarbons (73) have been titrated using tetracyanoethylene as a titrant.

The general principles and recent applications of photometric titrations have been reviewed (74).

A variation of this direct spectrophotometric analysis technique is one called *differential spectrophotometry* (75). The essential difference is that standard solutions of comparable absorbance are used for references in the *blank cell* instead of pure solvent. Only small absorbance differences are observed and measured which permits the determination of the unknown in a sample, in an accuracy reported to be higher than that obtained by the conventional procedure. By measuring the absorbance of an unknown sample relative to the absorbance of a reference sample of known concentration, there is an increase in the relative precision of the concentration measurement. This use of relative measurements compensates for systematic errors. The technique has been particularly useful, for example, in the study of the visual pigments in single rods and cones of the human retina (76).

3. Structure Assignment

After having established empirically several general correlations between molecular structure and absorption spectra (Section 3) one may use these relationships as a basis for the assignment of a structure to a given compound. Ultraviolet-visible spectra provide information only about the chromophoric system of a compound, of course, but often this is the basic information sought. In some instances, the spectrum may enable one to discern the extent of conjugation (electron delocalization) in a compound, whether or not there is intramolecular or intermolecular hydrogen bonding, or something about the intramolecular steric conditions. These and other types of information obtainable from ultraviolet-visible spectra, which make possible partial or complete structure assignments, will be illustrated in this section.

A. CONJUGATION

Probably the structural detail most often studied by ultraviolet-visible spectroscopy is the presence of a specific chromophore. It is common, for example, to distinguish an α,β-enone system from any other unsaturated or saturated ketone on the basis of the intense 220–260-mμ band of the α,β-enone group (cf. Section IV-4). Similarly, an α,β-unsaturated tertiary amine group can readily be distinguished from other amines by its stronger absorption band in the 225–238-mμ range (160).

	λ_{max}, mμ	ϵ
$\diagdown$C$=$C$-$NR$_2$	225–238	5100–9600
$\diagdown$C$=$C$-$C$-$NR$_2$ or saturated NR$_3$	213–218	1500–6100

A number of chromophoric systems can be identified in this fashion by their ultraviolet absorption characteristics. This is particularly the case for polyunsaturated terpenes (79) and steroids, in which λ_{max} can often be estimated in good agreement with observed values, or used as a guide in the assignment of a structure to a new compound. For illustration, α,β-enones and diene systems have a primary absorption band in ethyl alcohol near 215 mμ, and structural modifications can be expected to produce the following changes in λ_{max} (80):

$$\overset{\gamma}{-}\text{C}\overset{\beta}{=}\text{C}\overset{\alpha}{-}\text{C}=\text{O}$$

$$\diagdown\text{C}=\text{C}-\text{C}=\text{C}\diagup$$

Parent $\lambda_{max} = 207$ mμ (81)	$\Delta\lambda$, mμ	Parent $\lambda_{max} = 217$ mμ	$\Delta\lambda$, mμ
Additional conj. C$=$C	$+39$	Additional conj. C$=$C	$+36$
Cisoid diene	$+30$	Cisoid diene	$+30$
Exocyclic C$=$C	$+ 5$	Exocyclic C$=$C	$+ 5$
Substituent or C$_6$-ring		C-attached substituent	$+ 5$
residue α	$+ 8$		
β	$+10$		
γ	$+12$		
δ or higher	$+18$		

Calculated (in parentheses) and observed absorption maxima in mμ are given below for several examples (structure parameters also given in parentheses):

CH$_3$—CH$=$CH—CHO

$\lambda_{max} = 218$
(γ, 219)

$$(\text{CH}_3)_2\text{C}=\text{C}\overset{\overset{\displaystyle\text{CH}_3}{\displaystyle|}}{\underset{\underset{\displaystyle\text{CH}_3}{\displaystyle|}}{\text{C}}}=\text{O}$$

$\lambda_{max} = 245.5$
(α, β, 2γ, 249)

$$\text{CH}_2=\text{C}\overset{\overset{\displaystyle}{}}{\underset{\underset{\displaystyle\text{CH}_3}{\displaystyle|}}{}}\text{—CHO}$$

$\lambda_{max} = 216$
(β, 217)

$(CH_3)_2C$=CH—CHO
$\lambda_{max} = 235.5$
$(2\gamma, 231)$

CH_3—CH=$\overset{\overset{\displaystyle CH_3}{|}}{C}$—CHO
$\lambda_{max} = 226$
$(\beta, \gamma, 229)$

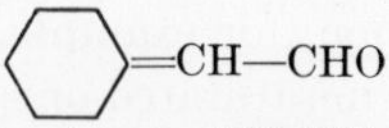

=CH—CHO
$\lambda_{max} = 238 (81)$
$(2\gamma, exo, 236)$

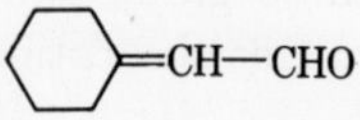

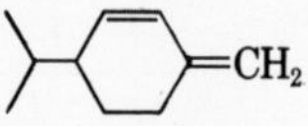

=CH—CHO

=CH$_2$
$\lambda_{max} = 231 (83)$
(2 C-attached,
exo C=C, 232)

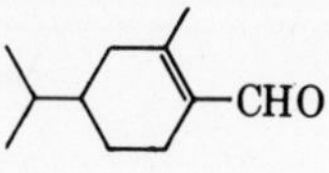

—CHO
$\lambda_{max} = 245 (84)$
$(\beta, 2\gamma, 241)$

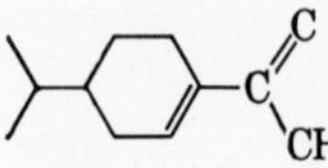

$\lambda_{max} = 235 (83)$
(3 C-attached, 232)

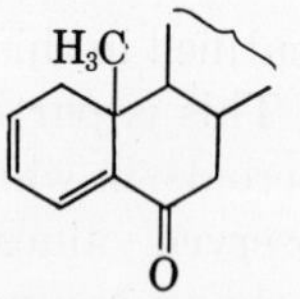

$\lambda_{max} = 315$
(cisoid, conj. C=C,
α, β, ϵ, exo C=C,
317)

$\lambda_{max} = 257$
(cisoid,
2 C-attached,
257)

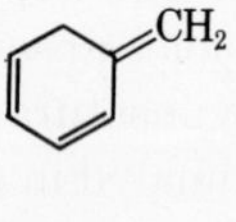

=CH$_2$
$\lambda_{max} = 303 (85)$
(cisoid, conj. C=C,
exo C=C, 2 C-attached,
298)

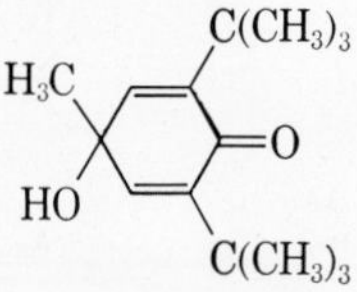

$\lambda_{max} = 234$
$(\alpha, \beta, \gamma, 237)$

Although these calculated values of λ_{max} may be correct only to ± 10 mμ, this is usually sufficiently close to permit a structure assignment with satisfactory confidence. For instance, two isomeric resin acids abietic and *l*-pimaric acid were shown to be tricyclic dienes, and chemical evidence lead to the two structures **18** and **19** (86).

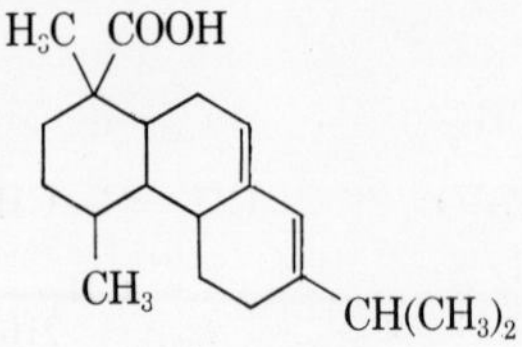

18

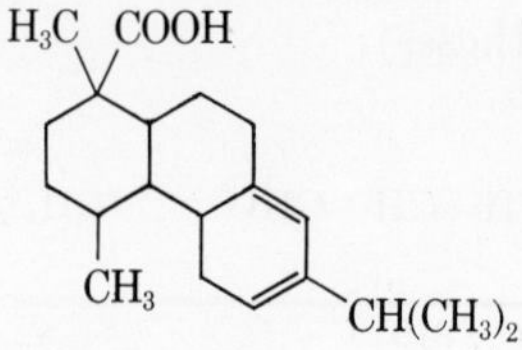

19

Abietic acid has a λ_{max} at 237.5 mμ (ϵ, 16,000) and l-pimaric acid at 272.5 mμ (ϵ, 7000). Calculated values for **18** and **19** are 242 and 272 mμ, respectively. On this basis, structure **18** could be assigned to abietic acid and **19** to l-pimaric acid. In another case, early chemical work on α-cyperone led to the possibility of **20, 21,** or **22** as alternative structures for this unsaturated ketone.

| | 20 | | 21 | | 22 |

In the absorption spectrum of α-cyperone, there is an intense band at 251 mμ ($\pi \rightarrow \pi^*$) and a low-intensity band at 312 mμ ($n \rightarrow \pi^*$) (87). Structure **20** is obviously incompatible with this data, which indicates an α,β-enone system. Structure **22** can be chosen in favor of **21** because **22** is a trisubstituted α,β-unsaturated ketone, calculated λ_{max} = 249 mμ, whereas **21** is only monosubstituted in the β position with a calculated λ_{max} = 227 mμ (88).

These generalizations about dienes do not apply to exocyclic cisoid diene systems because other strain factors complicate these correlations. Examine, for instance, the following examples:

| λ_{max}, mμ = | 220 (82a) | 224 (82b) | 260 (82c) |
| ϵ = | 10,500 | 10,500 | 5,700 |

In many cases, other properties substantiate the degree of resonance delocalization in these systems. For example, λ_{max} shifts to increasing longer wavelengths in the series acrolein, crotonaldehyde, and β-methylcrotonaldehyde. The infrared carbonyl frequencies also decrease in this same order (1704, 1696, and 1683 cm.$^{-1}$, respectively) (81). Generalized substituent effects on other chromophoric systems have also been developed (89). For example, a procedure was reported whereby the λ_{max} of 2,4-dinitrophenylhydrazones of aldehydes and ketones may be calculated to within 3 mμ of observed values (90), and the following empirical correlations for α,β-unsaturated nitriles have been noted (91):

$$\text{>C=C—C≡N}$$

Parent $\lambda_{max} = 203$ mμ

α or β substituent	$+ 2$
α,β or β,β disubstituted	$+ 7$
α,β,β trisubstituted	$+13$
⬡—C≡N	$+ 7$
⬠—C≡N	$+12\text{-}17$

In a different fashion, ultraviolet spectra can be used to ascertain the orientation of two groups in the benzene ring or to determine whether a given substituent is primarily electron-donating or electron-withdrawing. One of the principal effects noted by Doub and Vandenbelt in their collation of spectra of *ortho* and *para* disubstituted benzenes concerned the displacement of the first primary band of benzenes (92). Given $\Delta\lambda_1$, and $\Delta\lambda_2$ as the displacements for the two monosubstituted benzenes and $\Delta\lambda_{1,2}$ as the displacement for the corresponding disubstituted benzene, it was observed that when the two groups are of the same directing power in electrophilic substitution, then

$$\Delta\lambda_{1,2} \simeq \Delta\lambda_1 \text{ (or } \Delta\lambda_2, \text{ whichever is larger)}$$

and when the groups are of opposite types (i.e., o,p vs. m-orienting), then

$$\Delta\lambda_{1,2} > \Delta\lambda_1 + \Delta\lambda_2$$

That is, $\Delta\lambda_{1,2}$ tends to equal the larger between $\Delta\lambda_1$ and $\Delta\lambda_2$ in the first case, or to be greater than the sum of $\Delta\lambda_1$ and $\Delta\lambda_2$ in the second case. For example,

			mμ					mμ
ϕNO_2	$\Delta\lambda$	=	65		ϕNO_2	$\Delta\lambda$	=	65
ϕNH_2	$\Delta\lambda$	=	27		$\phi COOH$	$\Delta\lambda$	=	27
O_2N—◯—NH_2	$\Delta\lambda$	=	178		O_2N—◯—$COOH$	$\Delta\lambda$	=	61

On this basis, for example, it was shown that the hydrazone group (93), $>C=N-N-$, and the ferrocenyl group (94), $C_5H_5-Fe-C_5H_4-$ are strong electron-donating groups.

Along this same line, the m- and p-hydroxy-β-nitrostyrenes could easily be distinguished by their ultraviolet spectra, and particularly when the effect of base is noted on λ_{max}. For illustration, the λ_{max} values of some substituted β-nitrostyrenes are as follows (95):

R	Acid, mμ	λ_{max} Base, mμ
H	320	
p-COOH	313	319
m-COOH	316	318
p-OH	363	456
m-OH	318	331

Thus, the p-OH group not only has a much larger λ_{max} than the m-OH or m-directing groups, but base produces a tremendous bathochromic shift owing to the large interaction resonance between the NO_2 and O^- groups.

Ultraviolet spectroscopy was one of the first methods used to demonstrate the electron-delocalizing effect of a cyclopropyl group when attached to a multiple bond (96). It is found that the ultraviolet absorption by cyclopropyl derivatives is between that of the corresponding alkyl and vinyl derivatives (97). For instance, for primary bands:

$R-C=C$	$\overset{C}{\overset{/\backslash}{C-C-C=C}}$	$C=C-C=C$
λ_{max}, mμ = ᴖ175	>175	217

$R-C=O$	$\overset{C}{\overset{/\backslash}{C-C-C=O}}$	$C=C-C=O$
λ_{max}, mμ = 195	193–197	215
ϵ = ᴖ1,000	6,000–10,000	~15,000

This end-group conjugation between the cyclopropyl and unsaturated groups is also revealed by the chemical properties of the cyclopropyl derivatives. For example, cyclopropyl ketones add HBr as do α,β-enones (98), and vinylcyclopropane undergoes the Diels-Alder reaction (99). Now, although the cyclopropyl group exhibits this property of electron delocalization when attached to a multiple bond, it lacks the conjugative property of multiple bonds when not at the end of the conjugated system (100). The ultraviolet spectrum of tris-(thiocyclopropanone), 23 reveals with surprise the lack of electron delocalization by cyclopropyl groups attached to the sulfur atom (101).

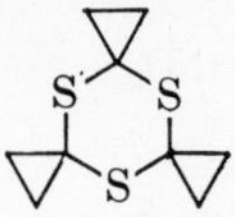

23

$\lambda_{max} = 231$ mμ

$\epsilon = 870$

This is shown by the λ_{max} values of compounds 23–26. The infrared spectrum of 26 also substantiates the presence of resonance interaction in this compound.

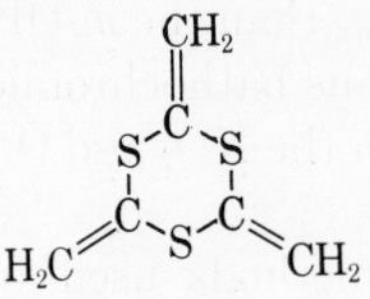

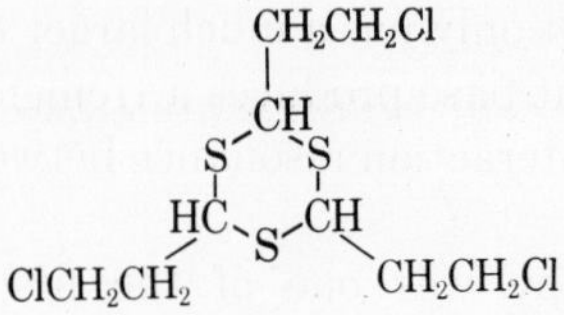

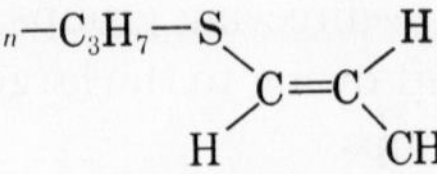

λ_{max}, mμ = 245	238	249.5
ϵ = 15,900	1,260	4,134
24	25	26 (102)

Another structural system which ultraviolet-spectroscopy helped to elucidate was that of the methoxy α- and γ-pyrones, 27 and 29, respectively.

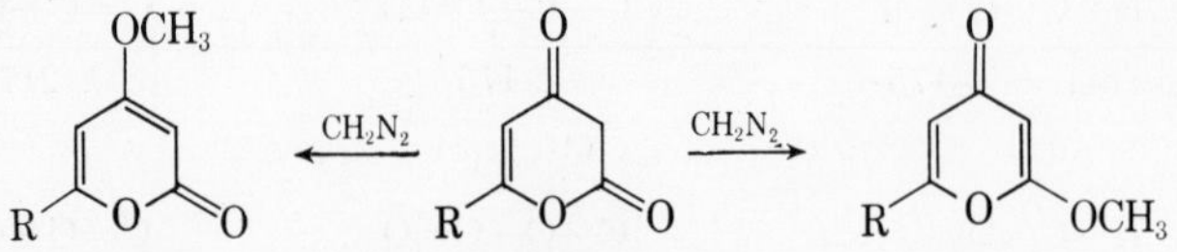

27   **28**   **29**

The parent 2,4-pyronone, 28, can give two isomeric methyl enol ethers, 27 and 29, and for some years there were conflicting reports about the identity of such isomeric pyrones (103). Finally, it was shown by a combination of spectral and chemical evidence that methylation of 2,4-pyrones with diazomethane usually yields mixtures of the two possible isomers, and that spectral data can be used to good advantage in differentiating between the two isomeric enol ethers of type **27** and **29** (104, 105). It is found, for example, that the 4-methoxy-α-pyrones **27** have a λ_{max} in alcohol at longer wavelengths than the 6-methoxy-γ-pyrones, **29** (106). This generalization is substantiated by infrared data which show that the carbonyl band of the α-pyrones occurs at lower frequencies (i.e., it has a greater single bond character owing to greater resonance of the enone system) than for the γ-pyrones (104, 105). These observations have provided supporting evidence in the elucidation of structure of certain natural products (105).

Another aspect of conjugation detectable in molecules by ultra-violet spectroscopy is the presence of two chromophores oriented approximately at right angles to each other. For illustration, it was observed in a study of the absorption spectra of tetracyclones, **30**, that substitution of groups into the *para* position of the 2-phenyl ring affects mainly the absorption band near 512 mμ whereas substituents in the *para* position of the 3-phenyl ring affect primarily the absorption band near 342 mμ (107).

(a)   (b)

$\xrightarrow{\quad x \quad}$

30

On this basis, one can associate the chromophore in the x direction as in **30a** with the shorter-waved band, and the chromophore in the y direction as in **30b** with the longer-waved band. In a similar fashion, x- and y-bands have been used to determine approximate perpendicular chromophores in other structural types, such as in anthracene (108), benzophenones (109), triarylmethanes (110), and polymethine dyes (111).

x path   *y* path

Ultraviolet spectroscopy has also revealed the occurrence of reso-nance interaction between groups not conjugated in the classical sense (cf. Section 4, regarding such electron delocalization in enone sys-tems). In particular, aryl groups separated by one and even two methylene groups exhibit spectral properties not shown by model isolated chromophoric systems. For instance, resonance of diphenyl-methane among structures **31** has been proposed to account for its

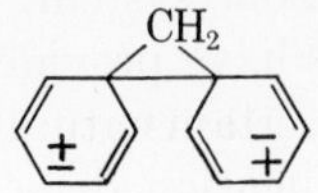

31

enhanced absorption over that of ethylbenzene (112). Similarly, in the spectra of di-9-anthrylmethanes there is observed a small batho-chromic shift relative to the spectra of the corresponding 9-ethylan-thracenes (112).

Ultraviolet spectroscopy provided additional evidence to show that phloroglucinol and its alkyl ethers are carbon-protonated in concen-trated acids rather than oxygen-protonated as are phenol and anisole (113). The spectra of phloroglucinol and its ethers in acid are

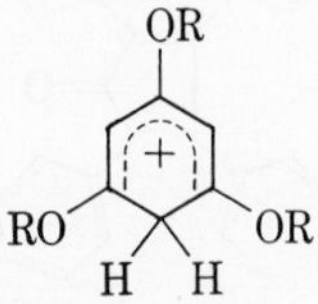

markedly different from those of phenol or anisole in acid, which are known to protonate on oxygen, and the former spectra are consistent with observed spectra of other C-protonated phenonium ions. Spec-trophotometric determination of pK_a's of these compounds also demonstrated the large enhanced basicity of the trialkoxybenzenes over that of phenol or anisole.

B. STERIC EFFECTS

The principal types of steric effects on spectra were discussed in Section III-2, so that merely a few less typical examples will be in-cluded in this section.

The strain observed in certain *ortho*-substituted acetophenones based on chemical reactivity studies (116) was confirmed by ultraviolet absorption measurements (117).   Thus, the chemical and spectral data showed that the steric hindrance to the carbonyl group in the acetophenones increases in the order **32** < **33** < **34** < **35**.

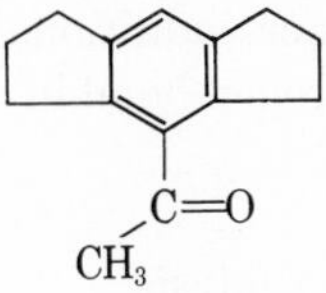

32

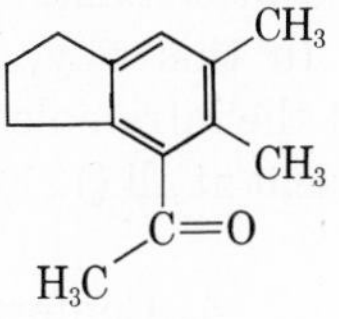

33

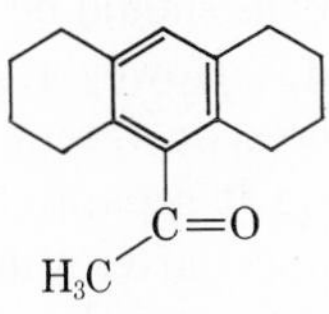

34

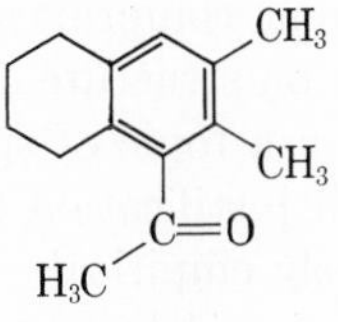

35

Several minor steric effects are readily detectable by ultraviolet spectroscopy, such as the buttressing effect (118).   This is a secondary steric hindrance, for example, like that from a *meta* group R′ in a biphenyl **36** which buffers or hinders an *ortho* group R from bending

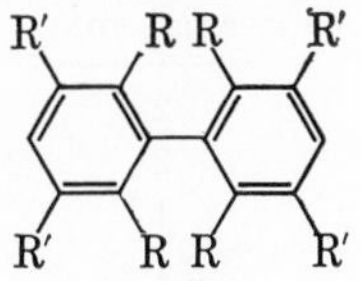

36

back to permit rotation about the bond between phenyl rings (119).

C. HYDROGEN BONDING

It was shown in Section III-3 that intramolecular hydrogen bonding between two *ortho* groups in the benzene ring can be detected in several ways.   One is to compare the spectra of the corresponding hydroxy and alkoxy compounds, in which case the intramolecularly hydrogen-bonded hydroxy derivative absorbs at longer wavelengths than the alkoxy analogue.   This is opposite to the spectral shift observed for the respective *para* derivatives.   A second method is to make a comparison of the *ortho* isomer with the *meta* or *para* hydroxy isomers (amino compounds, in the case of N—H···X bonding).   In this case, the *ortho* isomer absorbs at significantly longer wavelengths than the *meta* or *para* isomers. A third method is to study the effect of change of solvent. It has been shown that the intramolecular hydrogen bond absorption band is not appreciably affected by changes in solvent (120). In this way, for instance, additional evidence was found (120) that the intramolecular hydrogen bond in *o*-nitroaniline is very weak if present at all (121).

4. Conformational Analysis

Strictly speaking, conformational analysis should be taken up in the previous section on structure assignment. However, conformational analysis has been a topic of special interest in recent years and this provides a small justification for treating it separately. Again, the approach is purely empirical. For instance, after studying the spectra of a number of model compounds, it was generalized that the introduction of an axial substituent α to a carbonyl group of a cyclohexanone produces a bathochromic shift, whereas an equatorial substituent produces a hypsochromic shift (122):

| | $\Delta\lambda_{max}$ of the 280-mμ band of α-substituted cyclohexanone | |
α-Substituent	axial, mμ	equatorial, mμ
Cl	22	−7
Br	28	−5
OH	17	−12
OAc	10	−5

Information about the stereo structure of certain unsaturated ketones has been acquired almost solely from ultraviolet spectroscopy so far. Simple ketones have an intense band near 195 mμ ($\epsilon \backsim 10^3$) and a low-intensity $n \rightarrow \pi^*$ band at about 280 mμ ($\epsilon \backsim 20$–50).

$$\lambda_{max}, m\mu = 195, 275 \qquad 283 \qquad 295$$
$$\epsilon = 900, \ 22 \qquad 16 \qquad 27$$

In the case of a conjugated α,β-enone system, the $\pi \rightarrow \pi^*$ band of the C=C bond moves up to 200–260 mμ ($\epsilon \backsim 10^4$) and the $n \rightarrow \pi^*$ band of the C=O bond shifts to 300–350 mμ but is still of low intensity ($\epsilon \backsim 50$).

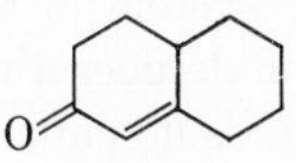

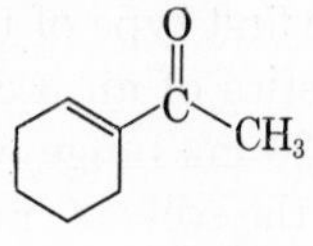

CH₃—CH=CH—CHO
(123)

λ_{max}, mμ = 217, 321	229, 337	232, 308
ϵ = 15,650, 19	16,500, 37	12,500, 50

Even though a C=C and a C=O group may not be conjugated in the classical sense in a given structure, if they are suitably oriented there can be some overlapping of the π orbitals in one of two ways: (i) π fashion, in which the molecular π orbitals are parallel end-to-end as in **37** or face–to–face as in **38–40**, or (ii) by s-type overlap of the carbonyl

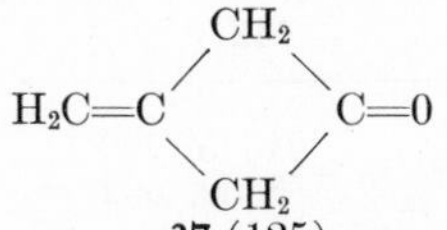

$$H_2C=C \underset{CH_2}{\overset{CH_2}{\diamondsuit}} C=0$$

37 (125)

λ_{max}, mμ = 214, 284
ϵ = 1500, 30

carbon and olefin carbon p orbitals (homoconjugation) as in **41–43**. This makes the p_n nonbonding carbonyl oxygen orbital and the C=C π orbital become almost parallel.

Compound (126)	Solvent[a]	λ_{max}, mμ	ϵ	λ'_{max}, mμ	ϵ'
38	H	209.5	3110	298	32
	A	214sh	1810	297	43
39	H	219	2720	302	27
	A	224.5	1455	297	33
40	H	239	3940	306	31
	A	244	2530	302sh	50

[a] H = hexane A = alcohol.

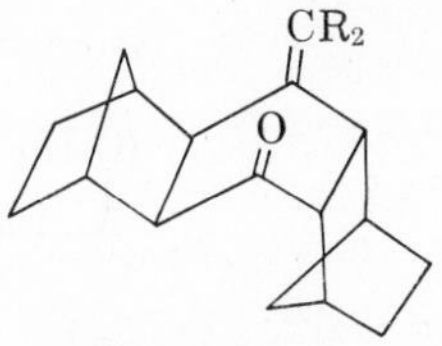

38, R = H
39, R = H, CH₃
40, R = CH₃

The first type of trans-annular interaction (π overlap) has the characteristics of an α,β-enone system in that it produces a band in the 200–230 mμ range, which undergoes a red-shift with increasing polarity of the solvent, and there is no enhancement of the intensity of the $n \rightarrow \pi^*$ band. These spectral properties are illustrated by the data for compounds 37–40.

The second type of transannular orbital overlap, homoconjugation, also shifts the $\pi \rightarrow \pi^*$ band to the 200–230 mμ region, but increases the intensity of the $n \rightarrow \pi^*$ band (see structures 41–43). Homocon-

41	42	43

| λ_{max}, mμ = | 202, 290 | 213.5, 290 | 223, 296, 307 |
| ϵ = | 3000, 110 | 5500, 562 | 2290, 267, 267 |

jugation in 43 is confirmed by the fact that the saturated diketone 44 has a spectrum of a typical simple ketone.

44

λ_{max}, mμ = 296
ϵ = 32

Consequently, the wavelength and intensity of the $n \rightarrow \pi^*$ band for these unsaturated *nonconjugated* ketones can be used to infer the spatial orientation of the carbonyl and unsaturated groups. For illustration, compounds 45 and 46 have enhanced $n \rightarrow \pi^*$ bands and it can be deduced that the carbonyl and phenyl rings are approximately

45 (127)	46

| λ_{max}, mμ = | 296, 305, 316 | 290 |
| ϵ = | 646, 437, 174 | 500 |

perpendicular to each other. This is substantiated by a molecular model as illustrated in the diagram.

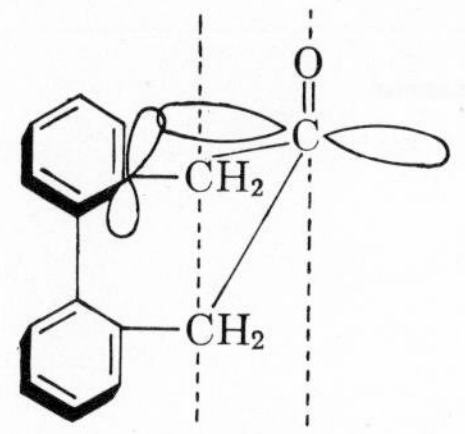

In contrast to **46**, the corresponding saturated compound **47** has only a simple carbonyl band.

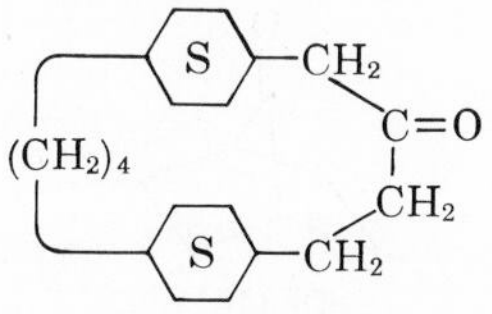

47

$$\lambda_{max}, \ m\mu \ = \ 280$$
$$\epsilon \ = \ \ 56$$

Similarly, from the spectra of the *cis* and *trans* 5-cyclodecenones, it can be deduced that the C=C and C=O bonds in the *trans* isomer

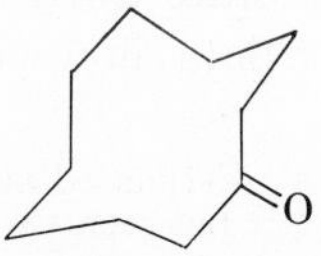

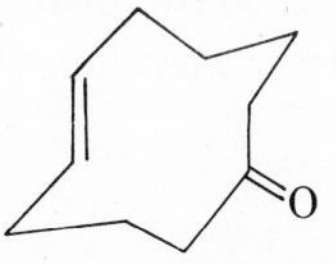

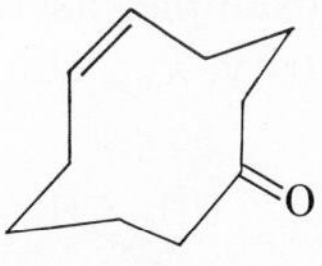

Cyclodecanone	*trans*-5-Cyclodecenone	*cis*-5-Cyclodecenone
$\lambda_{max}, \ m\mu \ = \ 288.3$	214.5, 270–80	289.9
$\epsilon \ = \ \ 15$	2300, 20	15

are oriented so as to give some π-type overlap, whereas the two groups are completely isolated in the *cis* isomer. Also, from its spectrum, one phenyl group in 2,2-diphenylcyclohexanone must be rotated such that there is σ-type overlap with the carbonyl group. This does not occur in the monophenylcyclohexanone. Similarly, the intensity of the carbonyl band of bicyclo[2.2.1]hept-2-en-7-one (**48**) and the lack of any selective absorption down to 200 mμ indicates that there is no s-type overlap of the pi orbitals of the C=O and C=C bonds.

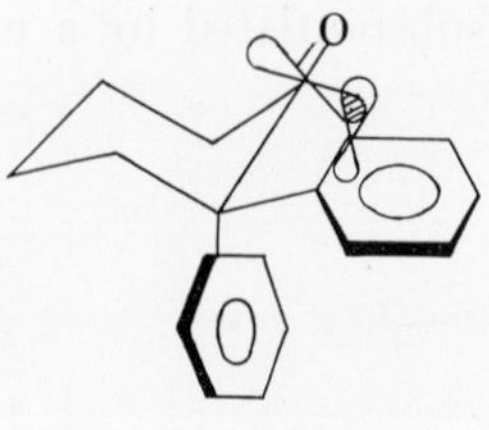

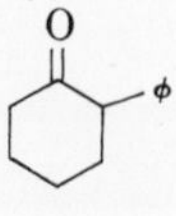

λ_{max}, mμ = 298
ϵ = 125

= 291
= 20

Thus, the roof-shaped C_6 ring allows s-type overlap when the $C{=}O$ bond is located in the 2 or 3 position but not in the 7 position of the bicyclohept-5-ene ring.

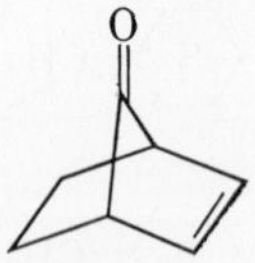

48 (161)

λ_{max}, mμ = 272
ϵ = 38.9

Ultraviolet spectra have been used in conformational analysis to provide qualitative information about the geometry in other systems. For example, as the two carbonyl groups in **49** rotate away from planarity, λ_{max} shifts to shorter wavelengths and the data show that as

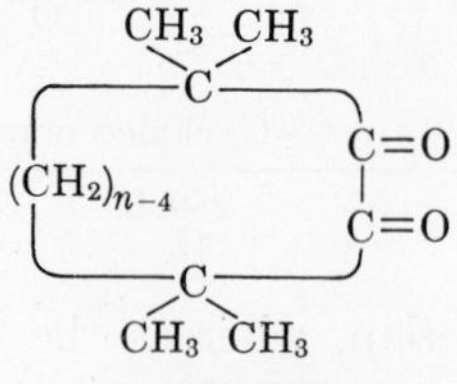

49 (162)

n	λ_{max}, mμ	Estimated angle between C=O groups from models
5	466	0–10° (angles)
6	380	0–60° (angles)
7	337	90–110° (angles)
8	343	100–140° (angles)
Acyclic	365	90–180° (angles)
18	384	100–180° (angles)

n increases the angle between carbonyl groups is gradually increased (primarily from repulsion between oxygen atoms) from 0°C. in the C_5 ring to an angle approaching 90°C. in the C_7 ring (162). In contrast to this, the spectra of the corresponding quinoxalines, in which the $C{=}N$ groups are constrained to a fairly planar position, are all quite

Quinoxalines

similar. In another case, the λ_{max} of *cis, trans*-cyclodecadiene shows that the two double bonds are not quite planar as they are in an acyclic diene (see Table IV).

cis,trans-Cyclodecadiene
λ_{max}, mμ = 222 mμ
ϵ = 7250

In some cases, ultraviolet spectroscopy has been used in a semi-quantitative way to estimate the angles of rotation of the two parts of a chromophoric system. It was shown in Table IX that partial steric hindrance may not appreciably affect λ_{max}, but merely decrease the band intensity. Consequently, the ratio ϵ/ϵ^0 can be taken as a measure of the reduction of resonance interaction between the parts A and B of a conjugated system A—B as the planes of A and B are rotated about a bond joining A and B, where ϵ and ϵ^0 are the absorptivities of the conjugated band for the nonplanar and planar systems. The angle of twist ϕ between A and B in the sterically hindered A–B molecule has been calculated from the relationship (128):

$$\epsilon/\epsilon^\circ = \cos^2\phi$$

For illustration, the absorptivities for some 4-nitroanilines in ethanol are given in Table X together with the ϵ/ϵ^0 ratios and the calculated angles ϕ between the nitro group and the benzene ring in each compound. Data from other types of measurements corroborate values of ϕ obtained this way. For instance, the Hammett substituent constant σ has been shown to be equal to $\sigma_I + \sigma_R$, where these two constants reflect the inductive and resonance contributions to the Hammett constant. If it is assumed that complete inhibition of resonance would reduce the Hammett constant to the inductive constant $\sigma_\pm$, then the quantity

$$\frac{\sigma_R{}^0 - \sigma_R}{\sigma_R{}^0}$$

should be a measure of the inhibition to resonance, where $\sigma_R = \sigma - \sigma_I$ for the resonance inhibited group and $\sigma_R{}^0 = \sigma^0 - \sigma_R{}^0$ for the uninhibited group. A comparison of the percentages of resonance inhibition in some *ortho* substituted compounds determined in this fashion and also as determined from ultraviolet absorptivities ($\epsilon^0 - \epsilon$)/ϵ^0 was made and the results are given in Table XI (130).

TABLE X

Absorptivities and Angles of Rotation Between Nitro and Phenyl Groups in Some 4-Nitroanilines (129)

R in $4\text{-}O_2N\text{—}C_6H_4\text{—}NH_2$	λ_{max} ⌒ 376–401 mμ	ϵ/ϵ^0	ϕ
H	15,500	1.00	(0)
2,3-Trimethylene	13,900	0.90	19
2,5-Trimethylene	13,600	0.88	21
3-Me	13,200	0.85	23
2,3-Tetramethylene	11,200	0.72	32
2,3-Di-Me	9,750	0.63	38
3,5-Di-Me	4,840	0.31	56
2,3,5,6-Tetra-Me	1,560	0.10	72
3,5-Di-*tert*-Bu	540	0.03	79

Quite good agreement is found for the percent of resonance inhibition in these compounds as determined by the two methods. Similarly, ϕ values were calculated for a number of substituted benzaldehydes and acetophenones from spectroscopic data and found to be in agreement with values deduced from dipole moment measurements (131). Thus, ultraviolet spectra can serve as a simple way to estimate the conformational angle between rotating parts of a conjugated system. This technique was used, for example, to determine the angle between phenyl rings in some bridged biphenyls (132):

n	ϕ
0	15°
1	49°
3	68°

TABLE XI

Percentages of Resonance Inhibition and Calculated Angles of Twist in Some
Ortho Substituted Compounds (130)

Compound	Hindered group	Per cent inhibition of resonance from		Angle of twist
		Substituent constants	Absorption intensities	
4-Nitroaniline:				
3-Me	NO$_2$	19	15	24
2,3-Di-Me	NO$_2$	42	37	39
3,5-Di-Me	NO$_2$	67	69	55
2,3,5,6-Tetra-Me	NO$_2$	89	90	72
4-CO$_2$Et—C$_6$H$_4$—NMe$_2$:				
2-Me	NMe$_2$	55	55	47
2,6-Di-Me	NMe$_2$	75	80	62
4-CO$_2$Et—C$_6$H$_4$—OCH$_3$:				
2,6-Di-I	OCH$_3$	30	38	35
2,6-Di-Me	OCH$_3$	60	62	51

5. Miscellaneous

There are several unrelated types of information about molecular structure which may be derived from ultraviolet-visible spectra, and some of these are taken up in this Section.

A. RESONANCE IN GROUND AND EXCITED STATES

Since ultraviolet-visible spectra involve ground and excited states, a reasonable knowledge about either state can be used to make deductions about the other. For illustration, acid strengths of 4- and 3-nitro-4'-hydroxybiphenyl when compared with the acid strengths of *p*-nitro- and *m*-nitrophenol, phenol, and 4-hydroxybiphenyl, indicate that there is little resonance between benzene rings in the biphenyl system in the ground state (133). This is confirmed by other types of physical properties such as heats of combustion data from which resonance energies may be calculated. On the other hand, 4,4'-disubstituted biphenyls with opposite orienting substituents (*o,p* vs. *m*-directing) absorb at considerably longer wavelengths than the corresponding 3,4'-disubstituted biphenyls (133):

	λ_{max}, mμ
3-Hydroxybiphenyl	250
4-Hydroxybiphenyl	260
3'-Nitro-4-hydroxybiphenyl	263
4'-Nitro-4-hydroxybiphenyl	340
2-Hydroxyfluorene	311
7-Nitro-2-hydroxyfluorene	370

Apparently, the ionic structures must make a large contribution to the excited states of these 4,4'-disubstituted biphenyls and give them a fairly large dipole moment in the excited state.

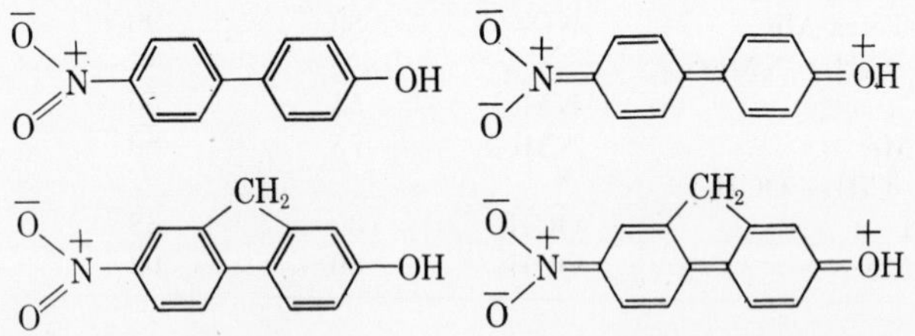

Chief contributors to   Chief contributors to
the ground state   the excited states

Likewise, resonance interaction as measured by relative basicities on the one hand, and by ultraviolet spectra on the other hand, in substituted stilbenes and stilbazoles, indicate that the contribution from ionic forms is much greater in the excited states than in the ground states (134).

In a different manner, ultraviolet spectra may shed light on the contribution of ionic structures to ground states. As pointed out earlier, the primary band of aryl compounds normally undergoes a bathochromic shift with increases in polar character of the solvent. This is observed to be the case for the ketones listed in Table XII, and the band is identified with the transition:

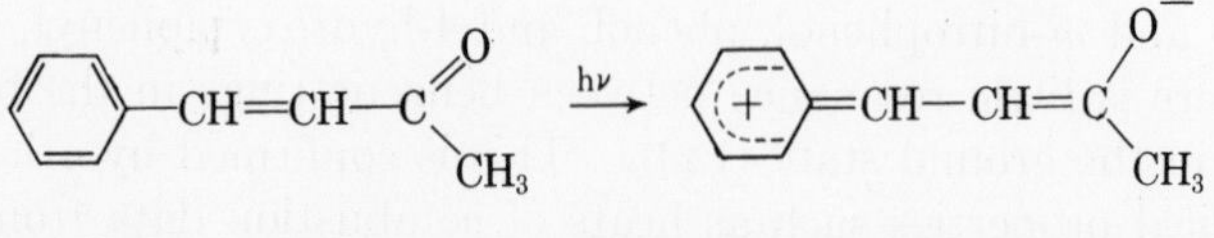

Thus, the change to the more polar solvent produces a definite red shift in the band for the ketones because the excited state is more polar than the ground state and increased solvent stabilization of the excited state decreases the transition energy. However, λ_{max} for the

TABLE XII
Wavelengths of the Primary Band of Some Ketones, Sulfones, Phosphine Sulfides, and Phosphine Oxides in Ethanol and Cyclohexane (135)

Compound	Cyclohexane λ, mμ	Ethanol λ, mμ
Ketones		
C_6H_5—$COCH_3$	239	243
p-CH_3O—C_6H_4—$COCH_3$	264	274
$(C_6H_5)_2CO$	249	253
C_6H_5—CH=CH—$COCH_3$	280	285
C_6H_5—CH=CH—CO—C_6H_5	300	310
$(p$-CH_3—$C_6H_4)_2CO$	258	265
$(p$-CH_3O—$C_6H_4)_2CO$	279	295
Sulfones		
C_6H_5—SO_2CH_3	217	217
p-CH_3O—C_6H_4—SO_2CH_3	238	240
$(C_6H_5)_2SO_2$	235	235
C_6H_5—CH=CH—SO_2CH_3	263	264
C_6H_5—CH=CH—$SO_2C_6H_5$	275	275
Phosphine oxides		
$(C_6H_5)_3PO$	224	224
$(p$-$CH_3C_6H_4)_3PO$	231	232
$(p$-CH_3O—$C_6H_4)_3PO$	244	246
Phosphine sulfides		
$(p$-CH_3—$C_6H_4)_3PS$	227	227
$(p$-CH_3O—$C_6H_4)_3PS$	240	242

other classes of compounds listed in Table XII remains virtually the same in the two solvents. This suggests that the ground and excited states of these molecules have approximately the same polar character. It can be deduced, then, that the ground states of these molecules have a significant polar nature and indicates that the sulfur–oxygen and phosphorus–oxygen bonds are largely coordinate–covalent rather than double bonds:

B. MOLECULAR-WEIGHT DETERMINATIONS

Many picrate charge-transfer compounds exhibit a strong absorption near 380 mμ and the same absorptivity ($\epsilon \backsim 38,440$) (136). Hence, the Bouguer-Beer law may be used to determine the molecular

$$A = c\,b\,\epsilon$$

where A = observed absorbance
c = molar concentration of the picrate
b = cell thickness = 1 cm.
ϵ = 38,440

weight of the picrate from which the molecular weight of the complexed amine or hydrocarbon may be computed. The procedure is quite simple and gives results accurate to $\pm 2\%$ (137). The same principle has been used to determine the molecular weights of sugars in the form of their osazones (138).

The number average molecular weight of certain polymers by end-group analysis has been done by spectrophotometric measurements (139). The procedure can be applied to polymers having sulfide end groups, and the method is based on the complex formed between molecular iodine and sulfide groups. Results are in agreement with osmotic molecular weights and offers certain advantages in technique.

C. IONIZATION POTENTIALS

The stability of charge-transfer complexes has been related to the ionization potential of the donor component and the electron affinity of the other component in a complex (140). When a series of complexes are prepared from one electron acceptor, e.g., trinitrobenzene, a plot of the wavelength of the CT band vs. the ionization potentials of the electron donors gives a straight line. From a relation of the type

$$\Delta E = I_b - E_a + \text{C}$$

where ΔE is the transition energy corresponding to the CT band, I_b is the ionization potential of the electron donor component, E_a is the electron affinity of the electron acceptor component, and C is a constant, ionization potentials of polynuclear hydrocarbons have been determined in good agreement with values from other methods (141). Ionization potentials are determined by several methods on vapors, which do not work well on hydrocarbons of low volatility.

Therefore, this indirect determination of ionization potentials of certain hydrocarbons from absorption spectra of their CT complexes satisfies an important need.

D. USE OF THE FAR ULTRAVIOLET REGION (142,143)

Recently, instruments have been developed which allow measurements to be made conveniently below 200 mμ into the *far ultraviolet* region. This extends the types of compounds which may be studied spectroscopically because almost all vapors have intense, characteristic spectra in this region. The coupling of vapor chromatography with far-ultraviolet spectroscopy permits the analysis of hot gases without their prior separation and is particularly advantageous for the analysis of gases in low concentration ranges. The observations of the highly excited states of polyatomic molecules have provided valuable evidence concerning the electronic structures of these molecules.

As in the near ultraviolet, chromophoric types tend to absorb in characteristic regions in the far-ultraviolet. Thus, the C=C and C=O bonds absorb near 180 and 195 mμ, respectively. Also, alkyl groups produce red shifts as they do in the regular region. References to reviews on far-ultraviolet spectroscopy have been cited by Kaye (142). He has also indexed the literature since 1941 and given references to spectra for over 280 compounds. Articles are scattered in the literature on the use of the far ultraviolet for analysis of steroids (163), unsaturated fatty acids (142), and numerous other substances. A bibliography for vacuum ultraviolet spectra has appeared recently (164).

References

1. Braude, E. A., in E. A. Braude and F. C. Nachod, eds., *Determination of Organic Structures by Physical Methods*, Academic Press, New York, 1955, Chap. 4.
2. Mason, S. F., *Quart. Rev. (London)*, **15**, 287 (1961).
3. Ferguson, L. N., *The Modern Structural Theory of Organic Chemistry*, Prentice-Hall, Englewood Cliffs, New Jersey, 1963, Chap. 5.
4. Doub, L., and J. M. Vandenbelt, *J. Am. Chem. Soc.*, **69**, 2714 (1947).
5. Beale, R. N., and E. M. F. Roe, *J. Chem. Soc.*, **1953**, 2760.

6. Bayliss, N. S., and E. G. McRae, *J. Am. Chem. Soc.*, **74**, 5803 (1952); *J. Phys. Chem.*, **58**, 1002 (1954); **61**, 562 (1957); F. A. Bovey and S. S. Yanari, *Nature*, **186**, 1042 (1960); K. Hirayama, *J. Am. Chem. Soc.*, **77**, 379 (1955); W. T. Simpson, *J. Am. Chem. Soc.*, **73**, 5359 (1951).

7. Brealey, G. J., and M. Kasha, *J. Am. Chem. Soc.*, **77**, 4462 (1955).

8. Kosower, E. M., *J. Am. Chem. Soc.*, **80**, 3261 (1958).

9. Kosower, E. M., *J. Am. Chem. Soc.*, **80**, 3253 (1958).

10. Ferguson, L. N., *Electron Structures of Organic Molecules*, Prentice-Hall, Englewood Cliffs, N. J., 1952, p. 313.

11. Brooker, L. G. S., and co-workers, 14th International Congress of Pure and Applied Chemistry, Zurich, 1955.

12. Schwarzenbach, G., H. Lutz, and E. Felder, *Helv. Chim. Acta*, **27**, 576 (1944).

13. Bohlmann, F., and H. J. Mannhardt, *Chem. Ber.*, **89**, 1307 (1956).

14. Kuhn, R., *J. Chem. Soc.*, **1938**, 605; and references cited therein.

15. Gillam, A. E., and D. H. Hey, *J. Chem. Soc.*, **1939**, 1170.

16. Clar, E., *Aromatische Kohlenwasserstoffe*, 2nd ed., Verlag Springer, Heidelberg, 1952.

17. Kamlet, M. J., J. C. Hoffsommer, and H. G. Adolph, *J. Am. Chem. Soc.*, **84**, 3925 (1962).

18. Schubert, W. N., and J. M. Craven, *J. Am. Chem. Soc.*, **82**, 1357 (1960).

19. Burawoy, A., and A. R. Thompson, *J. Chem. Soc.*, **1956**, 4313.

20. Morris, R. J., and W. R. Brode, *J. Am. Chem. Soc.*, **70**, 2485 (1948); see also R. J. Morris, F. R. Jensen, and T. R. Lusebrink, *J. Org. Chem.*, **19**, 1306 (1954).

21. Wepster, B. M., in W. Klyne and P. B. D. de la Mare, eds., *Progress in Stereochemistry*, Vol. 2, Butterworths, London, 1958, p. 99.

22. Brooker, L. G. S., F. L. White, R. H. Sprague, S. G. Dent, Jr., and G. Van Zandt, *Chem. Rev.*, **41**, 325 (1947).

23. Akermark, B., *Acta Chem. Scand.*, **15**, 985 (1961); A. Burawoy, in D. Hadzi and H. W. Thompson, eds., *Hydrogen Bonding*, Pergamon Press, New York, 1959, p. 259.

24. Cline, J. K., R. R. Williams, and J. Finkelstein, *J. Am. Chem. Soc.*, **59**, 1052 (1937), and earlier papers.

25. Ruehle, A. E., *J. Am. Chem. Soc.*, **57**, 1887 (1955).

26. Williams, R. R., E. R. Buchman, and A. E. Ruehle, *J. Am. Chem. Soc.*, **57**, 1093 (1935).

27. Shurcliff, W. A., *J. Opt. Soc. Am.*, **32**, 160 (1942).

28. Malinin, D. R., and J. H. Yoe, *J. Chem. Educ.*, **38**, 129 (1961).

29. *Anal. Chem.*, **33**, 1968 (1961) for latest recommendations on spectrometry nomenclature.

30. Kienitz, H., *Z. Anal. Chem.*, **164**, 80 (1958).

31. Sternberg, J. C., H. S. Stillo, and R. H. Schwendeman, *Anal. Chem.*, **32**, 84 (1960); P. D. Croit, *Trans. AICE*, **60**, 1235 (1941).

32. Hiskey, C. F., *Anal. Chem.*, **33**, 927 (1961); M. G. Mellon, ed., *Analytical Absorption Spectroscopy*, Wiley, New York, 1950.

33. Coggeshall, N. D., and A. S. Glessner, Jr., *Anal. Chem.*, **21**, 550 (1949); D. D. Tunnicliff, R. R. Brattain, and L. R. Zumwalt, *ibid.*, **21**, 890 (1949).

34. Ramsay, D. A., "The Spectra of Polyatomic Free Radicals," in H. W. Thompson, ed., *Advances in Spectroscopy*, Vol. 1, Interscience, New York, 1959, Chap. 1.

35. Bender, M. L., and J. M. Jones, *J. Org. Chem.*, **27**, 3771 (1962).

36a. Brice, L. K., *J. Chem. Educ.*, **39**, 632 (1962).

36b. Brice, L. K., *J. Chem. Educ.*, **39**, 634 (1962).

37. Jencks, W. P., *J. Am. Chem. Soc.*, **81**, 475 (1959).

38. Cope, O. J., and R. K. Brown, *Can. J. Chem.*, **39**, 1695 (1961).

39a. Blois, M. S., Jr., ed., *Free Radicals in Biological Systems*, Academic Press, New York, 1961.

39b. Beinert, H., and R. H. Sands, in M. S. Blois, Jr., ed., *Free Radicals in Biological Systems*, Academic Press, New York, 1961, Chap. 2.

40. Lang, L., *Absorption Spectra in the Ultraviolet and Visible Region*, Academic Press, New York, Vols. I and II, 1961; Vol. III, 1962; Vol. IV, 1963.

41. S. P. Sadtler and Sons, 1517 Vine St., Philadelphia 2, Pa.

42. Available from L. E. Kuentzel, Wyandotte Chemicals Corp., Wyandotte, Mich.

43. *Appl. Spectry.*, **15**, 56 (1961).

44. Friedel, R. A., and M. Orchin, *Ultraviolet Spectra of Aromatic Compounds*, Wiley, New York, 1951.

45. Monkman, J. L., *Appl. Spectry.*, **16**, 22 (1962); C. Karr, *ibid.*, **13**, 15, 42 (1959); A. L. Hayden, O. R. Summul, G. B. Selzer, and J. Carol, *J. Assoc. Offic. Agr. Chemists*, **45**, 797 (1962).

46. *Organic Electronic Spectra Data*, Vol. I, 1946–52, M. J. Kamlet, ed., 1960; Vol. II, 1953–55, H. E. Ungnade, ed., 1960; Vol. IV, 1958–59, J. P. Phillips and F. C. Nachod, 1963; Vol. III, in press; Interscience, New York.

47. Hershenson, H. M., *Ultraviolet and Visible Absorption Spectra Index for 1930–54*, 1956; *1955–59*, 1961, Academic Press, New York.

48. Gillam, A. E., and E. S. Stern, *Electronic Absorption Spectroscopy*, 2nd ed., Arnold Ltd., London, 1957, Appendix 1.

49. Clark, G. L., ed., *The Encyclopedia of Spectroscopy*, Reinhold, New York, 1960, pp. 1–79 for the visible-ultraviolet range.

50. Thompson, H. W., ed., *Advances in Spectroscopy*, Vol. I, 1959; Vol. II, 1962, Interscience, New York.

51. (a) G. M. Barrow, *Introduction to Molecular Spectroscopy*, McGraw-Hill, New York, 1962.

(b) R. P. Bauman, *Absorption Spectroscopy*, Wiley, New York, 1962.

(c) G. H. Beaven, E. A. Johnson, H. A. Willis, and R. G. J. Miller, *Molecular Spectroscopy*, Macmillan, New York, 1961.

(d) H. H. Jaffe, and M. Orchin, *Theory and Applications of Ultraviolet Spectroscopy*, Wiley, New York, 1962.

(e) A. Mangini, ed., *Advances in Molecular Spectroscopy*, Vols. 1, 2, 3, Pergamon Press, New York, 1962.

(f) C. N. R. Rao, *Ultraviolet and Visible Spectroscopy—Chemical Applications*, Butterworths, Washington, D. C., 1961.

(g) Scott, A. I., *Interpretation of the Natural Products*, Macmillan. New York. 1964.

52. G. F. Lothian, *Absorption Spectrophotometry*, 2nd ed., Macmillan, New York, 1958; A. E. Gillam and E. S. Stern, *Electronic Absorption Spectroscopy*, 2nd ed., E. Arnold, London, 1957.

53. (a) R. C. Blinn, in W. H. Butz and H. J. Noebels, eds., *Instrumental Methods for the Analysis of Food Additives*, Interscience, New York, Chap. IX.

(b) R. E. Dodd, *Chemical Spectroscopy*, Elsevier, New York, 1962.

(c) G. W. Ewing, *Instrumental Methods of Chemical Analysis*, 2nd ed., McGraw-Hill, New York, 1960.

(d) S. S. Penner, *Quantitative Molecular Spectroscopy and Gas Emissivities*, Addison-Wesley, Reading, Mass., 1959.

(e) H. A. Strobel, *Chemical Instrumentation: A Systematic Approach to Instrumental Analysis*, Addison-Wesley, Reading, Mass., 1960.

(f) P. M. B. Walker, in J. F. Danielli, ed., *General Cytochemical Methods*, Academic Press, New York, 1958, Chap. 3.

(g) H. H. Willard, L. L. Merritt, Jr., and J. A. Dean, *Instrumental Methods of Analysis*, 3rd ed., Van Nostrand, New York, 1958, Chap. 5.

(h) L. Schubert and I. May, in I. M. Kolthoff, and P. J. Elving, eds., *Treatise on Analytical Chemistry*, Part 1, Vol. 2, Section B, Interscience, New York, 1961.

(i) P. Delahay, *Instrumental Analysis*, Macmillan, New York, 1957, Chaps. 9 and 15.

(j) A. H. Becket and J. B. Stenlake, *Practical Pharmaceutical Chemistry— Quantitative Analysis*, Athlone Press, London, 1962.

(k) D. Chapman, in H. W. Chatfield, ed., *The Science of Surface Coatings*, E. Benn, London, 1962, Chapt. 19; *Treatise on Analytical Chemistry*, Part 1, Vol. 2, Sect. B, Interscience, N. Y., 1961, edited by I. M. Kolthoff and P. J. Elving.

54. McDonald, F. R., and G. L. Cook, *Appl. Spectry.*, **15**, 110 (1961).

55. Vosburgh, W. C., and G. R. Copper, *J. Am. Chem. Soc.*, **63**, 437 (1941); C. V. Banks and E. K. Byrd, *Anal. Chim. Acta*, **10**, 134 (1954); T. Moeller and R. W. Shellman, *Science*, **118**, 327 (1953).

56. Yoe, J. H., and A. E. Harvey, Jr., *J. Am. Chem. Soc.*, **70**, 648 (1948).

57. Ben-Bassat, A. H. I., and G. Frydman-Kupfer, *Chemist-Analyst*, **52**, 8 (1963).

58. Jones, M. M., *J. Am. Chem. Soc.*, **81**, 4485 (1959); L. Sommer and M. Hnilickova, *Bull. Soc. Chim. France*, **1959**, 36.

59. (a) A. E. Harvey and D. L. Manning, *J. Am. Chem. Soc.*, **72**, 4488 (1950); (b) A. E. Harvey and D. L. Manning, *ibid.*, **73**, 4744 (1952).

60. Kingery, W. D., and D. N. Hume, *J. Am. Chem. Soc.*, **71**, 2393 (1949); H. E. Bent and C. L. French, *ibid.*, **63**, 568 (1941).

61. Tobey, S. W., *J. Chem. Educ.*, **35**, 515 (1958); M. M. Davis and E. A. McDonald, *J. Res. Natl. Bur. Std.*, **42**, 595 (1949); M. M. Davis and H. B. Hetzer, **60**, 569 (1958); M. M. Davis, *J. Am. Chem. Soc.*, **84**, 3623 (1962).

62. Naqvi, N., E. L. Amma, Q. Fernando, and R. Levine, *J. Phys. Chem.*, **65**, 218 (1961).

63. Lawrence, A. R., and L. N. Ferguson, *J. Org. Chem.*, **25**, 1220 (1960); R. A. Robinson, M. M. Davis, M. Paabo, and V. E. Bower, *J. Res. Natl. Bur.*

Std., **64A**, 347 (1960); G. W. Stevenson and D. Williamson, *J. Am. Chem. Soc.*, **80**, 5943 (1958); S. B. Knight, R. H. Wallick, and J. Bowen, *ibid.*, **76**, 3780 (1954); M. T. Rogers, T. W. Campbell, and R. W. Maatman, *ibid.*, **73**, 5122 (1951).

64. Noyce, D. S., and M. J. Jorgenson, *J. Am. Chem. Soc.*, **84**, 4312 (1962), for a careful study of the accuracy of various procedures based on this spectro-photometric method.

65. McKinney, R. W., and C. A. Reynolds, *Talanta*, **1**, 46 (1958).

66. Reilley, C. N., and B. Schweizer, *Anal. Chem.*, **26**, 1124 (1954).

67. Mader, P. M., K. Schoenemann, and M. Eye, *Anal. Chem.*, **33**, 733 (1961).

68. Ellert, H., T. Jasinski, and K. Marcinkowska, *Acta Polon. Pharm.*, **17**, 29 (1960).

69. Hummelstedt, L. E. I., and D. N. Hume, *U. S. At. Energy Comm.*, Report AECU-4561, 1959.

70. Reynolds, C. A., F. H. Walker, and E. Cochran, *Anal. Chem.*, **32**, 983 (1960).

71. Hummelstedt, L. E. I., and D. N. Hume, *Anal. Chem.*, **32**, 1792 (1960).

72. Ozolins, M., and G. H. Schenk, *Anal. Chem.*, **33**, 1035 (1961).

73. Schenk, G. H., and M. Ozolins, *Talanta*, **8**, 109 (1961).

74. Headridge, J. B., *Talanta*, **1**, 293 (1958); A. L. Underwood, *J. Chem. Educ.*, **31**, 394 (1954); R. F. Goddu and D. N. Hume, *Anal. Chem.*, **26**, 1740 (1954); H. V. Malmstadt, in G. L. Clark, ed., *The Encyclopedia of Spectroscopy*, Reinhold, New York, 1960, p. 71 ff.

75. Jones, A. G., *Analytical Chemistry, Some New Techniques*, Academic Press, New York, pp. 47–74; J. W. O'Laughlin and C. V. Banks, in G. L. Clark, ed., *The Encyclopedia of Spectroscopy*, Reinhold, New York, 1960, p. 19; C. F. Hiskey, in G. Oster and A. W. Pollister, eds., *Physical Techniques in Biological Research*, Vol. 1, Academic Press, New York, 1955.

76. Brown, P. K., and G. Wald, *Science*, **144**, 45 (1964).

77. Carlson, R, L., R. S. Drago, et al., *J. Am. Chem. Soc.*, **84**, 2320 (1962); N. J. Rose and R. S. Drago, *ibid.*, **81**, 6138 (1959); M. Brandon, M. Tamres, and S. Searles, *J. Phys. Chem.*, **65**, 654 (1961); R. E. Merrifield and W. D. Phillips, *J. Am. Chem. Soc.*, **80**, 2778 (1958); P. D. Gardner, R. L. Brandon, N. J. Nix, and I. Y. Chang, *ibid.*, **81**, 3413 (1959); L. H. Klemm, J. W. Sprague, H. Ziffer, and B. I. Macgowan, *Anal. Chim. Acta*, **19**, 369 (1958).

78. Drago, R. S., and N. J. Rose, *J. Am. Chem. Soc.*, **81**, 6141 (1959); T. M. Cromwell and R. L. Scott, *ibid.*, **72**, 3825 (1950); C. Walling, E. R. Briggs, K. B. Wolfstirn, and F. R. Mayo, *ibid.*, **70**, 1537 (1948); M. Brandon, M. Tamres, and S. Searles, *ibid.*, **82**, 2131 (1960).

79. O'Connor, R. T., and L. A. Goldblatt, *Anal. Chem.*, **26**, 1726 (1954).

80. Fieser, L., and M. Fieser, *Advanced Organic Chemistry*, Reinhold, New York, 1961.

81. Forbes, W. F., and R. Shilton, *J. Am. Chem. Soc.*, **81**, 786 (1959); *J. Org. Chem.*, **24**, 436 (1959).

82. (a) W. J. Bailey and H. R. Golden, *J. Am. Chem. Soc.*, **75**, 4780 (1953).

(b) W. J. Bailey, E. J. Fetter, and J. Economy, *J. Org. Chem.*, **27**, 3479 (1962).

(c) E. Weltin, F. Gerson, J. N. Murrell, and E. Heilbronner, *Helv. Chim. Acta*, **44**, 1400 (1961).

83. Booker, H., L. K. Evans, and A. E. Gillam, *J. Chem. Soc.*, **1940**, 1453.
84. Kuhn, R., and A. Winterstein, *Ber.*, **67**, 344 (1934).
85. Bailey, W. J., and R. A. Baylouny, *J. Org. Chem.*, **27**, 3476 (1962).
86. Ruzicka, L., P. J. Ankersmit, and B. Frank, *Helv. Chim. Acta*, **15**, 1289 (1932).
87. Bradfield, A. E., B. H. Hegde, B. Rao, J. L. Simonsen, and A. E. Gillam, *J. Chem. Soc.*, **1936**, 667, 676.
88. Woodward, R. B., *J. Am. Chem. Soc.*, **63**, 1123 (1941).
89. Gillam, A. E., and E. S. Stern, *Electronic Absorption Spectroscopy*, 2nd ed., Arnold, London, 1957, Chap. 6.
90. Johnson, G. D., *J. Am. Chem. Soc.*, **75**, 2720 (1953); S. Yaroslavsky, *J. Org. Chem.*, **25**, 480 (1960).
91. Heilmann, R., J. M. Bonnier, and G. de Gaudemais, *Compt. Rend.*, **244**, 1787 (1957); O. H. Wheeler, *J. Org. Chem.*, **26**, 4755 (1961).
92. Doub, L., and J. M. Vandenbelt, *J. Am. Chem. Soc.*, **71**, 2414 (1949); see also A. R. Katritzky, *Chem. and Ind. (London)*, **1961**, 1267.
93. Hinman, R. L., *J. Org. Chem.*, **25**, 1775 (1960).
94. Little, W. F., and A. K. Clark, *J. Org. Chem.*, **25**, 1979 (1960).
95. Stewart, R., and L. G. Walker, *Can. J. Chem.*, **35**, 1561 (1957).
96. Carr, E. P., and C. P. Burt, *J. Am. Chem. Soc.*, **40**, 1590 (1918).
97. Kosower, E. M., *J. Am. Chem. Soc.*, **80**, 3261 (1958); M. F. Hawthorne, *J. Org. Chem.*, **21**, 1523 (1956).
98. Kohler, E. P., and J. B. Conant, *J. Am. Chem. Soc.*, **39**, 1409 (1917).
99. Sarel, S., and E. Breuer, *J. Am. Chem. Soc.*, **81**, 6522 (1959).
100. Eastman, R. H., and S. K. Freeman, *J. Am. Chem. Soc.*, **77**, 6642 (1955).
101. Price, C. C., and J. S. Vittimberga, *J. Org. Chem.*, **27**, 3736 (1962).
102. Sosnovsky, G., and H. J. O'Neill, *J. Org. Chem.*, **27**, 3469 (1962).
103. Beak, P., and H. Abelson, *J. Org. Chem.*, **27**, 3715 (1962) for leading references.
104. Herbst, D., W. B. Mors, O. R. Gottlieb, and C. Djerassi, *J. Am. Chem. Soc.*, **81**, 2427 (1959).
105. Bu'Lock, J. D., and H. G. Smith, *J. Chem. Soc.*, **1960**, 502.
106. Chmielewska, I., J. Ciéslak, K. Gorczyńska, B. Kontnik, and K. Pitakowska, *Tetrahedron*, **4**, 36 (1958).
107. Coan, S. P., D. E. Trucker, and E. I. Becker, *J. Am. Chem. Soc.*, **75**, 900 (1953).
108. Hirshberg, Y., and R. N. Jones, *Can. J. Res.*, **27B**, 437 (1949).
109. Katzenellenbogen, E. R., and G. E. K. Branch, *J. Am. Chem. Soc.*, **69**, 1615 (1947).
110. Lewis, G. N., *J. Am. Chem. Soc.*, **67**, 770 (1945).
111. Tuemmler, W. B., and B. S. Wildi, *J. Am. Chem. Soc.*, **80**, 3772 (1958).
112. Stewart, F. H. C., *J. Org. Chem.*, **27**, 3374 (1962) for pertinent references.
113. Kresge, A. J., G. W. Barry, K. R. Charles, and Y. Chiang, *J. Am. Chem. Soc.*, **84**, 4343 (1962).
114. Cram, D. J., N. L. Allinger, and H. Steinberg, *J. Am. Chem. Soc.*, **76**, 6132 (1954).
115. Brown, C. J., *J. Chem. Soc.*, **1953**, 3265, 3279.

116. Arnold, R. T., and P. N. Craig, *J. Am. Chem. Soc.*, **70**, 2791 (1948).
117. Forbes, W. F., and W. A. Mueller, *Can. J. Chem.*, **33**, 1145 (1955).
118. Forbes, W. F., and W. A. Mueller, *J. Am. Chem. Soc.*, **79**, 6495 (1957).
119. Rieger, M., and F. H. Westheimer, *J. Am. Chem. Soc.*, **72**, 19 (1950).
120. Dearden, J. C., and W. F. Forbes, *Can. J. Chem.*, **38**, 1837 (1960).
121. Hambly, A. N., *Rev. Pure Appl. Chem.*, **11**, 212 (1961), and references 18–21 cited by J. C. Dearden, and W. F. Forbes, *Can. J. Chem.*, **38**, 1837 (1960).
122. Cookson, R. C., *J. Chem. Soc.*, **1954**, 282; R. C. Cookson and S. H. Dandeganonker, *ibid.*, **1955**, 352.
123. Evans, L. K., and A. E. Gillam, *J. Chem. Soc.*, **1943**, 565.
124. Braude, E. A., E. R. H. Jones, H. P. Koch, R. W. Richardson, F. Sondheimer, and J. B. Toogood, *J. Chem. Soc.*, **1949**, 1890.
125. Caserio, F. F., and J. D. Roberts, *J. Am. Chem. Soc.*, **80**, 5837 (1958).
126. Winstein, S., L. Devries, and R. Orloski, *J. Am. Chem. Soc.*, **83**, 2020 (1961).
127. Mislow, K., M. A. W. Glass, R. E. O'Brian, P. Rutkin, D. H. Steinberg, J. Weiss, and C. Djerassi, *J. Am. Chem. Soc.*, **84**, 1455 (1962).
128. Wepster, B. M., in W. Klyne and P. B. D. de la Mare, eds., *Progress in Stereochemistry*, Vol. 2, Butterworths, London, 1958, p. 99, and pertinent references cited therein.
129. Wepster, B. M., in G. W. Gray, ed., *Steric Effects in Conjugated Systems*, Butterworths, London, 1958, p. 82.
130. Taft, R. W., Jr., and H. D. Evans, *J. Chem. Phys.*, **27**, 1427 (1957).
131. Braude, E. A., and F. J. Sondheimer, *J. Chem. Soc.*, **1955**, 3754.
132. Mislow, K., S. Seymour, and H. Schaeffer, *J. Am. Chem. Soc.*, **84**, 1449 (1962).
133. Kreiter, V. P., W. A. Bonner, and R. H. Eastman, *J. Am. Chem. Soc.*, **76**, 5770 (1954).
134. Katritzky, A. R., A. J. Boulton, and D. J. Short, *J. Chem. Soc.*, **1960**, 2954.
135. V. Baliah and P. Subbarayan, *J. Org. Chem.*, **25**, 1833 (1960); V. Baliah and Sp. Shanmuganathan, *J. Phys. Chem.*, **62**, 255 (1958).
136. Cunningham, K. G., G. W. Dawson, and F. S. Spring, *J. Chem. Soc.*, **1951**, 2304.
137. Boekelheide, V., and J. C. Godfrey, *J. Am. Chem. Soc.*, **75**, 3679 (1953); J. C. Godfrey, *Anal. Chem.*, **31**, 1087 (1959).
138. Barry, V. C., J. C. McCormick, and P. W. D. Mitchell, *J. Chem. Soc.*, **1955**, 222.
139. Rosenthal, I., G. J. Frisone, and J. K. Coberg, *Anal. Chem.*, **32**, 1713 (1960).
140. Briegleb, G., and J. Czekalla, *Angew. Chem.*, **72**, 401 (1960); R. Foster, *Tetrahedron*, **10**, 96 (1960).
141. Streitwieser, A., Jr., *J. Am. Chem. Soc.*, **82**, 4123 (1960); J. B. Birks and M. A. Slifkins, *Nature*, **191**, 761 (1960).
142. Kaye, W. I., *Appl. Spectry.*, **15**, 89, 130 (1961).
143. Price, W. C., in H. W. Thompson, ed., *Advances in Spectroscopy*, Vol. 1, Interscience, New York, 1959, Chap. 2.
144. Ferguson, L. N., and T. C. Goodwin, *J. Am. Chem. Soc.*, **71**, 633 (1949).
145. Scheibe, G., *Ber.*, **59**, 1333 (1926).
146. Henri, V., and L. W. Pickett, *J. Chem. Phys.*, **7**, 439 (1939).

476   LLOYD N. FERGUSON

147. Pesch, E., and S. L. Friess, *J. Am. Chem. Soc.*, **72**, 5756 (1950).
148. Cope, A. C., and L. L. Estes, Jr., *J. Am. Chem. Soc.*, **72**, 1128 (1950).
149. Blomquist, A. T., and A. Goldstein, *J. Am. Chem. Soc.*, **77**, 998 (1955).
150. Bartlett, M. F., S. K. Figdor, and K. Wiesner, *Can. J. Chem.*, **30**, 291 (1952).
151. Meites, L., *Handbook of Analytical Chemistry*, McGraw-Hill, New York, 1963.
152. Boltz, D. F., *Rec. Chem. Progr.* (*Kresge-Hooker Sci. Lib.*), **24**, 167 (1963).
153. Ma, T. S., *Organic Functional Group Analysis*, Wiley, New York, 1964.
154. Feigl, F., R. Belcher, and W. I. Stephen, in C. N. Reilley, ed., *Advances in Analytical Chemistry and Instrumentation*, Vol. 2, Interscience, New York, 1963, Chap. 1.
155. Rossotti, F. J. C., and H. Rossotti, *The Determination of Stability Constants*, McGraw-Hill, New York, 1961; L. Sommer and T. Jin, *Chem. Listy*, **55**, 574 (1961).
156. Conrow, K., G. D. Johnson, and R. E. Bowen, *J. Am. Chem. Soc.*, **86**, 1025 (1964); and references cited therein.
157. Headridge, J. B., *Photometric Titrations*, Pergamon Press, New York, 1961.
158. Boltz, D. F., *Anal. Chem.*, **36**, 256 (1964).
159. Reynolds, C. A., *Rec. Chem. Progr.* (*Kresge-Hooker Sci. Lib.*), **24**, 157 (1963).
160. West, J. A., *J. Chem. Educ.*, **40**, 194 (1963).
161. Bly, R. K., and R. S. Bly, *J. Org. Chem.*, **28**, 3165 (1963).
162. Leonard, N. J., and P. M. Mader, *J. Am. Chem. Soc.*, **72**, 5388 (1950).
163. Ulrich, W. F., in J. R. Ferraro and J. S. Ziomek, eds., *Developments in Applied Spectroscopy*, Plenum Press, New York, 1963, pp. 130–141.
164. Hirt, R. C., and R. G. Schmitt, No. AD 401,498, obtainable from the Office of Technical Services, U. S. Dept. of Commerce, Wash. 25, D. C.
165. Gordon, S., E. J. Hart, M. S. Matheson, J. Rabani, and J. K. Thomas, *J. Am. Chem. Soc.*, **85**, 1375 (1963).
166. Sawicki, E., *Rec. Chem. Progr.* (*Kresge-Hooker Sci. Lib.*), **22**, 249 (1961).

Manuscript received by Publisher May 5, 1964.

AUTHOR INDEX*

A

Abelson, H., 454 (ref. 103), *474*
Abrahamson, E. W., 22 (ref. 76), *33*
Ackermann, R. J., 400 (ref. 23), *409*
Adams, R., 132, *212*
Adamski, T., 21, *33*
Adolph, H. G., 424 (ref. 17), 425 (ref. 17) *470*
Akerlöf, G., 302, 303, *362*
Akermark, B., 431 (ref. 23), *470*
Aleshin, S., *362*
Alicino, J. F., 93 (ref. 1), *112*
Allinger, N. L., 430 (ref. 114), *474*
American Petroleum Institute, 407 (ref. 33), *410*
Amma, E. L., 444 (ref. 62), *472*
Analytical Chemistry, 438 (ref. 29), *470*
Analytical Methods Committee, 84 (ref. 2), 95 (ref. 2), 97, *112*
Anderson, O. L., 216 (ref. 3), 307 (ref. 3), *362*
Angst, W., 264
Ankersmit, P. J., 450 (ref. 86), *474*
Ansevin, A., 42 (ref. 8), 63 (ref. 8), 67 (ref. 8), 68 (ref. 8), *73*
Anson, F. C., 3, *31*
Anson, M. L., 37, *73*
Applied Spectroscopy, 440 (ref. 43), *471*
Archer, E. E., 82, 87 (ref. 4), 93, 94 (ref. 4), 97 (ref. 4), *112*
Arnold, R. T., 456 (ref. 116), *475*
Azo, L. G., 215 (ref. 165), *368*

B

Baddenhausen, H., 110 (ref. 52), *113*
Bailey, W. J., 450 (ref. 85), 451 (ref. 82), *473*, *474*
Baliah, V., 467 (ref. 135), *475*

Balodis, R. B., 95 (ref. 28), 98 (ref. 28), 99 (ref. 28), *112*
Banks, C. V., 442 (ref. 55), 448 (ref. 75), *472*, *473*
Bar-Gadda, I., 125 (ref. 3), 126 (ref. 3), *210*
Bark, L. S., 14 (ref. 39), 29 (ref. 39), *32*
Barney, J. E., II, 84, 88 (ref. 5), 103 (ref. 5), 105 (ref. 5), 106 (ref. 5), *112*
Barnicoat, C. R., 13, *32*
Barrow, G. M., 441 (ref. 51), *471*
Barry, D. L., 84 (ref. 60), 97 (ref. 60), 107 (ref. 60), 109 (ref. 60), *113*
Barry, G. W., 456 (ref. 113), *474*
Barry, V. C., 468 (ref. 138), *475*
Bartels, U., 93 (ref. 7), 106 (ref. 6), *112*
Bartlett, M. F., 429 (ref. 150), *476*
Bartužek, Z., 78 (ref. 120), 87 (ref. 120), 88 (ref. 120), 94 (ref. 120), 97 (ref. 120), *115*
Basargin, N. N., 90 (ref. 112), 93 (refs. 112, 113), *115*
Bass, E. A., 90 (ref. 141), 93 (ref. 141), 100 (ref. 142), 102 (ref. 142), *115*
Bates, R. G., 215 (ref. 4), 222 (ref. 4), *362*
Battles, J., 400, *409*
Bauer, S. H., 399, *409*
Bauman, R. P., 441 (ref. 51), *471*
Bayliss, N. S., 417 (ref. 6), *470*
Baylouny, R. A., 450 (ref. 85), *474*
Beak, P., 454 (ref. 103), *474*
Beale, R. N., 416 (ref. 5), *469*
Beaven, G. H., 441 (ref. 51), *471*
Beck, W., 108 (ref. 125), *115*
Becker, E. I., 455 (ref. 107), *474*
Becket, A. H., 441 (ref. 53), *472*
Beckman Instrument Co., 267, 268, 351 (ref. 5), *362*

* *Italic* numbers refer to the bibliographies of the different articles.

477

W

Vosburgh, W. C., 442 (ref. 55), *472*
Votoček, E., 78, 84 (ref. 152), 94 (ref. 152), 95 (ref. 152), *116*

W

Wacks, M., 399, *409*
Wagman, D. D., 327 (ref. 157), 329 (ref. 157), 336 (ref. 157), 337 (ref. 157), *367*
Wagner, H., 90, 91, 93, *116*
Wald, G., 448 (ref. 76), *473*
Walker, F. H., 447 (ref. 70), *473*
Walker, L. G., 453 (ref. 95), *474*
Walker, P. M. B., 441 (ref. 53), *472*
Wallick, R. H., 444 (ref. 63), *473*
Walling, C., 446 (ref. 78), *473*
Walnut, T. H., 22 (refs. 80, 81), *33*
Walsh, P. N., 382 (ref. 6), 400 (ref. 6), *409*
Walton, H. F., 308 (ref. 202), *369*
Walton, J. H., 351 (ref. 50), 352 (ref. 50), 355 (ref. 50), 361 (ref. 50), 362 (ref. 50), *364*
Washizuka, S., 19, *33*
Wasmuth, C. R., 25, *33*
Webb, T. J., 129 (ref. 62), *212*
Weir, H. E., 88 (ref. 154), *116*
Weiss, H. V., 25, 26 (refs. 90–96), *33*, *34*
Weiss, J., 460 (ref. 127), *475*
Weltin, E., 451 (ref. 82), *473*
Wepster, B. M., 428 (ref. 21), 463 (ref. 128), 464 (ref. 129), *470*, *475*
West, J. A., 449 (ref. 160), *476*
West, T. S., 100 (ref. 12), 102 (ref. 12), 106 (ref. 15a), 107 (ref. 15a), 108 (ref. 15a), *112*
Westheimer, F. H., 457 (ref. 119), *475*
Weyl, W. A., 306 (ref. 205), 336 (refs. 203, 204), 346, *369*
Wheeler, O. H., 452 (ref. 91), *474*
White, D. C., 92, 93 (ref. 155), 96 (ref. 156), 98 (ref. 157), *116*
White, D. O., 382, 400, *409*
White, F. L., 429 (ref. 22), *470*
Wiesner, K., 429 (ref. 150), *476*
Wildi, B. S., 455 (ref. 111), *474*
Wiley, W. C., 375, *409*
Wilkinson, J. V., 93 (ref. 149), 94 (ref. 149), 107 (ref. 150), *116*

Willard, H. H., 3 (ref. 1), 4, *31*, 441 (ref. 53), *472*
Willard, J. E., 307 (ref. 104), *366*
Willemart, R., 99 (ref. 158), *116*
Willermain, M., 129, *212*
Williams, M., 4 (ref. 5), *31*
Williams, R. R., 432 (refs. 24, 26), 435 (ref. 24), *470*
Williamson, D., 444 (ref. 63), *473*
Willis, H. A., 441 (ref. 51), *471*
Wilson, D. W., 350 (ref. 123), 351 (ref. 123), 354, 358, 359, *366*
Winkler, A., 85, 88 (ref. 42), 94 (ref. 42), 97 (ref. 42), 106 (ref. 42), *113*
Winsor, P. A., 123, *211*
Winstein, S., 459 (ref. 126), *475*
Winterstein, A., 450 (ref. 84), *474*
Wittmann, H., 104 (ref. 122), 105, *115*
Wolfstirn, K. B., 446 (ref. 78), *473*
Wollish, E. G., 100 (ref. 132), 102 (ref. 132), *115*
Wong, S. L., 351 (ref. 50), 352 (ref. 50), 355 (ref. 50), 361 (ref. 50), 362 (ref. 50), *364*
Woodward, R. B., 451 (ref. 88), *474*
Wyatt, E. I., 21 (ref. 74), *33*

Y

Yamamura, S. S., 90 (ref. 47), 92 (ref. 47), *113*
Yanari, S. S., 417 (ref. 6), *470*
Yaroslavsky, S., 451 (ref. 90), *474*
Yasuda, S. K., 100 (ref. 123), 101, 102 (ref. 123), 107 (ref. 159), *115*, *116*
Yoe, J. H., 437 (ref. 28), 442 (ref. 56), 443 (ref. 56), *470*, *472*
Young, J. C., *364*
Yudis, M., 131, *212*

Z

Zamochnick, S. B., 355 (refs. 154a, 154b), 356 (ref. 154d), *367*
Zarembo, J. E., 82 (ref. 90), 90 (ref. 90), 93 (refs. 90, 91), *114*
Ziffer, H., 442 (ref. 77), *473*
Zuck, D. A., 150 (ref. 34), 151 (refs. 33, 34), *211*
Zumwalt, L. R., 438 (ref. 33), *470*

SUBJECT INDEX

A

Abietic acid, structure of, 450
Acetic anhydride, photometric titration with, 447
Acetophenones, spectra of, 425
8-Acetoxyquinaldine, hydrolysis of, 17
7-Acetoxyquinoline, hydrolysis of, 25
8-Acetoxyquinoline, hydrolysis of, 16–17, 25
Acrolein, wavelength of, 451
Air spectrum on oscilloscope, 392
Alicyclic diene system, intramolecular strain exhibited by, 429
Alizarin fluorine blue, color reaction for fluoride, 102
Alizarin sulfonic acid, use as a titrant, 93
Alkali cations, effect of alcohol on electrode response to, 300–301
Alkaline earth cations, theoretical specificity of, 338–339
Alkaline earth sulfates, precipitation of, 20
Alkaline error, 218, 220
  enhancement of, 218–220
Alkali silicate glass, interstitial position in, 339
  lattice-breaking position in, 339
Alkaloids, titration of, 447
Alkyl fluorides, analysis of, 100
Aluminosilicate-glass electrodes, selectivities of, 256
Aluminum, effect of replacing by other elements, 347
Aluminum 8-hydroxy-quinolate, precipitation of, 17, 18
Aluminum oxide-containing glasses, for alkali metal cations, electrode properties of, 248–272
  for hydrogen ion, electrode properties of, 248–272

responses to alkaline earth cations, 285–289
responses to silver ion, thallium ion, and ammonium ion, 272–285
responses to substituted ammonium ions, amines, and amino acids, 289
summary of silver ion, thallium ion, and ammonium ion sensitivities, 285
Aluminum oxide-silicon dioxide glasses, composition changes in, 224
Aluminum, precipitation of, 16
Amberlite IR-120(H) resin, removal of zinc ions on, 100
Amides, complex formation with, 205–206
Amine groups, tertiary α,β-unsaturated, distinguished from other amines, 449
Ammonia, volatilization of, 12
Ammonium, precipitation titration of, 355
Ammonium ion, electrode response to, 284
  equilibrium selectivities for, 337
  glass electrodes response to, 280–285
  measurement of, 352
  selectivity isotherm, 287
  silver ion and thallium ion, combined selectivity isotherms for, 287
  substituted, electrode responses to, 294
  theoretical specificity of, 335–338
Ammonium ion–hydrogen ion mixtures, electrode potentials in 286
Analog output, 383–388

495

Advances in Analytical Chemistry and Instrumentation

CUMULATIVE INDEX, VOLUMES 1-4

Author Index

Subject Index